THE NATURE
AND GROWTH OF
MODERN MATHEMATICS

Volume 1

Fawcett Premier Books
by Edna E. Kramer:

THE MAIN STREAM OF MATHEMATICS

THE NATURE AND GROWTH OF MODERN
MATHEMATICS
Volumes 1 and 2

THE NATURE AND GROWTH OF MODERN MATHEMATICS

Volume 1

by Edna E. Kramer

A FAWCETT PREMIER BOOK

Fawcett Publications, Inc., Greenwich, Connecticut

To

My husband,

Benedict Taxier Lassar

THE NATURE AND GROWTH OF MODERN MATHE-MATICS, Volume 1

CONTENTS for Volume 1

7

Forefathers of Modern Mathematics and Their Legacy

8

A Calculus for Heaven and Earth

15

Demons, Energy, Maxwell, and Gibbs   477

The foremost native American mathematical physicist / Carnot's
thermodynamics / Maxwell's demon / Maxwell-Boltzmann law as
a multivariate frequency function / The Josiah Willard Gibbs
Lectureship / "Hermaphrodite monster" or major simplification? /
Chef-d'oeuvre / Statistical physics: Brownian motion, Einstein's
statistical discoveries and his subsequent point of view / Stochastic
processes / Discrete and continuous parameter processes / Special
simplicity of Gibb's stochastic process / Gibbs's initial assumptions
and his deductions therefrom / His "conservation" laws / Too
many variables / Phase, phase-space, phase-trajectory / Linear
motion and plane trajectories / Conservative systems / Gibbs's
ensembles / Microcanonical distribution / Canonical distribution /
Entropy / Ensemble versus time averages / Ergodic hypothesis /
The ergodic theorems of von Neumann and Birkhoff / Wilson
and his reminiscences of Gibbs

Preface

The Nature and Growth of Modern Mathematics traces the development of the most important mathematical concepts from their inception to their present formulation. Although chief emphasis is placed on the explanation of mathematical ideas, nevertheless mathematical content, history, lore, and biography are integrated in order to offer an overall, unified picture of the mother science. The work presents a discussion of major notions and the general settings in which they were conceived, with particular attention to the lives and thoughts of some of the most creative mathematical innovators. It provides a guide to what is still important in classical mathematics, as well as an introduction to many significant recent developments.

Answers to questions like the following are simple and will be found in this book:

Why should Pythagoras and his followers be credited with (or blamed for) some of the methodology of the "new" mathematics?

How do modern algebras (plural) generalize the "common garden variety"?

What single modern concept makes it possible to conceive in a nutshell of *all* geometrics, plain and fancy—Euclidean, non-Euclidean, affine, projective, inversive, etc.?

What is the nature of the universal language initiated by a thirteenth-century Catalan mystic, actually formulated by Leibniz, and improved by Boole and De Morgan?

How did Omar Khayyám solve certain cubic equations?

What are the common features of any boy's "engagement problem," the geishas' pantomime of baseball, and modern engineering decisions?

Who are the "Leonardos" of modern mathematics?

How did Queen Dido set a precedent for mathematicians and physicists?

Why should isomorphism, homomorphism, and homeomorphism be an intrinsic part of the vocabulary of every mathophile?

How did Maxwell's "demon" make the irreversible reversible?

Why did the mere matter of counting socks lead a millionaire mathematical genius to renounce mathematics in favor of finance?

What are the beautiful "ideals" formulated by Richard Dedekind and advanced by Emmy Noether?

Proceeding from illustrative instances to general purposes, let us state that the author's objectives are:

1. To survey the entire field of mathematics, with emphasis on twentieth-century ideas.

2. To furnish the type of exposition that should make it possible for a layman who is educated but not a specialist in mathematics to gain insight into the manifold aspects of modern mathematics, including its essential relationship to all areas of scientific thought. This objective was formulated because the "new" mathematics which has become the vogue in our schools is not really new, and those who seek popular treatment of contemporary mathematics can find only occasional superficial articles in periodicals. Books offering fuller exposition, including the author's *Main Stream of Mathematics*, have generally terminated with material from the early decades of the present century. In the potentially democratic world which men of good will envision, the man in the street must be entitled to more mathematical stimulation than the puzzle column in a Sunday newspaper, an occasional profile of a Nobel prize winner, an enigmatic summary of some recent discovery in applied mathematics—whether that man is an engineer in a remote village in India who is seeking to fill loopholes in his mathematical knowledge, a retired physician anxious to convince himself he is a mathematician *manqué*, a high school senior in quest of a research topic for a science talent contest, a nun whose objective is to inspire her students with an account of the accomplishment of women mathematicians, or a stockbroker eager to indulge in some pure mathematics.

(Such are some of the individuals who have corresponded with the author *in re* mathematical information.)

3. To stress "human interest" and thereby to reveal mathematics as a living, growing endeavor, holding a strong place in man's culture. This aim was conceived because there is danger to the humanities in the present educational crash programs designed to produce a large number of mathematicians, physical scientists, engineers, and technical workers. Our times make such programs a necessity, and the leaders who suggest the concentrated curricula or write the texts are rendering an inestimable service. Although these men understand the value of the pure mathematical content of the courses of study they prescribe, can the same be said of the students or of the teachers in elementary and secondary schools, or of the general public? They must have the opportunity to realize that there is more purpose to the "new" mathematics than recounting the tale of Little Red Riding Hood in terms of set theory or computer language. Thus, part of the third objective of the present work is to supply material which can serve as a cultural background or supplement for all those who are receiving rapid, concentrated exposure to recent advanced mathematical concepts, without any opportunity to examine the origins or gradual historical development of such ideas. Hence, although designed for the layman, this book would be helpful in courses in the history, philosophy, or fundamental concepts of mathematics.

At this point I should like to express my indebtedness to a number of persons. First and foremost, there is my husband, Dr. Benedict T. Lassar, through whose advice and assistance the manuscript has received a "fondest father's fondest care." I appreciate the many valuable suggestions made by Linda Allegri, who served as mathematics editor, as well as those of C. B. Boyer. The author is especially grateful to the mathematicians who gave their kind permission to quote from important articles they have written. Exact references to those mathematicians and the particular papers are provided at appropriate points in the body of the work. Thanks for the special permission must also be extended to the organizations sponsoring the publications in which the articles appeared, namely, the Royal Society of London, the Université de Paris, the American Mathematical Society, the Mathematics Association of America, and to the editors of *Biometrika*, *Econometrica*, the *Annals of Mathematical Statistics*, the *Journal of the American Oriental Society*, *Scripta Mathematica*. Oxford University Press graciously gave permission to quote from the author's previous book, *The Main Stream of Mathematics*. A most valuable form of assistance was rendered by those who encouraged the author to initiate or to continue (through long years) the writing of this book. They are Hanna Neumann, Bernhard H. Neumann, Peter M. Neumann, Jean Leray, Christie J. Eliezer, Sigekatu Kuroda, John M. Danskin, Stanislaw Ulam, Wilhelm Magnus, Fred Kerner, the late E. B. Wilson. Finally, thanks are due to William Taylor for the careful preparation of the diagrams, and to Beth Goldberg for the translation of barely decipherable scribbling into neat, accurate typescript, for noting errors, and for making suggestions.

New York   E. E. K.
January, 1970

Introduction

The era in which we live has variously been described as the age of the common man, the age of anxiety, the nuclear age, the space age, and so on. To this list of appellations one might well add the *age of mathematics*. At no other time in history has the man in the street been informed emphatically and repeatedly that the further progress of mathematics concerns him vitally because it is sure to have effects, direct or indirect, on his material comforts, his mode of thought, and his very survival. The nonspecialist cannot help wondering at this sudden prominence of a subject whose higher branches have always seemed to belong to a world apart, a sphere where physical scientists find advanced mathematics a useful tool, while philosophers and numerical geniuses indulge in it as an art or as an intellectual hobby. The present phenomenon may have been precipitated by the political and economic circumstances of our day, but the major role of the new mathematics is no fortuitous overnight occurrence. It represents the cumulative effect of some four thousand years of scientific thought.

Circles of Thought

Most interest must center on the outcome of this long period of fruition, and therefore emphasis must be placed on mathematical activity as it exists today. However, since many classic aspects of mathematics have stood the test of time, they are actually part of the present and must be considered in relation to it. Some of the older notions pave the path for recent developments, and others clarify the new replacements or generalizations. In order to integrate the traditional with the modern in mathematics, a "spiral" organization is used by the author in tracing the progress of concepts from their origins in antiquity or some period prior to the twentieth century up to their ultimate formulation. In some instances the first presentation of a topic may be compared to a trip around one of the small inner whirls of a spiral. After this initial full circle, the subject may be dropped until later chapters where new convolutions are examined and the original journey continues through one or more additional broader circles of thought.

Something Old, Something New

The use of the spiral sequence necessitates the juxtaposition of "something old, something new" in a number of chapters. For example, since certain Pythagorean problems are similar to issues handled by Dedekind and Cantor in the late nineteenth century, it seems logical to discuss some aspects of the earlier and later viewpoints side by side. If Euclid's discoveries in the higher arithmetic were first generalized by the great Russian mathematician Tchebycheff, there seems no reason to defer all mention of the nineteenth-century analytical number-theorist simply because he lived much later. If Euler, the most prolific of mathematicians, was "analysis incarnate" but nevertheless employed intuitive methods with grave logical defects, why not reveal at once just how these faults were remedied a couple of centuries later, after they had produced a veritable crisis in mathematics? In the same way, the games of chance played by primitive man and his more civilized successors are linked with the more sophisticated games of military, industrial, or economic strategy, whose theory has been studied by Borel, Wald, and above all, by von Neumann, heroic figures in recent mathematical history.

Thus the mode of organization makes it impossible to adhere to strict chronological order. Continuity of subject matter seems a more important criterion than sequence in time. When, for example, Newtonian mathematical physics is specified as a set of "deterministic" laws, an obvious way to secure emphasis and clarification is to proceed to the "indeterminacy" in a vast major modern area. Therefore a treatment of probabilistic or statistical thought follows the discussion of the deterministic "differential equation type" of mechanics produced by Newton, Euler, Lagrange, Laplace, and Hamilton. Thus, relatively early in the book there appear the names and discoveries of some recent probabilists, statisticians, and researchers in statistical mechanics, whereas mathematical ideas which developed earlier are deferred for later presentation.

Treatment of Biography and Mathematical Lore

As for the biographical material, it is not necessary, in a layman's cyclopedia, to present details of the lives of all the mathematicians in history, and a few of the more usual favorites are given only brief mention in order to give more space to the newer names. It is inevitable, moreover, for an author to have individual enthusiasms and personal preferences. Again, history has left more detailed information about the lives of some mathematicians, or else they were particularly fortunate in having had friends or contemporary biographers to record facts before they were lost forever. In a few instances where the biographical material on record may be apocryphal or, on the other hand, has been repeated again and again as part of the anecdotal stock-in-trade of mathematical writers, the present author has employed an imaginative narrative instead of a biography. For example, there is the story of Hypatia, influenced inevitably by Charles Kingsley's Victorian version.

Integration of Exposition with Source Material

Popularization need not, and should not, be vulgarization, and the quotation of original sources is one method that is often used to maintain a scholarly level of exposition. But since recent mathematical research is exceedingly advanced and abstract in nature, the actual symbolic or technical format in which the creators clothe their ideas might baffle a general reader. If first formulations cannot be used on account of their difficulty, it is sometimes possible to examine how the foremost mathematicians of our era present popularization of ideas related to their own. Some of their narrative or expository writings, quoted occasionally in the present work, were not originally directed to the man in the street.

Nevertheless they constitute popularizations in the sense that they were prepared for an audience of biologists, psychologists, economists, engineers, philosophers, chemists, physicists or for mathematical readers who were not specialists in the field under discussion. This sort of secondary source serves the dual purpose of indicating the clarity of such exposition and bringing recent mathematical leaders into the story by having them speak for themselves as well as for those whose research they are evaluating or eulogizing.

In making use of such source material, it is not feasible, in most cases, to quote material *in toto*, with assistance merely from prefatory or supplementary notes. Instead, one may need to combine statements by a number of mathematicians or else interrupt the course of a discussion in order to provide clarification or amplification at the exact points where difficulties may arise. What is done resembles the plotting of a detective story. When a Scotland Yard sleuth is congratulated on his solution of a case, he will respond modestly: "Oh, but if not for your questions, I should never have been able to find the answers, for you have a perfect talent for failing to understand at the very instant when clarification is most needed."

Special Features

As in the matter of biographies, so in the question of topics to be discussed, it is necessary to make some choice. The writer of a popular work on mathematics must select subjects at varied levels of difficulty and present these with varying degree of completeness in order to appeal to a wide audience. That is why, in a few instances, the life and times of a creative thinker are given more space than the advanced mathematical theories to which he gave birth. Again, an informal, anecdotal, even discursive introduction may be the best approach to certain topics. As for variety in exposition, a general work can enjoy a freedom which mathematical textbooks have never had. It seems to the author that even in books for students at school much would be gained by banishing a pattern that makes each chapter a "pedagogic" stereotype. *The Nature and Growth of Modern Mathematics* avoids such a pattern, and hence a discussion is sometimes initiated with a biography or a narrative while at other times the story of the discoverers is told last, not first. Or if mathematicians have worked in the same or related fields, it may be interesting to consider their biographies simultaneously. Where ideas are particularly dramatic, one should plunge into them without preliminaries. The flashback technique, used so frequently in nonmathematical literature, is employed occasionally in the present work in order to emphasize the culminating result of decades, even centuries, of preliminary theorizing, or to give the most general concepts priority over the special cases from which they evolved, or to reveal the goal of a particular chapter or portion of the book.

An Overall Picture

It is the author's opinion that one can provide an appreciation of the development of mathematics and its position in our present culture without according full technical treatment to every mathematical specialty in existence at the present time. To attempt more than brief reference to certain areas would be impracticable and might, moreover, have the effect of confusing or overpowering a general reader. Nevertheless, the origins and elementary aspects of the most important subjects are presented in broad outline. Also there is explanation of why the "multivalence" of modern pure or completely abstract theories makes them all-encompassing so that, in actuality, consideration of a single theory implies a vast content in the specific models to which it applies. This is one reason why the mathematical present can be properly termed the age of abstractness. But the author does not limit the material or adjust the style in accordance with the current emphasis on pure mathematics, and the book deals with much that can be described as "applied mathematics." Although the present abstract trend may have potent effects on the future of mathematics, we are where we are just now because "applied" problems, especially in astronomy and mechanics, are part of our cultural heritage and were, in the past, the motivating factors which stimulated the growth of mathematics toward its present magnitude and condition.

In any comprehensive presentation of mathematics as it exists today, it is inevitable that certain phases of "higher" mathematics must be treated. A reader need not be fearful on this account, however, since part of the present picture is the fact that some of the new advanced mathematical ideas are easier to comprehend as well as far more stimulating than many technical fine points of traditional elementary mathematics.

THE NATURE AND GROWTH OF
MODERN MATHEMATICS

Chapter 1

From Babylonian Beginnings
to Digital Computers

"Schoolboy, where did you go . . . ?"
"I went to school."
"What did you do in school?"
"I read my tablet, ate my lunch,
 prepared my tablet, wrote it, finished it; then . . .
 upon the school's dismissal, I went home,
 entered the house, [there] was my father sitting.
 I spoke to my father . . .
 read the tablet to him, [and] my father was pleased;
 truly I found favor with my father. . . .
 [I said]: 'I want to go to sleep;
 wake me early in the morning,
 I must not be late, [or] my teacher will cane me.'
 When I awoke early in the morning,
 I faced my mother, and
 Said to her: 'Give me my lunch, I want to go to school. . . .'
 My mother gave me two 'rolls,' I went to school.
 In the tablet house, the monitor said to me: 'Why are you
     late?' I was afraid, my heart beat fast.
 I entered before my teacher, took [my] place.
 My 'school-father' read my tablet
 . . . [and] caned me. . . .
 The teacher, in supervising the school duties,
 looked into house and street in order to pounce upon
     someone,
 . . . [and] caned me. . . .
 [He] who was in charge of drawing [said]: 'Why when I
     was not here did you stand up?' [He then] caned me.
 [He] who was in charge of the gate [said]: 'Why when I
     was not here did you go out?' [He then] caned me."

The above is taken from the opening passages of a short story* recently deciphered by the noted Assyriologist Samuel Noah Kramer, who gives 2000 B.C. as its probable date of creation. It must have been a popular work in ancient Mesopotamia, for numerous cuneiform copies of the original tablet have been found and its title was listed in an early Sumerian literary catalogue.

Babylonian mathematical tablets of approximately the same era as "Schooldays"* will be discussed in this chapter. Hence it will be interesting to examine the rest of that tale not only for its intrinsic charm and its indication of the invariance in human characteristics through four millennia, but also for its picture of a cultural setting in which mathematics was able to thrive.

The story of the young scribe continues with his recital of added woes. In all, he is caned three times by the teacher and half a dozen times by other members of the school staff. When the anxious father seeks a solution for the alleged juvenile delinquency, the son suggests that the teacher be invited to dinner and, if possible, engaged for extracurricular tutoring.

The father consents, summons the instructor, uses diplomatic finesse to bring about better teacher-pupil rapport. Having placed the pedagogue in the seat of honor at the dinner table, the Sumerian parent thanks the "school-father" (parent surrogate) for educating the boy in the "recondite details of the tablet-craft, counting and accounting." Subsequently a banquet is arranged where the servants are ordered to

"Pour out for him [the teacher] good wine, . . .
Make flow the good oil in his vessel like water . . ."
They pour out for him good date-wine, . . . [then]
he [the father] dressed him in a new garment, put a band
    about his hand.
The teacher with joyful heart gave speech to him:

"Young man, because you did not neglect my word, did not
    forsake it,
May you reach the pinnacle of the scribal art, achieve it
    completely. . . .
May Nidaba, the queen of the guardian deities,
. . . show favor to your fashioned reed. . . .

* S. N. Kramer, "Schooldays, A Sumerian Composition Relating to the Education of a Scribe," *Journal of the American Oriental Society*, Vol. 69 (1949), pp. 199 ff.

Of your brothers, may you be their leader,
Of your companions, may you be their chief,
may you rank the highest of [all]."*

Whether or not this particular scribe ever fulfilled his teacher's hopes, it is certain that Babylonian mathematics did "rank the highest of all" in the world of 2000 B.C. and that Sumerian computers were leaders of all their ancient "brothers" in the field. The mathematical historians Otto Neugebauer and F. Thureau-Dangin (1872–1944) have deciphered and interpreted cuneiform tablets which show that during the two millennia before the Christian era the Babylonians evolved a remarkable body of arithmetical and algebraical procedures and, in the last centuries of that epoch, an incredible mathematical astronomy.

Whenever Babylonian mathematics is mentioned, one must realize that the term "Babylonian" is a generic one. The civilization from which the mathematical cuneiform tablets come was preceded by an earlier culture, the Sumerian. According to some theories, the Sumerians are supposed to have migrated from the Ural-Altaic region of north-central Asia to the more fertile Tigris-Euphrates valley. Whatever their country of origin, a non-Semitic people did live just north of the Persian gulf for many centuries prior to the days of Babylonian mathematical achievement. These early inhabitants of lower Mesopotamia founded the Chaldean cities of Ur, Nippur, and Babylon; they developed a culture in which weights and measures, bills, receipts, legal contracts, promissory notes, interest (simple and compound) were commonplace. Semites who occupied Akkad (Assyria), the upper portion of the land between the rivers, built Nineveh as a rival to Babylon, as well as other important cities like Assur, Calah, and Arbela. Eventually the Assyrian Semites conquered their neighbors to the south, and the combined kingdom of Sumer and Akkad was formed. When Hammurabi became supreme ruler of that united kingdom, he chose Babylon, a Sumerian metropolis, as his capital, and from the renown of this city the entire country came to be known as Babylonia.

Historians disagree on the date of Hammurabi and give it variously as some time between 2000 B.C. and 1700 B.C. His era was the golden age of "Old Babylonian" culture. In the field of mathematics, quadratic equations were being solved

* S. N. Kramer, *loc. cit.*

by the equivalent of the formula we use today; all sorts of tabulations assisted the accountant, the statistician, the algebraic theorist; some cuneiform tablets were akin to our logarithmic tables, and interpolation was used to "read between the lines"; a considerable knowledge of practical geometry was available for application to engineering and architecture.

There is a saying that no subject loses more when divorced from its history than mathematics. Certainly mathematics does not flourish in a vacuum, and some would have us believe that its subject matter developed to solve the everyday problems of advancing civilization. But this is only part of the story. Even in ancient Babylonia a considerable body of theoretical mathematics was built up without any thought of immediate practical application. Whether the Mesopotamian "pure" mathematicians held the belief that their discoveries would ultimately be useful, we do not know. But if we realize that Babylonian creativeness extended to other fields—astronomy, religion, government, and law—we can gain some idea of the cultural level which a society must reach for mathematics to be more than a tool, for mathematics to advance along the lines that have made it the logical, philosophical, and universal subject of modern times.

Details of the truly advanced status of mathematics in ancient Babylonia will be presented at many points in this book. We shall subsequently see that great ideas formerly credited to the Greeks were undoubtedly of Mesopotamian origin, that Babylonian algebra was probably an influence in India as late as the twelfth century A.D., and that the western world did not contribute notably to the subject before the time of the Renaissance. In the present chapter we shall first examine those mathematical ideas that form the logical background for the sophisticated mathematical activity of Hammurabi's day (and that of the suffering schoolboy). Then, in order to provide a specific example of the mathematics of that era, we shall explain the Babylonian concept of a "positional" system of numeration, an idea essential for the efficiency of computation (whether by reference to cuneiform tablets or by use of digital computers) and one which has important logical by-products, such as a pattern for the decisions of an "electronic brain."

Since Mesopotamian number mastery was not a sudden development, it would be proper to consider origins, but here one is handicapped by a lack of documentary evidence.

Nevertheless, latter-day ethnological studies suggest the sort of gradual evolution of ideas that may have taken place among the Sumerians or their predecessors or the even more remote ancestors of the Babylonians. We may conjecture that those earliest forebears, like some aborigines whose mores modern anthropologists have studied, had a rather limited conception of number. Some tribal languages, in fact, show a complete lack of number words. A time must come, however, when even a tribesman may want to keep track of his wives, children, clubs, canoes, flocks. The idea of number arose from his need to count those particular aggregates that were important to him.

Reference has just been made to various collections of objects which may occur in a primitive environment. We shall have occasion to consider many different *sets* of things related to fundamental mathematical ideas, both in this chapter and throughout our book. The logic of modern mathematics indicates that the notion of *set* must play a basic role because so many other concepts can be defined or explained in terms of it. As we have just seen, the idea is involved even in the earliest use of numbers.

A *set* is a collection of objects, empirical or conceptual, which are called *elements* or *members* of the set. As synonyms for the word "set," there are the terms *aggregate, class, ensemble, collection.* Thus one can refer to aggregates of people, classes of students, collections of paintings, sets of ideas, and so on. We shall even consider sets whose members are sets, for example, a set of sets of china, the set of all classes in a school, a collection of boxes of matches, the set of all twins in a town.

Finite sets can be specified by listing their members. But one cannot provide a full roster of the numbers used for counting. We shall call that collection the *natural number aggregate* and state that it is symbolized as {1, 2, 3, 4, . . .} (where the three dots after 4 are to be read as "and so on") to signify that the sequence of symbols is unending. Although we are unable to list all elements of the set in question, we have defined it by giving a property, "are used for counting," shared by the numbers in the set and *not* characteristic of other numbers. The use of a defining attribute is the only means of specifying the membership of an aggregate whose roster is unending or "infinite." But one can proceed in the same fashion even for finite sets. For example, reference to the first two presidents of the United States defines a unique pair of individuals, and it is not necessary to list their names.

For many mathematical purposes, a set and a property defining it are used interchangeably. But there is an essential difference in the fact that a particular collection is a unique entity, whereas its elements may share many different common characteristics. In the instance of an aggregate defined in the previous paragraph, one might specify the same set as "the United States presidents elected during the eighteenth century." Or if, say, Samuel Jones has written a recent best-selling book about George Washington and John Adams, one might define the aggregate in question as the "subjects of Jones's study."

Let us now return to the issue that launched our discussion of the set concept, namely, primitive man's need to enumerate particular sets in his immediate environment. Anthropologists have found that, among many tribes, if a savage wishes to state that he has felled *two* trees, has *two* children, owns *two* canoes and *two* clubs, he may use a different word for "two" in each of the four connotations. He has not yet arrived at a *pure* or *abstract* concept of "twoness," a property common to many aggregates, for example, a man's eyes, hands, feet, ears, twin children, and so on.

Primitive man progresses toward a more abstract notion of number when he applies one and the same word for "two" to *any* aggregate of objects that matches some standard collection symbolized by {. .} or {||}. He may think of the things pictured within the braces as pebbles or sticks. In fact, || or = may ultimately become his written symbol for "two."

The procedures for matching and counting described above can be formalized by means of a suitable definition: Two sets are said to be in *one-to-one correspondence* if and only if the elements of those two aggregates can be paired (matched) so that every member of either set has a unique partner in the other set. In that case, the two sets are said to contain the same *cardinal number* of objects. For example, the set of seats in a theater is in one-to-one correspondence with the set of tickets printed for a particular performance and, in a specific case, the cardinal number of either set might be symbolized by the numeral 1250.

In modern mathematical philosophy the cardinal number of a given set is sometimes described as an attribute which that set shares with all sets that can be put into one-to-one correspondence with it. That description would interpret a particular cardinal number as a defining property for a whole class of matching sets. Or, from the point of view of Bertrand Russell, who credits the same idea to the German logician Gottlob Frege (1848–1925), the cardinal number of a given set *is* the aggregate of all sets that can be matched with it. We observe that the individual members of that collection are sets, one of which is the given set (since it can be matched with itself). Russell's conception is an instance of a fact mentioned earlier, the interchangeability of a set and one of its defining properties.

It may seem an anachronism to consider the counting procedures of early man as the basis for the modern, sophisticated Frege-Russell conception of cardinal number. But here we are reminded of Molière's *Bourgeois Gentilhomme,* who discovered belatedly that he had been talking *prose* all his life. Ordinary prose and tribal arithmetic may, of course, lack elegance. Nevertheless, children learn to talk by imitating the former, and we shall do well to use primitive counting in the further analysis of the meaning of number.

To determine the size or cardinality of a given set by means of matching (one-to-one correspondence), our remote forebears made comparisons with ever-ready standard models—the eyes for *two,* the legs of an animal for *four,* the fingers of one hand for *five,* etc. Let us, for the sake of uniformity, imagine a tribe that used pebbles to form the collection of standard sets, {.}, {. .}, {. . .}, and so on. Then if a flock of sheep was to be counted, the tribesman would attempt to match the flock with some set of pebbles in the collection. The matching might fail because there were either more or fewer sheep than pebbles in the standard set selected. Then it would be necessary to try matching with some other standard set, and the procedure would be repeated until a one-to-one correspondence was obtained.

The method of counting just described would be a good one in a primitive society where all aggregates of interest are small, for then matching would call for only a few standard sets and not too many trials. Otherwise, just as a draftsman or mechanic arranges his tools neatly in a kit, modern man must put some law and order into his aggregate of standard sets. Then, too, if one is to be able to make ready reference to some cardinal number, he will want to name it by a word or a symbol.

Instead of trial and error with a few standard sets, primitive or modern man may count the elements in a given set by a process of tallying, that is, by placing pebbles or sticks on the ground one by one, which is the same as putting ink dots or pen strokes on a piece of paper. In this way one can actually construct standard sets in an orderly fashion by starting with one dot or stroke and adding one more repeatedly until he arrives at the standard set matching the aggregate he wishes to count. If he does this with dots, he will be building up the standard sets we have suggested above. If he does his tallying with strokes, he will simultaneously be recording successive numerals in the match-stick notation used by the Chinese, later adopted by the Japanese and used by them as recently as the eighteenth century. Or, if he does his counting orally, he will say "one, two, three, four," etc. Here "two" signifies "one and one," "three" means "two and one," "four" signifies "three and one," etc. Thus, by the process of starting with the cardinal number we call "one" and adding "one" repeatedly, the standard sets are built up in the orderly fashion of Figure 1.1, where names in the English language, match-stick numerals, and the Hindu-Arabic numerals we use today are recorded for the first few sets.

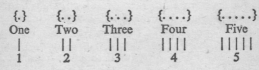

Figure 1.1

If we are to be truly modern, we should precede the standard sets in Figure 1.1 by { }, called the *null set*, or *empty set*. The special symbol $\emptyset$ is usually used to designate this vacuous aggregate, that is, $\emptyset = \{ \}$. To the cardinal number of $\emptyset$ we give the name *zero*, represented by the numeral 0. Although we do not usually count "*zero*, one, two, three," we actually begin with the empty set in the process of tallying, since placing the *first* pebble or stick on the ground might be considered as adding one object to the empty set in order to obtain the next standard set in the sequence of standard sets.

In logic, there is much emphasis on the distinction between an entity and the word or symbol used to name it.

Thus the word "Henry" is not identical with the man named. Also, he may be designated in many ways, for example, "Hal" or "Mr. Brown" or by his social security number, and so on. Again, in the sense of Frege and Russell, the cardinal number of {. . .} is the collection of sets matching {. . .}. Surely that aggregate is not the same as the symbol "three" or the numeral 3. In practice, however, constant emphasis on the distinction between a name and the object named makes for pedantry. Hence, once the matter is understood, a mathematician will habitually indulge in a pardonable "abuse of language" by speaking of the "cardinal number 3" instead of the "cardinal number symbolized by the numeral 3." We shall, in fact, use the simpler form of expression in the very next paragraph.

The cardinal numbers, 1, 2, 3, 4, . . . , are called *counting numbers* or *natural numbers*. But from a more sophisticated point of view, *zero* should be included as a counting number and should precede 1 in the sequence above. Thus the natural numbers would be identical with the set of (finite) cardinal numbers. However, since zero has not been traditionally associated with the process of counting, the aggregate, {0, 1, 2, 3, 4, . . .}, is sometimes described as the class of *whole numbers*.

When the standard sets in Figure 1.1 are generated in orderly fashion by adding one "pebble" repeatedly, each set can be matched (placed in one-to-one correspondence) with a part or *proper subset* of its immediate successor which can, in turn, be matched with a proper subset of the next set, and so on. Therefore a standard set can be matched with a proper subset of any set further to the right in the sequence. Or the cardinal number of any standard set is *less than* the cardinal number of any set further on in the sequence. For example, {. . .} can be matched with part of {. . . . . .}, and hence 3 < 7 (3 is *less than* 7).

One would say that the relation "is a proper subset of" gives some structure to the collection of standard sets by arranging them in order. The relation < establishes a similar order among the natural numbers. Therefore, as far as order is concerned, the ordered standard sets are said to be *isomorphic* to the natural numbers arranged in increasing order, which means that the two systems have the same *form* or are *abstractly equivalent*. Isomorphism is an exceedingly important concept in modern mathematics, since reasoning in a single system establishes corresponding facts in all systems that are isomorphic to it, and sometimes it is easier to handle a particular system rather than one of its abstract equivalents.

We have described two isomorphic systems that provide two equivalent ways of counting. One method is tallying, that is, building up standard sets, and the other is recitation of number words in sequence—one, two, three, four, etc. Either technique is satisfactory if one has only small aggregates to count. Otherwise, think of the quantity of pebbles, sticks, or pen strokes necessary to tally a million objects, or the need to memorize, in order, a million different number words! As far as we know, the Babylonians were the first people in history to realize that such suffering is unnecessary, and that only a few symbols can suffice to represent all counting numbers however large. Again, it is fairly certain that their ideas were anticipated, in a small way, by primitive predecessors. Economy of words and symbols is practiced by the savage who counts on the fingers of one hand, then ties a knot in a rope and starts counting again, repeating the *same number words* used originally. When he reaches "five" once more, a second knot it tied, and he starts anew. We would say that he has chosen *five* as the *base* or *radix* of his system of numeration. Because fingers and toes are used in counting, *five* or *ten* or *twenty* is the most usual choice of radix.

The ancestors of the Sumerians must have proceeded in just the way we have described except that their choice of base was *ten*. This is indicated in the Sumerian-Babylonian numerals. Symbols for the first nine numerals are akin to match-stick notation, except that the vertical strokes are wedge-shaped or *cuneiform*, ▼.▼▼.   ▼▼▼   Then (in

lieu of knotting a rope), the primitives in question made a mark, ≺ , and started the count anew. When they arrived at another count of *ten*, they made another mark, so that ≺≺ represented twenty and, with the orderly condensation of cuneiform symbols, ≼ ▼ represented fifty. The repetitive

scheme of numeration continued with fifty-one,   ≼ ▼
and went on up to fifty-nine ≼ ▼▼▼
                                    ▼▼▼

Only when larger numerals had to be represented was there evidence that *sixty* was used as the radix of a "positional" system whose nature will be explained below.

Since primitives have only small sets to count, they do not carry a good idea like counting by tens to a general conclusion. On the other hand, if we were faced with the task of counting a large set of cards or coins, we would almost automatically place them in packages of ten until we had ten such sets, when we would fuse the objects into a single set of one hundred. Then we would start counting out sets of ten until we had another hundred, and so on.

Our system of numeration with Hindu-Arabic numerals is a *positional* one with radix *ten*. This signifies that there are *ten*, and *only ten* symbols:

$$0, 1, 2, 3, 4, 5, 6, 7, 8, 9$$

With the use of these symbols in different positions, all finite cardinal numbers can be represented. The same few ciphers have different significance according to *position*. In counting, as we have illustrated, objects are grouped into tens, and tens of tens (hundreds) and tens of tens of tens (thousands), etc. In "place-value" notation, the grouping is indicated by the position of the number symbols. Thus, 8,439 means 8 thousands, 4 hundreds, 3 tens, and 9 units.

If man had had six fingers, *six* might have been the radix of our number system. The written symbols would have conveyed different meanings, but the abstract mathematical concepts and procedures would have been the same. We would have used six symbols and only six—0, 1, 2, 3, 4, 5—to write all numbers. Then *six* would be written as 10 (1 six and 0 units); twelve would be written as 20 (2 sixes and 0 units); eighteen would be written as 30; thirty-five would be 55 (5 sixes and 5 units). Since this is the largest two-digit number we can write with the six symbols available, thirty-six, the next higher number, would have to be written as 100. Continuing in the same way, 555 (5 thirty-sixes + 5 sixes + 5 units) would be the largest three-digit number, and the next number would have to be written as 1000. It would be equivalent to our six × six × six.

On the other hand, if man had had six fingers on each hand, we might have had *twelve*, not six, as base. Although the Aphos of Benue, an African tribe, do not have twelve fingers, they use twelve as their number base and thereby seem to indicate some remarkable arithmetic intuition in the choice of a superior base. For the use of the base twelve, we would need twelve symbols,

$$0, 1, 2, 3, 4, 5, 6, 7, 8, 9, *, \#$$

and we should write twelve as 10 (1 twelve and 0 units); thirteen would be 11, twenty-four would be 20 (two twelves and 0 units); one hundred forty-three would be ## (eleven twelves and eleven units). As this is the largest two-digit number that can be represented with the twelve symbols available, the next number, one hundred forty-four, would be written 100.

The reader may amuse himself by checking the following sample exercises.

System with Base Six

35	Five + two = seven, written as 11 in this system.
+ 52	Put down 1 and carry 1.
131	Three + five + one = nine, written as 13 in this system.

43	Three × three = nine, written as 13 in this system.
× 3	Put down 3 and carry 1.
213	Three × four = twelve. Twelve + one = thirteen, written, as 21.

System with Base Twelve

8*	Ten and one are eleven. Eight and four are twelve.
+ 41	
10#	

	Eleven fives = fifty-five, written as 47 in this system.
35	Put down 7 and carry 4. Eleven threes = thirty-three.
× #	
317	Adding four, the result is thirty-seven, written as 31 in this system.

In our decimal system, positions to the right of the decimal point represent tenths, hundredths, thousandths, etc. Thus 0.462 stands for the *sum* of 4 tenths, 6 hundredths, and 2 thousandths. Using the customary exponential symbolism of algebra, we can summarize the nature of the decimal system by stating that successive places to the left of the decimal point have the values 1 (or 10^0), 10^1, 10^2, 10^3, 10^4, etc., whereas those to the right have the values 1/10 (or 10^{-1}), 1/100 (or 10^{-2}), 1/1000 (or 10^{-3}), etc. Thus 7084.91002 means

$$7(10^3) + 8(10^1) + 4(10^0) + 9(10^{-1}) + 1(10^{-2}) + 2(10^{-5})$$

In general, if the base of a number system is represented by b, successive places to the left of the "decimal" point have the values, b^0, b^1, b^2, b^3, b^4, etc., and those to the right have the values b^{-1}, b^{-2}, b^{-3}, b^{-4}, etc.

In the Sumerian-Babylonian notation sixty was the radix for natural numbers above fifty-nine and also for the sexagesimal fractions. Now in a modern sexagesimal system of numeration the symbol 54 would signify 5 sixties and 4 units. It would be the symbol for our decimal number three hundred four. Again, in a sexagesimal system, 8.49 would mean the sum of 8 units, 4 sixtieths, and 9 thirty-six hundredths. As a matter of fact, our method of angular measure is derived from the Babylonian sexagesimal system. In order to avoid confusion, however, we would *not* write 8.49 but instead would employ the symbol

$$8° \ 4' \ 9''$$

and read it as 8 degrees, 4 minutes, 9 seconds. This is identical in meaning with the above 8 units, 4 sixtieths, 9 thirty-six hundredths, since a *degree* is the unit of angular measure and a *minute* and a *second* are one sixtieth and one thirty-six hundredth, respectively, of the angular unit.

The cuneiform symbol for sixty was the same as for *one*, namely, ▼ . The only way to realize that sixty was meant, and not one, was from the context. For example, in a textbook tablet where the natural numbers were listed in order, one could judge that the single vertical wedge succeeding fifty-nine represented sixty. Again, the group of cuneiform symbols, ▼▼◄◄▼▼▼ , might be interpreted as our $2(60)^1 + 23(60)^0 = 143$ but *other* interpretations are possible, for example, $2(60)^2 + 23(60)^1 = 8580$. What the Babylonians needed was a symbol for *zero*. Ultimately such a sign was developed, for it appears in the Seleucid mathematical tablets and there is some evidence that it may possibly have been created as early as 700 B.C. But even in the final phase of Babylonian writing there were no zero symbols at the ends of numbers. To put this weakness into modern dress, let us imagine our decimal system without a zero. We write

1 2 3

Is this one hundred twenty-three, or ten thousand two hundred three, or one thousand two hundred thirty? In the first case, the Babylonians would have avoided difficulties by writing the symbols close together. The second number would have been symbolized by 1-2-3, that is, by using a zero symbol that is akin to our dash. But in the third instance, the ambiguity was never removed.

The Babylonians' choice of radix is now attributed to the adjustment of their arithmetic to their monetary units. In the earliest days the basic medium of exchange was barley, but pieces of precious metals like silver were used later on. Since coinage had not yet been invented, value was measured according to weight. In the table of weights, sixty *shekels* were equivalent to one *mina* and sixty *minas* to a *talent*. This counting of weights (and ultimately of minted coins) in groups of sixty was the origin of the sexagesimal system. Formerly, the use of sixty as base was erroneously attributed to the Babylonian estimate of the year as 360 days, involving the subdivision of the apparently circular orbit of the sun into 360 equal parts. Today it is known that this phase of Babylonian astronomy occurred in the last centuries B.C., whereas the use of a sexagesimal number system is found in the earliest cuneiform tablets.

How did the Babylonians handle arithmetic computation? They seem to have had little trouble with addition and subtraction. For multiplication and more advanced arithmetic operations, they made extensive use of *tables*. Whereas the modern schoolboy memorizes tables for multiplication by 2, 3, . . . , 9, the Babylonian scribe would have consulted a cuneiform tablet like the one now on view in the Brussels collection. In that table, the products of 7, 10, 12½, 16, 24, by 2, 3, . . . , 9, 10, 20, . . . , 50 are listed.

The Babylonians were very modern in their idea that it is *not* necessary to introduce a division operation providing one is able to carry out multiplication with whole numbers and common fractions. For example, one need not consider $7 \div 2$ because one can instead perform the multiplication, $7 \times \frac{1}{2}$. The thought is that division by a number is equivalent to multiplication by its *reciprocal* or *multiplicative inverse*. Moreover, except for *zero*, every number x of elementary arithmetic has a multiplicative inverse, $1/x$, that is, a number such that $x \cdot 1/x = 1$. Thus the multiplicative inverses or reciprocals of 3, 4, 1/5, 2/9 are respectively 1/3, 1/4, 5, 9/2.

Many Babylonian tables of reciprocals have been unearthed and deciphered. When transcribed into our symbols, the first entries in one of those tables would appear as follows:

Number	Sexagesimal Reciprocal
2	30
3	20
4	15
5	12
6	10
8	7, 30
9	6, 40

Here the multiplicative inverse of each number in the first column is expressed as a sexagesimal fraction in the second column. Interpreting that column in terms of angular measure with degrees, minutes, and seconds may serve as a helpful artifice. Thus the reciprocal of 2 is 1/2 and $(1/2)° = 30'$. The reciprocal of 3 is 1/3 and $(1/3)° = 20'$, that for 8 is $(1/8)° = 7'30''$, etc. The transcription of the Babylonian procedure for obtaining $7 \div 2 = 3 \ 1/2$ and $9 \div 8 = 1 \ 1/8$ is

$7 \times (1/2)° = 7 \times 30' = 210' = 3° \ 30'$, which is equivalent to our
$\qquad\qquad\qquad 3 \ 1/2$

$9 \times (1/8)° = 9 \times 7'30'' = 63' \ 270''$
$\qquad\qquad = 63' + (4'30'')$
$\qquad\qquad = 67' \ 30''$
$\qquad\qquad = 1° \ 7'30''$, which is equivalent to our 1 1/8.

We observe that 7 and its reciprocal were omitted from the Babylonian tabulation. We can conjecture why this is so if we try to convert $(1/7)°$ into minutes and seconds, using only whole numbers. This cannot be done, since the result is 8′34 2/7″. Babylonian tables listed only "regular" reciprocals and omitted "irregular" ones like 1/7, 1/11, etc., with the statement that these involve "impossible" divisions. However, in such cases, sexagesimal approximations like 8,34 for 1/7 were used much as we might use the decimal 0.14 as an approximation of 1/7. Some of the reciprocal tablets are very extensive; one from the Seleucid period contains about fifty pairs of numbers. A row near the end of this tablet bears an entry which we transcribe as 2, 59, 21, 40, 48, 54 with reciprocal 20, 4, 16, 22, 28, 44, 14, 57, 40, 4, 56, 17, 46, 40. This means that the number in question should be interpreted by us as

$$2(60)^5 + 59(60)^4 + 21(60)^3 + 40(60)^2 + 48(60)^1 + 54(60)^0$$

and its reciprocal as equal to

$$20(60)^{-6} + 4(60)^{-7} + 16(60)^{-8} + 22(60)^{-9} + 28(60)^{-10}$$
$$+ \cdots + 46(60)^{-18} + 40(60)^{-19}$$

We must admit that this is fearless arithmetic. But then tables of squares and square roots, cubes and cube roots, as well as exponential and compound interest tables had been a commonplace 1500 years before this reciprocal table was prepared!

As far as the pure mathematician is concerned, it is the "place-value" *concept* that is an all-important contribution of the Babylonians to arithmetic; the fact that they based their system on sixty is immaterial. If they had used a radix of four or five or twelve or twenty (or any other number that is not too large), their creation would have been equally valuable as a means of condensing the tasks of enumeration and computation. In algebraic terminology, a numeral in *any* positional system of notation represents a number

$$a_n b^n + \cdots + a_2 b^2 + a_1 b^1 + a_0 b^0 + c_1 b^{-1} + c_2 b^{-2} + \cdots + c_m b^{-m}$$

where b represents the number chosen as radix, and an a or a c is either zero or an integer between 1 and $b - 1$. (The subscripts are a customary algebraic device for indicating position.) The great advantage of using any positional system lies in the fact that only b symbols are required. The formula above tells the entire story in a nutshell.

Is there possibly a best choice of radix? Pure mathematicians have indicated that a *prime* base (one like 7, 11, 13,

17, etc., with no divisors but 1 and itself) would have led to greater unformity in arithmetic procedures. Practical reformers, on the other hand, have been in general agreement that *twelve* would have been a better base than ten, since it has the divisors 2, 3, 4, and 6, a fact that would have made work with fractions easier than it is with base ten (divisors 2 and 5). The learning of only two additional symbols would be worthwhile, compared to the tremendous saving in other arithmetic effort. Charles XII of Sweden was supposed to have been contemplating, at the time of his death, the abolition of the decimal system in all his dominions, in favor of the duodecimal. A universal change to the base twelve, or to any base, however, is just as impracticable as the general use of Esperanto. If a choice were possible, a duodecimal or a prime system would be the scale of civilization, but quinary, decimal, and vigesimal systems are the scales of nature.

In the United States in colonial days, the Reverend Hugh Jones (1692–1760), professor of mathematics at the College of William and Mary, was an ardent advocate of the *octary* system (radix *eight*), which is, in fact, used today in connection with certain electronic computers. Jones was a reformer who argued that ordinary arithmetic had already become "mysterious to Women and Youths and often troublesome to the best Artists." Without going into detail, it can be asserted that the base eight makes fractional work simpler because octary fractions are just a matter of halving again and again. Thus, one-quarter is just one-half of a half, and one-eighth is just one-half of a half of a half, etc. Moreover, computation is facilitated because the radix eight is a perfect cube, that is, $8 = 2 \cdot 2 \cdot 2$, and four, which is one-half the radix, is a perfect square ($4 = 2 \cdot 2$). Still another advantage of repeated halving is seen in the fact that arithmetic is made consistent with the British system of weights, in which an ounce is one-sixteenth of a pound, and so on. The Reverend Jones showed that, as far as England and its colonies were concerned, many arithmetic difficulties arose from the use of the British system of weights, measures, and coinage.

Whereas the Reverend Jones saw advantages in octary arithmetic, and British mathematicians* today are still arguing about the virtues of decimal versus duodecimal systems,

* See B. H. Neumann, "On Decimal Coinage," *Matrix*, Melbourne University Mathematical Society, 1964, pp. 16–18.

one of the mathematical immortals, Gottfried Wilhelm Leibniz (1646–1716) had advocated the binary or dyadic system, the type of numeration with two as base, which, according to anthropologists, was used by the most primitive of primitive groups. Among such people a tribesman would count "one, two," then "two and one," "two and two," "two and two and one," "two and two and two." At about this point the strain became too great and every higher number was called "heap," a lot. Then what advantages could Leibniz see in the primitive dyadic system? For one thing, it appeared to hold mystic significance for him. But mathematicians today are inclined to view his imaginative statements merely as a poetic formulation of aspects of the algebra of sets (Chapter 6). From still another point of view, Leibniz realized that the utter simplicity of binary arithmetic must hold definite practical advantages, and in this, as well as in his thoughts on symbolic logic, he anticipated present developments in applied and pure mathematics.

As a preliminary to the explanation of the recent applications of numeration with base two, a few decimal numbers and the corresponding binary numerals are listed below.

Decimal Number	Binary Representation
Zero	0
One	1 (one unit)
Two	10 (one "two" and no units)
Three	11 (one "two" and one unit)
Four	100 (one $(two)^2$)
Five	101
Six	110
Seven	111
Eight	1000
Nine	1001
Ten	1010
Eleven	1011
Twelve	1100
Thirteen	1101
Fourteen	1110
Fifteen	1111
Sixteen	10000

To obtain the decimal equivalent of any binary number one need only apply the basic formula for the meaning of a number in a positional system of numeration (page 38). Here, if we think in terms of our decimal system, $b = 2$ and each a will have either the value 0 or the value 1, that is, the only symbols needed in a binary system are 0 and 1. Successive places proceeding toward the left, starting at the decimal point, have the values 2^0, 2^1, 2^2, 2^3, etc. Thus the binary number 10111 has, according to the fundamental formula, the decimal value

$$1(2)^4 + 0(2)^3 + 1(2)^2 + 1(2)^1 + 1(2)^0 =$$
$$16 \ + \ 0 \ + \ 4 \ + \ 2 \ + \ 1 \ = 23$$

and 11.1001 has the value

$$1(2)^1 + 1(2)^0 + 1(2)^{-1} + 0(2)^{-2} + 0(2)^{-3} + 1(2)^{-4} =$$
$$2 \ + \ 1 \ + \ \frac{1}{2} \ + \ 0 \ + \ 0 \ + \ \frac{1}{16} = 3\frac{9}{16}$$

The first advantage of a binary system of numeration is that only two symbols are needed, namely 0 and 1. Another is that children studying binary arithmetic would have very few tables to memorize. The addition table reduces to

$$0 + 0 = 0 \qquad 0 + 1 = 1 \qquad 1 + 1 = 10$$

All multiplication tables are embodied in the three statements

$$0 \times 0 = 0 \qquad 0 \times 1 = 0 \qquad 1 \times 1 = 1$$

But, on the other hand, there is the *length* of a numeral! Our thousand would have to be written as

$$1,111,101,000$$

In our modern electronic "children"—our digital computers or mechanical brains, and so on—a lengthy binary numeral would, however, constitute no serious problem. With 1 and 0 represented by "on" and "off" respectively, a long numeral merely means a more extensive bank of telegraph-type relays or radio-type tubes. To see how this occurs, let us suppose, for simplicity, that one wishes to register or signal any number from zero to seven. Then, using the binary representations, and a row of three electric light bulbs with "on" for 1 and "off" for 0, the signals are as follows:

Decimal Number	Binary Representation	Signal
Zero	000	0 0 0 (off, off, off)
One	001	0 0 ● (off, off, on)
Two	010	0 ● 0 (off, on, off)
Three	011	0 ● ●
Four	100	● 0 0
Five	101	● 0 ●
Six	110	● ● 0
Seven	111	● ● ● (on, on, on)

The binary representations are the same as those previously given, except that 0's have been added on the left in the case of the first four numbers so that every number may have three places.

One might think, alternatively, that one of the numbers from zero to seven is to be fed into a computer by means of a punch card with three dots where 1 and 0 are represented by punching or not punching the dot. Then the above "signals" show the appearance of the punch card for the different numbers. Similarly, one could use a punch card with ten dots, or a row of ten bulbs to register all binary numerals up to 1,111,111,111. Some decimal names and binary equivalents would be as shown on the bottom of p. 42.

To understand the extreme importance of Leibniz' favorite radix *two* in the present age of automation, one must realize that the name "computer" is misleading, and "thinking machine" or "giant brain" are substitute terms that give a better idea of the remarkable services the electronic devices in

Decimal	Binary	Signal
Zero	0,000,000,000	0 0 0 0 0 0 0 0 0 0
One	0,000,000,001	0 0 0 0 0 0 0 0 0 ●
Two	0,000,000,010	0 0 0 0 0 0 0 0 ● 0
...	....	....
...	....	....
...	....	....
Thousand	1,111,101,000	● ● ● ● ● 0 0 0 0 0
...	....	....
1023	1,111,111,111	● ● ● ● ● ● ● ● ● ●

question can render. It is true that binary numbers like those above may be fed into a machine or stored in its registers or signaled, and so forth. But these binary figures (or their decimal equivalents) are often merely code numbers for names or words or messages or mathematical propositions or general statements of some sort.

A digital computer receives its problems through "input" devices like punched cards, punched paper tape, magnetic tapes, magnetic wire, or photographic film. The reason for the almost universal use of binary representation is that the equipment generally employed in digital computers has *two* states. The punched cards and tapes are either punched or not in each position, and magnetic equipment distinguishes a pulse from a nonpulse; relays are open or shut, and electronic circuits are built with two stable states. Computers are designed to do much more than calculation. They can make selections or *decisions* providing questions are put to them properly. The binary computers must be asked to make comparisons between *pairs*, much as the last rounds in a sequence of basketball games compare teams in order to select the winning team.

All this may seem a long way from Hammurabi's era and Babylonian mathematics. Digital computers, however, are direct descendants of the cuneiform tablets, linked by the dominant idea of the place-value notation, which is basic to all schemes of simplifying the practical calculations required in each period of history. Practicality must be the concern of the applied mathematician, and therefore he sees a positional scheme as a superior one, and points with pride to the speedy, painless performance of electronic computers where astronomic figures are involved. The point of view of pure mathematics, however, provides unity for the subject by pronouncing ancient and modern systems merely different examples of a *single* abstract pattern, in other words, by calling the systems *isomorphic* with respect to the arithmetic operations of addition and multiplication.

That a one-to-one correspondence can be established between two systems of numeration with different radices, or between a set of numerals and a set of electric signals, is indicated by previous tabulations (page 42). Isomorphism or structural identity exists because there is matching not only of number symbols, but of operations (the addition and multiplication operations in the two systems) and the results of operations. Thus the decimal statements

$$2 + 3 = 5 \qquad 2 \times 3 = 6$$

correspond to the binary

$$10 + 11 = 101 \qquad 10 \times 11 = 110$$

and, again, these match, symbol for symbol, operation for operation, with certain computer signals and operations.

What we have been discussing, then, is the matter of varied interpretations of a single pure or abstract system, the one usually described as the additive and multiplicative arithmetic of the whole numbers and the common fractions. This particular structure is not the entire story, however, and this makes it inadequate for important theoretical issues associated with measurement in the physical world. The nature of certain geometric problems arising from questions of measure will now be considered; it will be seen that it was not Babylonian but rather Hellenic science that revealed and succeeded in solving related numerical paradoxes, thereby making possible the logical derivation of formulas for lengths, areas, and volumes.

Chapter 2

Mathematical Method and
Main Streams Are Launched

At the beginning of our story, a Sumerian document was seen to present a picture of what the life of a schoolboy was like in 2000 B.C. The ancient story was a case of fiction imitating fact. But what is the life of today's schoolboy like, almost four thousand years later? Are the blows of the cane being replaced by stinging intellectual impacts? Are parents still involved in the backlash of pedagogical methods?

To face only the mathematical aspect of these questions, one must consider the United States educational phenomenon called "the new mathematics." Perhaps the evidence we shall adduce will be a case where facts appear to imitate fiction, since we now propose to show that basic features of the "new" program must be given a date at least as early as the sixth century B.C. As we have seen, pebble devices for picturing cardinal numbers go back to prehistoric man. But school children who are now using such representations in order to "discover" patterns or mathematical laws are emulating procedures followed by the ancient Pythagorean Society.

That organization, part secret brotherhood, part institute for advanced study, had a membership of wealthy men whom Pythagoras (*ca.* 550 B.C.) had gathered about him in Crotona, a Greek city in southern Italy. The avowed purpose of the Pythagorean school was to carry on scientific research in number theory, geometry, music, and astronomy. It is known that Pythagoras made many trips to the Middle East, and therefore it is not surprising that some of the ideas he presented to his disciples had a strong Babylonian flavor.

But in one respect the Babylonians exerted no influence, since the Society showed no interest in techniques of practical computation, and devoted itself instead to the logical and philosophical aspects of the *theory* of numbers.

Our own objective in the present chapter is to show how discoveries of the Pythagorean brotherhood led to the "real number system," the rock on which most of mathematics, old or new, is built. So great were the Pythagorean birth pangs that they could only be alleviated by the panacea of a second major conception, one which crystallized for all time the method of *proof* that is used in mathematics. Although the Babylonians and Egyptians based mathematical conclusions on experiment and observation, the Pythagoreans discovered that certain intuitive ideas about measurement will produce an apparent paradox. Therefore Pythagoras decided, once and for all, that empirical observations cannot furnish pure mathematical *proof*, which must be provided instead by deductive chains of reasoning. Hence he went forward with a task that Thales (*ca.* 600 B.C.), his teacher, had initiated, and which Hellenic thinkers up to the time of Euclid (300 B.C.) were to pursue. The program was the organization of geometry into a logical pattern in which, after a few assumptions and definitions are laid down, all further statements are deduced.

"Number rules the universe," said Pythagoras. To some extent this was an expression of the deep emotion with which mathematicians react to their specialty, but mainly it was an assertion of the major dogma of the Pythagorean brotherhood, the belief that all of mathematics and science could be based on the natural numbers, $\{1, 2, 3, \ldots\}$. It was in their study of some of the elementary properties of the natural numbers that the Pythagoreans set the example for the "method of discovery" in the "new mathematics." Since *pattern* was the objective, and *geometry* was a fundamental interest, the brotherhood formed *figurate numbers*, designs in the form of *polygons*. Thus, by counting the dots and observing the shape in each of the diagrams of Figure 2.1, we see why 10, 16, 20, 22, and 28, are described as *triangular*, *square*, *rectangular*, *pentagonal*, and *hexagonal* numbers. The Society used such diagrams in the derivation of formulas related to certain number series.* But here we shall be more

---

* See, for example, E. E. Kramer, *The Main Stream of Mathematics*, Oxford University Press, New York, 1951, pp. 196 ff.

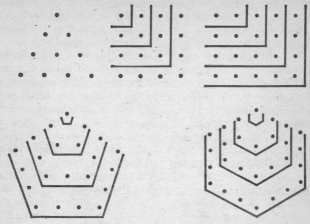

Figure 2.1   Figurate numbers

concerned with how today's schoolboy is applying figurate numbers.

Our kindergartners, like the Pythagoreans, may construct figurate numbers by adding *one* pebble at a time. The Society held that *one* is therefore a *source* of numbers but is *not* itself a counting number, since there is no need to count in a set containing a unique, solitary pebble. In the course of building numbers, our children may recite appropriate rhymes or ditties. The Pythagoreans chanted prayers that incorporated oriental mystic beliefs about the natural numbers.

The gist of their faith was that *one* represented reason, *two* stood for man, *three* for woman, *five* represented marriage, since it is formed by the union of two and three. *Four* stood for justice, since it is the product of equals. All the *even* numbers were regarded as soluble, therefore ephemeral, *feminine*, pertaining to the earth; *odd* numbers were indissoluble, *masculine*, partaking of celestial nature. *Ten*, inevitably a number *base*, was pictured with *four* rows of pebbles as in Figure 2.1 and hence called the *tetraktys*. It was considered the sacred "fourfoldness," because its four rows represented a totality of the reason and justice of man and woman, and also, in Pythagorean metaphysics, cosmic creation through the four basic elements—fire, water, air, and earth. The ritual of the brotherhood included a special prayer to the "holy ten, the keyholder of all."

Mathematics was mixed with mysticism in the activities of Pythagoras' followers, and later in the present chapter we shall see how the "eternal feminine," that is, the characteristics of the even numbers, led them to the most startling of their discoveries. Opinion to the contrary, we do not bring sex into the kindergarten today and hence do not visualize counting numbers as male and female. Instead, we use the term *even* for 2, 4, 6, . . . and all natural numbers that are multiples of 2, and we refer to the other natural numbers—1, 3, 5, . . .—as *odd*. But we can agree with the Pythagoreans in picturing an even number as a rectangle with two columns (Figure 2.2.*a*) and an odd number as such a rectangle supplemented by a single pebble (Figure 2.2*b*).

Figure 2.2*a*
Even number 6

Figure 2.2*b*
Odd number 7

Any sophisticated use of Pythagorean figurate numbers presupposes that the meaning of *addition* and *multiplication* of natural numbers is understood. Therefore today's school children are being encouraged to "discover" the meaning of 3 + 4, for example. They know that 3 is the symbol for the (cardinal) number corresponding to the set {. . .}, and 4 is the number for {. . . .}. If they unite these sets by placing the pebbles or dots in the second aggregate to the right of those in the first, they are constructing the united set or *union* of the two sets, namely, {. . . . . . .}. The sum 3 + 4 can then be defined as the cardinal number of the union, and that number is 7. The "discovery" is that 3 + 4 = 7.

Children are told that the above united set or union might have been pictured as

or in a variety of different ways. No particular pattern is required in forming the union of two sets. That being the case, the diagrams we have just indicated (or the original picture) might just as well correspond to the sum $4 + 3$. Therefore $4 + 3 = 7$ and $3 + 4 = 4 + 3$.

In passing, let us remark that, in modern mathematics, the symbol $=$ can be read as "equals" but is understood to signify that the words or symbols on either side of the equals sign are names for the same object. Thus $4 + 3$ is not identical with the symbol 7. Nevertheless the same thing is named in either case—specifically, a certain cardinal number.

A child may enjoy repeating the steps of his "discovery" with suitable variations for the sake of interest. If he wishes to "discover" the meaning of $3 + 3$, say, he will wish to unite $\{. . .\}$ and $\{* * *\}$. (We recall from the previous chapter that 3 is the cardinal number of *many* different matching sets.) Here what should be emphasized is that in defining addition of cardinal numbers, the sets that are united must be *disjoint* or nonoverlapping, that is, must have no members in common. That fact enables one to say that $3 + 3$ corresponds to the picture,

$$\left\{ \bullet \quad \bullet \quad \bullet \quad * \quad * \quad * \right\} \quad \text{or} \quad \left\{ \begin{matrix} \bullet \\ * \quad * \quad \bullet \\ \bullet \quad * \end{matrix} \right\}$$

and so on, and therefore $3 + 3 = 6$.

After uniting many varied pairs of disjoint sets in order to find different sums, the child is supposed to make more significant "discoveries," namely, those that are laws or general rules for *all* pairs of natural numbers. Thus the fact that $3 + 4 = 4 + 3$, $1 + 2 = 2 + 1$, $2 + 5 = 5 + 2$, etc. should suggest the "discovery" that the order of terms is immaterial in adding a pair of natural numbers. Here we have the *commutative law* of addition of natural numbers: If a and b are any two natural numbers, then $a + b = b + a$.

Our illustrative examples have indicated that addition can be described as a *binary operation* because basically it combines only *two* numbers at a time. Now if one is to drive a car or operate any machine, it is always advisable to check in advance that it is in good operating order. By crude analogy, if addition is to be considered a proper, well-defined binary operation on the natural numbers, one should know, at the start, that it is possible to perform it with *every* pair of natural numbers. There should be no stalling or disastrous results where a sum is some "monster" unknown to the world of counting numbers. Nor should one arrive at a dilemma where there are two possible natural numbers that might serve as the sum. This is all so obvious that the reader may wonder why it is mentioned at all. The point is that one is not going to stop with addition. One will subsequently define and carry out $8 - 2$, $6 - 3$, etc. But what about $2 - 8$, and $3 - 6$? Will a child in the lower school grades be asked to "discover" how to remove 8 pebbles from a set of 2? Evidently one cannot say that subtraction is a well-defined binary operation on the natural numbers. One way of handling such a situation in the newest "new mathematics" is to say that subtraction of natural numbers cannot be honored with the title of binary operation. An older method starts all studies of a particular operation with a "closure" law.

Returning to *addition* of natural numbers, the latest style would merely summarize the situation by stating: Addition is a *binary operation* on the set of natural numbers. The older fashion would provide the implicit content of this statement by asserting the closure law: The aggregate of natural numbers is *closed* under addition. This means that the sum of any two natural numbers is a unique natural number.

In a *logical* treatment of the arithmetic or algebra of natural numbers, the above closure law will naturally precede the commutative law of addition or any other law relating to addition, for how can one say that $a + b = b + a$ for *all* a and b unless one is sure that $a + b$ and $b + a$ have meaning in the aggregate under consideration? Because a closure law should logically come first, one finds very often that teachers and textbooks expect such a law to be one of the first "discoveries" made by children. Thus young students who carry out a dozen or more pebble additions corresponding to $1 + 1$, $3 + 4$, $4 + 3$, $7 + 5$, etc. are coaxed into "discovering" that one can *always* (sic) carry out the pebble process and obtain a unique result. The fact is that only one very young pupil in a million would realize that there is any need to demonstrate the closure property of addition, and that pupil would realize the "discovery" to be a hasty generalization based on limited evidence. For our own information, the closure law is a postulate or assumption. It could only be demonstrated if we made other assumptions. As far as the average schoolboy is concerned, the logical sequence is not always the pedagogical one. It seems to this author that the time to "discover" the closure law for addition is *after* the failure of closure in the case of subtraction and division of natural numbers has been "discovered." Such counterexamples as $2 - 3$ and $2 \div 3$ can motivate reconsideration of addition of natural numbers.

Granted that addition of natural numbers has closure or is a *binary operation*, how is the child to assign a meaning to $3 + 4 + 2$, the sum of *three* (not two) numbers? It is a simple exercise to draw pebble diagrams that "associate" the first two numbers and then combine their sum with the third. In other words, $(3 + 4) + 2$ is pictured, and after the first binary addition is performed, one has $7 + 2$, a second binary addition, yielding the result 9. Alternatively, children consider the interpretation $3 + (4 + 2) = 3 + 6 = 9$, which is the same as the answer previously obtained. After carrying out repeated additions of three terms with the two different interpretations, pupils "discover" the *associative* property (or law) of addition of natural numbers: If a, b, and c are any three natural numbers, then

$$(a + b) + c = a + (b + c)$$

which says that the result of adding the third number to the sum of the first and second is identical with the outcome of adding the first to the sum of the second and third.

Since so many of the "discoveries" may seem obvious or intuitive, it is always important to provide counterexamples by varying the set or the operation. Thus there is noncommutativity in "adding" to one's feet "shoes + stockings" rather than "stockings + shoes" and nonassociativity in the sums, "(baking powder + milk) + other cake ingredients" and "baking powder + (milk + other cake ingredients)."

As in the case of addition, Pythagorean figurate diagrams are helpful in defining the *multiplication* of natural numbers and discovering its properties. In fact, multiplication can be interpreted as repeated addition, although a more general definition that mirrors a "multiplication" of sets will be given in Chapter 7. Here, we shall say that $2 \times 3 = 3 + 3$ and $3 \times 4 = 4 + 4 + 4$, as pictured in Figures 2.3a and 2.3b. Hence, in general, if a and b are natural numbers, then $a \times b$, usually written as ab, can be pictured as a rectangular figurate number with a columns containing b dots each. It is then a simple matter to "discover" the closure, commutative, and associative laws for the multiplication of natural numbers.

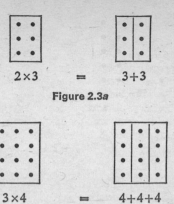

$2 \times 3 \quad = \quad 3 + 3$

Figure 2.3a

$3 \times 4 \quad = \quad 4 + 4 + 4$

Figure 2.3b

Perhaps the most interesting law is the one that connects the two binary operations on the natural numbers. It is called the *distributive law* and it states:

$$a(b + c) = ab + ac$$

where a, b, and c are any natural numbers. Figure 2.4 pictures a pebble diagram for a special case.

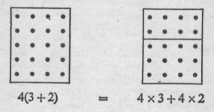

$4(3 + 2) \quad = \quad 4 \times 3 + 4 \times 2$

Figure 2.4

Products which were of special interest to the Pythagoreans were those that could be pictured as *square numbers*, namely, 1×1, 2×2, 3×3, 4×4, etc., or 1^2, 2^2, 3^2, 4^2, etc. Children can diagram these squares, and then after many transformations like those in Figures 2.5a and 2.5b, they can make the "discovery," that is, arrive at the inductive generalization: The square of an odd number is odd and the square of an even number is even.

Because the "discovery" just described was actually made

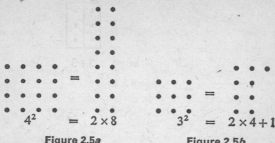

Figure 2.5*a*   Figure 2.5*b*

by the Pythagoreans who verified the validity of the induction by providing a *deductive* proof, let us do likewise. We shall, however, employ modern *algebraic* symbolism and state that $2x$ and $2x + 1$ represent even and odd numbers if x is replaced by any one of the whole numbers $\{0, 1, 2, 3, \ldots\}$. Then the *square* of an even number is symbolized by $(2x)^2$ and the square of an odd number by $(2x + 1)^2$. But $(2x)^2 = 4x^2 = 2 \cdot 2x^2$, an *even* number, and $(2x + 1)^2 = 4x^2 + 4x + 1 = 2(2x^2 + 2x) + 1$, an *odd* number.

If the reader should weary of pebble diagrams and Pythagorean preoccupation with even and odd numbers, he will be interested in the following dialogue from one of the comedies written by Epicharmos (540–450 B.C.), dramatic poet, philosopher, and member of the Pythagorean school:

"When you have an even number or, for all I care, an odd number, and someone adds a pebble or takes one away, is the original unchanged?"

"May the gods forbid it!"

"Now if some one adds to a length or cuts off a piece, will it measure the same as before?"

"Why, of course not."

"But look at people. One may grow taller, another may lose weight. . . . Then by your argument, you, I, and others are not the same people we were yesterday and we shall be still different individuals in the future."

Epicharmos may have been poking fun at his fellow Pythagoreans, but the dialogue does reveal some of their beliefs. The two questions asked indicate that the brethren distinguished between numbers for counting (the even and odd natural numbers) and numbers for *measuring* various magnitudes—lengths, areas, volumes, weights. When we think of modern measurements like 2.43 cm., 5⅛ sq. ft., etc., fractions make their appearance. But now we must ask whether such results of measurement did not, somehow, conflict with the Pythagorean belief that *natural numbers* must suffice in all situations.

For example, when the brotherhood discovered that, other conditions being equal, sounding musical strings measuring 1/2, 2/3, 1 (octave, fifth, fundamental, or *do, sol, do*) in unison or in succession produces a pleasing or "harmonic" effect, it would seem that common fractions were being used. But, to the Pythagoreans and their Hellenic successors, a fraction was a *ratio* (hence our term *rational number*) of lengths or areas or volumes, that is, of geometric magnitudes of the same kind. The fraction 1/2, for example, might mean that if the length of a particular musical string is taken as the unit of measure, and another string measures 2 units, then the ratio of lengths is 1 unit: 2 units. This is more like our 1 foot: 2 feet than the "pure" or abstract fraction 1/2, a symbol which can have many different concrete interpretations. An abstract logical definition of a ratio or common fraction would describe it as an *ordered pair* of natural numbers, for example, (1, 2) or (5, 7), in the order (antecedent, consequent) or (numerator, denominator), and this conception would in no way conflict with the Pythagorean faith in the natural numbers.

In a modern logical treatment of arithmetic, one would define addition and multiplication of the number pairs representing common fractions and also show that closure, associative, and commutative laws apply to such addition and multiplication. The natural numbers are part of the new system only when they are used for comparison or measurement. Then instead of {1, 2, 3, . . .} one would have ordered pairs like {(1,1),(2,1),(3,1), . . .}. There is need to consider the special point that a *number*, whether it is cardinal or fractional, is an abstract entity that can be symbolized or named in many different ways. We have already pointed out that III or 3 or 2 + 1 or *drei* are merely different names for the *same* cardinal. In the case of fractions, we may say that

$$\frac{1}{2} = \frac{3}{6} = \frac{70}{140} = \frac{5}{10} \text{ or } 0.5, \text{ etc,}$$

that is, (1,2) = (3,6) = (70,140) = etc., because these symbols, although not identical, name the same entity.

Although the Pythagoreans and their Hellenic successors

considered some of the special properties of natural numbers
and their ratios, the name of Pythagoras is more likely to be
associated with geometry than with arithmetic. The abstract
conception of fraction may seem novel to some laymen, but
they will all recall school days when they, like Gilbert's
"model of a modern major-general," were

> teeming with a lot of news
> with facts about the square of the hypotenuse.

Those facts were known to the Babylonians even before
Hammurabi's day and possibly to the Egyptians and Chinese
of a somewhat later date. But it is traditional to ascribe to
Pythagoras the first logical, deductive proof of the theorem
which asserts: In any and every right triangle, *the square on
the hypotenuse is equal to the sum of the squares on the
other two sides.* Like Gilbert, we shall consider the classic
proposition in its algebraic form and refer to the square "of"
rather than the square "on" the hypotenuse. Then the
theorem can be expressed algebraically as

$$c^2 = a^2 + b^2$$

where c stands for the length of the hypotenuse, a and b for
lengths of the "legs" or "arms" of any right triangle.

Now we come to that historic day when the Pythagoreans,
in attempting to apply "facts about the square of the hypotenuse" to an apparently simple problem of measurement, experienced a trauma for themselves, a crisis that challenged
their beliefs. Some say that the fateful day occurred *after*
Pythagoras had given his proof and made the theorem a
favorite with the brotherhood. But it is more likely that the
"facts" were first accepted on Babylonian authority and that
when they produced a crisis in elementary measurement,
doubt as to their validity provided the motivation for examining the whole issue of what constitutes *proof.* Probably

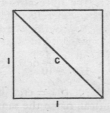

Figure 2.6

failure produced the moment of truth when Pythagoras, rejecting inductions based on observation, called for deductive chains of reasoning and gave an example of the latter kind of demonstration by proving his famous theorem.

Before or after that decisive moment, Pythagoras proposed to find the length of the diagonal of a square whose side measures 1 unit. Figure 2.6 indicates that the diagonal is the hypotenuse of a right triangle whose legs each measure 1 unit and hence

$$c^2 = 1^2 + 1^2$$
$$c^2 = 2$$

In accordance with Pythagorean beliefs it was now merely a matter of expressing the length c as a common fraction. Since $1^2 = 1$, $2^2 = 4$, the fraction should be larger than 1 and smaller than 2. We can try to guess or approximate its value, but the Pythagoreans had an *algorithm* or standardized procedure for doing so. If we should guess $1\frac{1}{2}$ and multiply it by itself, the result would be $2\frac{1}{4}$. Therefore the value of c must be smaller than $1\frac{1}{2}$. If we next try 1.4, then $(1.4)^2 = 1.96$. Hence our approximation is too small. We may then try 1.41, 1.42, etc., and find that $(1.41)^2 = 1.9881$, $(1.42)^2 = 2.0164$. No matter how we try, our estimates will apparently always be a little too small or a bit too large. Is it possible that our decimal scheme of approximation is at fault? Perhaps if we were to use ternary fractions or sexagesimal fractions (Chapter 1), we might be able to express the length of c exactly. Or maybe perfect measurement will only be possible by employing a fraction with some very special, huge denominator, like 10,032,571, for example. In effect, what we are asking is whether, with the side of the square as our "foot rule," we may not, perhaps, be able to hit on a scheme of exceedingly fine subdivision into tiny parts of suitable fractional denomination and thus (in theory) be able to measure the length of c. Our questions are a modern version of what the Pythagoreans asked themselves. For the answer they resorted to *deductive* proof. They were horrified when they were able to demonstrate that *no* common fraction (decimal or otherwise) will give the value of c, that is, measure the diagonal of the unit square. In other words, if the side is the unit of measure, the diagonal is *incommensurable*.

A deductive proof that no common fraction can possibly give the value of c in $c^2 = 2$ is usually attributed to the

Pythagoreans. At any rate, it was known to Aristotle (384–322 B.C.) and included in a more general theorem in Euclid's *Elements* (X-9). The argument is as follows: Suppose that c is actually equal to a common fraction. Then that fraction can be reduced to lowest terms so that its numerator and denominator have no common divisor. Then

$$c = \frac{m}{n}$$

where m and n are natural numbers with no common divisor. Hence $c^2 = 2$ becomes

$$\frac{m^2}{n^2} = 2$$

Therefore

$$m^2 = 2n^2$$

From this point on, the proof applies Pythagorean theorems about "feminine" numbers. Thus $2n^2$, being a multiple of 2, is "feminine" or *even*. But the above equation implies that m^2 names the same *even* number.

What about m itself? If it were odd, then m^2, its square, would be an odd number by virtue of the special property proved earlier in this chapter. But we have just established that m^2 is, in fact, even. Therefore m cannot be odd, and hence must be even. Let us then represent it by $2x$ and substitute this new form in the equation above. The result is

$$4x^2 = 2n^2$$

or

$$2x^2 = n^2$$

Here $2x^2$ is a multiple of 2 and hence even. Thus n^2 is even, and by an argument similar to the previous one, we conclude that n is an even number.

The net result is that m and n are both even, that is, are both exactly divisible by 2. But this *contradicts* the fact with which we started, namely, that m and n have no common divisor whatsoever. We have a *reductio ad absurdum!* Therefore the assumption leading to the contradiction must be false, and it is *not* true that the length of c is a common fraction, the ratio of two natural numbers.

"Natural numbers and their ratios rule the universe," Pythagoras believed. Hence what he had proved was a challenge to his faith. The numbers which he worshiped were in-effectual in a simple situation! If the side of a square is the unit of measure, the diagonal of the square is *incommensurable*. In terms of number, the lengths of the diagonal is "without ratio" or *irrational*. If $c^2 = 2$, then, employing modern algebraic symbolism, $c = \sqrt{2}$. Our proof has demonstrated that this symbol is *not* just another name for some common fraction, the ratio of two natural numbers. The symbol $\sqrt{2}$ represents something new. It measures a definite length, but should it be called a "number"? That question plagued the Pythagoreans, the more so since the irrationality of $\sqrt{2}$ implies the existence of an endless number of other irrationals. It is merely a matter of doubling, trebling, quadrupling, . . . , bisecting, trisecting, . . . , etc. the side of the unit square, to arrive at squares whose diagonals correspond to $2\sqrt{2}$, $3\sqrt{2}$, $4\sqrt{2}$, . . . , $\frac{1}{2}\sqrt{2}$, $\frac{1}{3}\sqrt{2}$, ... Also, the square-root spiral (Figure 2.7) indicates how repeated application of the Pythagorean theorem gives rise to other square-root irrationals like $\sqrt{3}$, $\sqrt{5}$, $\sqrt{6}$, ... (The reader can establish the incommensurability or irrationality of those lengths by imitating the proof for the irrationality of $\sqrt{2}$.)

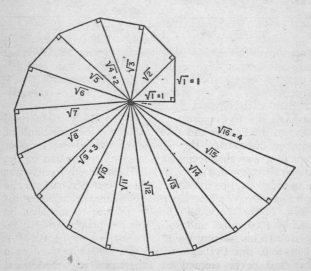

Figure 2.7   Square-root spiral

The Greeks used the term *logos* (word, speech) for the ratio of two natural numbers. Hence when incommensurable lengths were described as *alogon*, the term had a double meaning—"not a ratio" and "not to be spoken." The latter meaning, *unutterable*, was applied with dire consequences to a particular member of the Pythagorean Society. Legend has it that when Hippasus uttered the unutterable by revealing the brotherhood's difficulties with the handling of incommensurables, he was assassinated. After that, the brethren were free to worry about the *alogon* in secret. They never resolved their difficulties in that area, but later in this chapter we shall see how Eudoxus (*ca.* 370 B.C.) gave a brilliant answer to that most challenging question: What is number? For the moment, however, let us rest with the assumption that, given any line segment, there is some "number" that will describe its length.

As mathematics developed, it became apparent that not all incommensurable lengths are square roots. There are cube-root, fourth-root, fifth-root, irrationals, etc., and irrationals not expressible by roots of any order. A proof similar to that for $\sqrt{2}$ can establish the incommensurability of $\sqrt[3]{5}$, for example. But there are more complicated root irrationals, such as

$$\sqrt[7]{6 - \sqrt[4]{5 + \sqrt{11}}}$$

Furthermore, there are irrationals that cannot be expressed as finite combinations of root irrationals. These may be solutions of algebraic equations of fifth degree or higher, or they may be numbers like the π of geometry, which is *transcendental*, completely beyond algebra, so to speak.

Although the Pythagoreans progressed from the natural numbers to their ratios and then made the most profound of all number discoveries, they failed to extend the number concept in a way that seems almost trivial compared to the giant step that revealed the irrationals. Although Pythagoras made so many trips to the *east*, and then traveled back to the *west*, he never gave direction to the numbers describing his journeys. Today we would find it natural to say that he traveled $+1000$ miles and subsequently proceeded -1000 miles back to his starting point, as indicated by $(+1000) + (-1000) = 0$. But Pythagoras did not recognize zero as a number and never seemed to experience any theoretical motivation for giving direction to the numbers he used for measurement. One wonders whether, in this respect, he once again rejected the worldly practicality of mathematicians he met in the Middle East. There is some evidence that they may have understood "signed" numbers, since one interpretation of cuneiform tablets (from 1600 B.C.) now at Yale University points to algebraic equations in which negative numbers appear.

Suppose, then, that we have accepted zero (0) as a number, and that signs or directions have been given to other numbers previously considered. Then the natural number aggregate can be extended to the set of *integers*, {. . . —3, —2, —1, 0, +1, +2, +3, . . .}, where each natural number has produced a pair of "opposite" integers like +1 and —1, +2 and —2, etc. For convenience, one often identifies the natural numbers {1, 2, 3, . . .} with the *positive integers* {+1, +2, +3, . . .}. The set of all rationals now includes both +1/2 and —1/2, and the irrationals also come in directed pairs like $+\sqrt{6}$ and $-\sqrt{6}$, $+\sqrt[3]{5}$ and $-\sqrt[3]{5}$, $+\pi$ and $-\pi$, etc.

All the numbers we have discussed thus far—the integers, the rational fractions (positive or negative), and the directed irrationals—are described as *real numbers*. The reason for the appellation "real" will become apparent in Chapter 4.

To conceive of the *totality* of all real numbers, to put some law and order into that aggregate, and to hold on to our notion of a "number" as the length of a line segment, we shall now picture such lengths as distances on a *number line* (Figure 2.8), or as *coordinates* of points on such a line. For this purpose we can use any straight line, X'X (Figure 2.8),

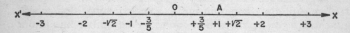

Figure 2.8   Number line

as number line, and set up a "system of coordinates" on that line in the fashion first given marked emphasis by René Descartes (1596–1650) and Pierre de Fermat (1601–1665). We begin by selecting O, any point on the number line, as the *origin* of coordinates, or representative of the number *zero*. The origin divides the number line into two *rays* or "half-lines," OX and OX'. On OX we select any point A (distinct from O) and call the length of OA the *unit dis-*

tance. We think of A as the representative of the integer $+1$, or alternatively, in accordance with our previous conception, we consider $+1$ as the directed distance from O to A. The ray OX passing through O and A gives the *positive* direction on the number line, and the other ray OX' gives the *negative* direction. In Figure 2.8 a *number scale* is formed by starting at O and marking off unit distances successively to right and left. The points labeled $0, +1, +2, +3, \ldots$ and $-1, -2, -3, \ldots$ can be considered to represent the numbers named, or alternatively, one can picture the numbers as the directed distances from the origin to the representative points. These directed distances or the numbers measuring them are called the *coordinates* of the respective points.

To obtain a point whose coordinate is a rational number that is not an integer, for example, $+3/5$, we can, if we wish, carry out a Euclidean construction. Before Euclid had incorporated the geometry of Thales, Pythagoras, and later Hellenic mathematicians into the *Elements*, Plato had exerted an influence that caused Euclidean constructions to be limited to those that can be carried out by straight-edge (line without a scale) and compasses. It would be possible (in theory) to use such tools to divide OA [Figure 2.8] into five equal parts. Then the directed distance from O to the terminal point of the third part would be $+3/5$, or that terminal point would represent $+3/5$. (One might, instead, divide the segment from O to the point $+3$ [Figure 2.8] into five equal parts and take the terminal point of the first part.) If, starting at O, the length of $+3/5$ is measured off on OX', the point whose coordinate is $-3/5$ is obtained. Any rational number, positive or negative, can be constructed in analogous fashion.

If we consider the points plotted on the number line thus far, we can observe certain important properties. First, there are the *integral* points which convert the number line into a *number scale*, the points corresponding to the integers arranged in order of size, namely, $\{\ldots -3, -2, -1, 0, +1, +2, +3, \ldots\}$. These points are spaced on the number line in such a way that each integer has a unique predecessor as well as an immediate successor. For example, -5 is preceded by -6 and followed by -4. This characteristic is described by saying that the integers or integral points form a *discrete* set. The property of discreteness no longer holds after the constructions described in the previous paragraph are carried out, that is, when all the fractional points are added to the picture. In the enlarged set of *all rational numbers* ordered according to size, we can name neither a specific antecedent nor a consequent to a particular number like 0.5, say. If we examine a fraction slightly larger than 0.5, for example, 0.50001, this is not the next number of the set, since the arithmetic mean of the two numbers, 0.500005, is still closer to 0.5. In turn, this new number is not the immediate successor to 0.5, since 0.5000025 is still closer, and we can continue the process of averaging *ad infinitum,* obtaining at each step a rational number closer to 0.5 than the fraction under consideration, so that the latter is *not* consecutive to 0.5 in the set of ordered rationals. Thus we see that it is hopeless to try to find, among the rational numbers, a next number after 0.5. Similarly, no fraction can be singled out as the immediate predecessor of 0.5.

The characteristic that between any pair of rational numbers there are always others (in fact, an infinite number of others) is usually described by saying that the rational numbers are *dense.* Now in spite of the close packing of integral and fractional points everywhere on the number line, there are *gaps,* an infinity of them, as we shall soon see. Since $\sqrt{2}$ is *irrational,* it is *not* included in the dense rational set. But a Euclidean construction can locate a point whose coordinate is $+\sqrt{2}$. With the Platonic tools one can construct a unit square (where the unit is OA in Figure 2.8), and then, starting at O, the length of the diagonal of this unit square can be measured off on OX. Using that same length, one can readily construct the points whose coordinates are $+2\sqrt{2}, +3\sqrt{2}, +4\sqrt{2}, \ldots, -\sqrt{2}, -2\sqrt{2}, \ldots$. All of these points fill gaps in the dense rational aggregate. The square-root spiral would enable us to fill other gaps by constructing $+\sqrt{3}, +2\sqrt{3}, +3\sqrt{3}, \ldots, -\sqrt{3}, -2\sqrt{3}, \ldots$, and, in fact, an "infinity" of points whose coordinates are multiples of $+\sqrt{5}$ or any other square-root irrational. But the Platonic tools are too limited for the construction of most irrational distances. Still we can imagine that there might nevertheless be a point whose coordinate is $+\pi$, and a point whose coordinate is $-\sqrt[5]{1 + \sqrt[3]{2}}$. It is all a matter of the definitions or rules which we lay down.

Therefore, if we are to give an exact definition of "real number," we must provide a formulation that will make it possible (in theory) to locate a point of the number line (measure off a directed distance from the origin) for every such number. In reverse, we would like to be able to provide

a real number for any specified point or distance from the
origin, since we want no gaps in the number line. We must
avoid the Pythagorean predicament of having no numbers
available for the exact measurement of certain line segments.
What we seek then is a definition that will put the real
numbers into *one-to-one correspondence* (Chapter 1) with
the points of the number line so that the numbers will form
a "continuum" (page 71).

To provide an exact definition of "real number" we shall
follow the Pythagorean example of defining new numbers in
terms of old. First there were the natural numbers and then
the fractions (positive rationals) became pairs of these. Then
a fraction or rational number led to an approximation of an
irrational, $\sqrt{2}$. In our own struggle with $\sqrt{2}$ we used approximations that were *decimal fractions*, and we shall now employ such fractions once again because they are familiar to
us. We remark that our formulations could be made equally
well in terms of binary, ternary, sexagesimal, etc. fractions,
that is, in a system of numeration whose base is not ten.

The division algorithm of school arithmetic would enable
the reader to express any rational fraction in decimal form.
Thus $5/16 = 0.3125$. When the fraction $1/7$ is converted
into a decimal, it becomes $1/7 = 0.142857142857142857 \ldots$,
where the figures 142857 are repeated over and over again
forever. Every rational fraction must have one of these two
types of decimal expression but *cannot* have a nonterminating
or infinite decimal expansion that is not repeating. To see
why this is so, consider the division for decimalization
of $5/16$,

$$\frac{0.3125}{16\,\overline{)5.0000}}$$

and then that for $1/7$,

$$\frac{0.1428571 \ldots}{7\,\overline{)1.0000000 \ldots}}$$

In the former case the process ceases when there is no remainder. In the latter the first six steps yield the quotients,
0, 1, 4, 2, 8, 5 and the remainders 1, 3, 2, 6, 4, 5. The seventh
step yields a quotient of 7 and a remainder of 1. This is a
repetition of the first remainder obtained in the conversion
to a decimal. Therefore, beginning with the eighth step the
original steps will be repeated up to the point where a re-

mainder of 1 occurs again when the same original steps will be repeated once more, and so on. In general, in the case of decimalization of *any* rational fraction whatsoever, division by an integer n can yield at most a *finite* number of different remainders, namely $1, 2, 3, \ldots, n-1$ (not necessarily in this order). Some or all of these remainders may occur in the first steps of the decimalization, but eventually, if the process does not terminate, one of the above remainders must *recur* because the variety of possible remainders is not infinite, and when this remainder recurs, there will be a repetition of some or all steps in the decimalization, and so forth.

Conversely, terminating and repeating decimals can always be converted into ordinary fractions. This is obvious for the terminating case. For example, $3.0217 = 3 \ 217/10,000$ or $30,217/10,000$. To see how the conversion might be carried out for a repeating decimal, consider

$$x = 0.217217217 \ldots \text{ forever}$$

Multiplying this equation by 1000 gives

$$1000x = 217.217217 \ldots \text{ forever}$$

or

$$1000x = 217 + 0.217217 \ldots \text{ forever}$$

or

$$1000x = 217 + x$$

and

$$999x = 217$$
$$x = \frac{217}{999}$$

Consider once more the case where a rational fraction is expressed as a terminating decimal, for example, $2/5 = 0.4$. We can convert this terminating decimal into a *nonterminating* repeating decimal in two ways. There is the obvious way of writing $0.40000 \ldots$, where the zeros after the 4 are repeated forever. But it is *not* obvious that $0.4 = 0.3999 \ldots$, where the 9's are repeated forever. Let us prove that this is the case, by stating that

$$0.39999 \ldots = 0.3 + 0.09999 \ldots$$
$$= 0.3 + x$$

where

$$x = 0.09999 \ldots$$
$$10x = 0.9999 \ldots$$
$$100x = 9.999 \ldots = 9 + 0.999 \ldots = 9 + 10x$$
$$90x = 9$$
$$x = \frac{1}{10} = 0.1$$

Therefore

$$0.39999 \ldots = 0.3 + 0.1 = 0.4$$

We can proceed similarly in other cases. Therefore every rational fraction can be expressed as a *nonterminating* repeating decimal. If our division algorithm leads to a terminating decimal like 0.4 or 5.2018, we shall substitute the *nonterminating* decimal where zeros are repeated, for example, 0.4000 . . . or 5.2018000 . . . . Although we might write 0.3999 . . . or 5.2017999 . . . we shall, for the sake of uniqueness, exclude the latter type of representation where the repeating part consists of 9's.

Since all rational numbers can be expressed as *nonterminating, repeating* decimals, and conversely, such decimals (positive or negative) can be considered as *defining* what is meant by a rational number, the only type of nonterminating decimal excluded by this definition is that which is *nonrepeating*. Therefore it is possible to define an *irrational* number as a *nonterminating, nonrepeating* decimal. The rationals and irrationals constitute the *real numbers*.

We have finally arrived at one goal. At long last, the *real numbers* can be *defined* as the set of all positive or negative nonterminating decimals.

It remains to indicate that this definition makes it possible to establish a one-to-one correspondence between the real numbers and the points of a number line, that is, there must be a point for every nonterminating decimal and such a decimal for every point. Suppose, then, that a real number is defined by some nonterminating decimal which we can carry out to as many places as we please, and that the first few places are given by 2.6314. . . . The decimal gives us a sequence of *rational* approximations to the real number, namely, 2, 2.6, 2.63, 2.631, 2.6314, ... In other words, the first approximation in the sequence places the real number in the interval (2, 3), and then 2.6 gives the approximating interval (2.6, 2.7), etc. Thus we have the sequence of *nested intervals*, (2, 3), (2.6, 2.7), (2.63, 2.64), . . . , illustrated in Figure 2.9. The adjective *nested* describes the fact that each interval lies within the preceding one. We observe also that the lengths of successive intervals are 1, 0.1, 0.01, 0.001, 0.0001, ... Since we are considering a *nonterminating* decimal, the nest of intervals will ultimately contain an interval of length 0.000 000 001 and then there will be still smaller intervals, so that interval length shrinks toward zero. As the innermost intervals get smaller and smaller, one can imagine their bounding walls approaching collision or, at any rate, getting close enough to "trap" a point of the number line. It is postulated, that is, *assumed*, that there is a unique point contained in all intervals of the nest. If there is such a point, we see that it must be unique, for if there were

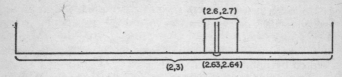

Figure 2.9   Nested intervals

another distinct point, it would be separated from the first by some distance, 0.000 01, say. But ultimately some interval of the nest will be smaller than that number, and the first point must be contained in that very small interval. Then the second point would be too far away to be inside the interval and hence would not be contained in every interval of the nest. Since every nonterminating decimal will give rise to a sequence of nested intervals like the one described, there will always be a unique point of the number line corresponding to every real number.

Conversely, if we are given any point P on the number line, then we can show that there will be a nonterminating decimal or real number corresponding to this point. If P is at one of the integral positions on the line, like 3 or — 4, then the corresponding nonterminating decimal would be 3.0000 . . . or — 4.0000. . . . Now suppose that P is not an integral point but lies on the number line somewhere between 1 and 2. Divide the interval (1, 2) into ten parts each measuring 0.1. If, by chance, P should be at the right endpoint of the third small part, then our task would be finished,

for the corresponding nonterminating decimal would then be
1.3000. . . . But let us suppose instead that P lies within the
seventh interval (1.6, 1.7). Divide that interval into ten parts
each measuring 0.01. If P lies within the fourth of these intervals, (1.63, 1.64) we can subdivide that interval into ten
equal parts and perhaps locate P in the interval (1.638,
1.639), etc. We can keep on subdividing each new interval
into ten equal parts. If, at any step, P is at the end-point of
some interval, the corresponding real number is rational.
Thus P might turn out to be 1.6382, that is, 1.6382000. . . .
If P is not the end-point of any interval, the corresponding
real number is irrational, and the left end-points of successive intervals give the corresponding decimal expansion.
Thus, if ultimately P is found to be in the interval
(1.6382704, 1.6382705), the real number corresponding to P
is 1.6382704. . . . Hence, in this case, and in every case, to a
point of the number line there will correspond a nonterminating decimal (real number). Having argued both
ways, we have indicated a one-to-one correspondence between points of the number line and real numbers as represented by nonterminating decimals.

To provide some structure for the real number system, one
can define addition and multiplication in this system and
show that closure, associative, commutative, distributive, etc.
laws are satisfied. We shall merely suggest how this is done.
Thus, to conceive of the *sum*, $\sqrt{2} + \sqrt{3}$, one would consider
that

$$\sqrt{2} = 1.41421 \ldots$$
$$\sqrt{3} = 1.73205 \ldots$$

leads to the two sequences of nested intervals:

$\sqrt{2}$	$\sqrt{3}$
(1.4, 1.5)	(1.7, 1.8)
(1.41, 1.42)	(1.73, 1.74)
(1.414, 1.415)	(1.732, 1.733)
(1.4142, 1.4143)	(1.7320, 1.7321)
etc.	etc.

Then adding lower boundaries of the corresponding intervals, and doing the same for upper boundaries, the sum
$\sqrt{2} + \sqrt{3}$ is defined by the following sequence of nested

intervals: (3.1, 3.3), (3.14, 3.16), (3.146, 3.148), (3.1462, 3.1464), etc. In similar fashion, one can define a sequence of nested intervals for $\sqrt{2} \cdot \sqrt{3}$ and in general, for sums, differences, products, quotients of real numbers, whether these are rational or irrational. Only division by zero is excluded.

The formulation of real numbers by using nested intervals or nonterminating decimals is relatively new mathematics—late nineteenth century. The idea is due to Georg Cantor (1845–1918), whose profound conception of *infinite* sets will be discussed in a later chapter. It is apparent that nested intervals and Cantor's theory are a far cry indeed from the Pythagorean despair on first encountering the *alogon*. But while Greek geometers of 500 B.C. regarded irrationals with dread, Eudoxus (*ca*. 370 B.C.) created a brilliant method for handling incommensurables and thus defining the meaning of and operations on the real numbers. The Eudoxian ideology, which is incorporated in Book V of Euclid's *Elements*, is in essence the same as the theory of Richard Dedekind (1831–1916), one of Cantor's contemporaries. The point of view of Eudoxus and Dedekind is mathematically more sophisticated than Cantor's conception of real number.

Dedekind observed that when the rational numbers are represented as points on the number line, any one of these points, for example, 0.6, produces a "cut" in the number line that divides it into two distinct parts, every rational point in one portion lying to the left of all rational points in the other. The point 0.6 can be considered either the last point in the left section or the first in the right. In general, then, *any* rational number effects a *Dedekind cut* in the aggregate of rational numbers by dividing that set into two subsets, A and B, so that every rational in A is less than every rational in B. The rational number producing the cut may be either the largest rational in A or the smallest in B. We observe that it is *impossible* to have *both* a largest rational a in A and a smallest rational b in B. For, as we have seen in establishing the density of the rationals (page 62), $\frac{1}{2}(a + b)$ would lie midway between a and b, and being greater than a and less than b, it would not belong to either A or B, which is impossible.

When Dedekind had observed that every rational number effects a cut in the set of rationals, he considered the converse situation. This involves the question: If, by some criterion or other, the rational aggregate is divided into two subsets A and B so that every number in A is less than every number in B, is there always a greatest rational in A or a smallest rational in B? The answer to that question is in the negative, as we shall now illustrate. But Dedekind, desiring *continuity* of the number line, postulated (assumed) that in *every case* the cut (A, B) *defines* or, from a purely logical viewpoint, actually *is* a real number. When A has no maximum rational and B has no minimum rational, there is a gap in the rational series, a puncture in the number line which must be filled. In that case, the cut (A, B) is said to define (or to be) an *irrational* number.

For illustrative purposes, suppose that the criterion for forming a cut in the rationals is as follows: Positive rationals whose square is greater than 2 are assigned to class B, and all other rationals to A. Then $-5, -3, 0, +1, +1.4, +1.41, +1.414$, for example, will be in class A, and $+1.415, +1.42, +2, +3$, etc. will be in B. There is no maximum in A and there is no minimum in B, and the cut (A, B) is irrational. It is, in fact, that classic irrational $\sqrt{2}$.

To-emphasize the nature of irrational cuts and to avoid belaboring $\sqrt{2}$, the reader should seek other criteria for bringing about a cut (A, B) where A has no last member and B has no first. For example, all rationals whose cubes are less than 7 can be assigned to A, and all others to B. Then $(A, B) = \sqrt[3]{7}$.

For Dedekind, then, the real number system was the set of all possible cuts (A, B) in the rational aggregate. He was able, in terms of his conception, to define addition and multiplication of real numbers, that is, of cuts (A, B), and to establish that those operations satisfied the fundamental laws of arithmetic—closure, commutativity, associativity, etc. To illustrate Dedekind's formulations, there is his definition of addition: Given any two cuts or real numbers (A_1, B_1), and (A_2, B_2), if C is the set of all rationals of the form $(a_1 + a_2)$ where a_1 is in A_1 and a_2 in A_2, and D is the set of remaining rationals, then the real number defined by the cut (C, D) is said to be the sum of the given real numbers.

We shall not give further details of the Dedekind treatment of the real numbers except to emphasize once more that it is in essence, if not in symbolism or wording, a modern-dress version of Eudoxus' theory. We shall return to Dedekind in later chapters. Before leaving Eudoxus, however, we must indicate that his theory of the real numbers is not the only contribution which places him among the mathematical "greats." The Pythagoreans may have begun the emphasis on deductive demonstration which led ultimately to the modern axiomatic method. But it was Eudoxus who fostered such methodology by making suitable assumptions and furnishing deductive proofs of numerous theorems, all for the purpose of resolving the Pythagorean crisis with $\sqrt{2}$. In still another anticipation of modern mathematics, Eudoxus established a method of finding areas and volumes that, perfected by Archimedes, was tantamount to the basic notion of Newton's seventeenth-century integral calculus. As if all of this were not enough, we have the Eudoxian theory of planetary motion which, revised and elaborated by Hipparchus in 140 B.C. and Claudius Ptolemy about 150 A.D., was to dominate astronomical theory until the time of Copernicus.

We are more certain about the scientific contributions of the mathematical giant of the fourth century B.C. than we are of the details of his personal life. Eudoxus was a native of Cnidus in Asia Minor, and some biographers give his life span as 408-355 B.C. In early youth he moved to Athens, where he became a protégé of Plato. Legend has it that the great philosopher and the young mathematician were companions on a journey to Egypt but parted company on their return to Athens. The termination of their friendship is attributed by some to Plato's envy of Eudoxus' brilliance, while others feel that the younger man's belief in pleasure as the *summum bonum* aroused the ire of Plato, just as later on it provoked the criticism of Aristotle.

Eudoxus, influenced by his teacher Archytas and his pupil Menaechmus, made the suggestion that geometry would be more of a pleasure if the number of mechanical tools permitted were increased. It was Plato, we recall, who had set the precedent of limiting all geometric constructions to those possible with straight-edge and compasses. When Archytas, Eudoxus, and Menaechmus proposed the use of other curves, Plato inveighed against them with great indignation and persistence. He accused them of employing "devices that require much vulgar handicraft." At any rate, such is the statement of Plutarch, who recounts further that "in this way mechanical devices were expelled from geometry, and being looked down upon by philosophers, were used to promote military science."

Whatever the reason, Eudoxus was unpopular in Athens and ultimately returned to Asia Minor, this time to Cyzicus, where, emulating Plato, he established an academy of his own. He communicated to the students his discoveries in mathematics, astronomy, and physics; he also found time to enter local politics and practice medicine. Specific details concerning his activities as a physician are lacking, but one might conjecture that he picked up medical knowledge on his trips to Egypt. He may have been more of a medicine man than a physician, in the sense of the latter term today. In the fourth century B.C. and for almost two millennia thereafter, astronomers were usually astrologers as well, and often engaged in medicine as a sideline. They treated patients in accordance with astrological rules rather than from any real knowledge of the human body. This was true even of Copernicus in the sixteenth century, who, during his lifetime, was more renowned as a physician than as an astronomer.

Eudoxus, Dedekind, and Cantor all developed theoretical concepts for the purpose of filling the gaps in the ordered set of rationals so that the final geometric picture is a straight line which is *continuous* or unbroken, in the intuitive sense. For this reason, one speaks of the real number *continuum*. More formally, Dedekind considered a one-dimensional or *linear continuum* to be, like a line segment, a *dense* aggregate with *no gaps*. (Cantor was more stringent and required an additional property.)

It may seem that we have wandered far afield in arriving at the Cantor and Dedekind concepts of the real number continuum when the original point of departure was the Pythagorean procedures which today's "new mathematics" emulates. But it was a Pythagorean discovery that motivated exact definition of the continuum and, in fact, produced a sort of schism in mathematical activity that was to last up to the present day. One school of thought has been devoted to working out the implications of Pythagoras' original belief that the framework of the universe is to be found in the natural numbers: {1, 2, 3, 4, . . .}. This sequence and also the set of integers ordered according to size, are described as *discrete*. That adjective is applied to *any* sequence and also to any ordered set in which every term (except the first, if any) has a unique predecessor, and every term (except the last, if any) has an immediate successor. For example, any finite set (arranged in any order) is discrete.

Because of their devotion to the natural numbers, the followers of Pythagoras are sometimes called *discretists*. In contrast to their point of view, there are those who would base science on the real number continuum. Although certain mathematicians have been polemic in their advocacy of the discrete rather than the continuous, or vice versa, mathematical history indicates that it is more a case of specialized interest in, or a talent for, one type of mathematics rather than another. The discretists have had a flair for the classic theory of numbers, algebra, and logic. Geometers, analysts, and physicists, on the other hand, are likely to be devotees of continuity. Although physicists tend to use continuous models, there are important exceptions. Matter has been thought of as discrete or atomistic since the day of Democritus (*ca.* 400 B.C.), and modern quantum theory is the example par excellence of the physics of the discrete or discontinuous.

The present domain of mathematics is so vast and varied that today no one attempts to define the subject precisely. In the past, however, mathematics was sometimes described as the "science of discrete and continuous magnitude," and its evolution was pictured as the progress of two dichotomous mainstreams, with Pythagoras and his associates as the source of both. Since an influence that lasts over 2400 years is bound to give rise to legends, it seems fitting to close the present chapter with some of the lore that has gradually accumulated around the ancient master's name.

Of Pythagoras' early life we know little except that he was born on the Greek island of Samos and traveled extensively in Egypt and surrounding countries, where it is almost certain that he was exposed to both the excellent Babylonian algebra and the crude Egyptian beginnings of mathematics. In administering the famous brotherhood, Pythagoras, according to some stories, was in favor of disseminating mathematical knowledge freely and was willing to lecture to any audience interested in what he had to say. But a different spirit was present among the brethren, who felt that the Society should be aristocratic in nature and that the members should keep their discoveries secret from the general public.

The brotherhood was pledged to vegetarianism, and it has been said that animal food was taboo because it was believed that men and beasts are kin. The Pythagoreans lived an ascetic and disciplined existence to purify their souls and fit them for the hereafter of which Pythagoras told when he preached the doctrine of the immortality and transmigration of the soul.

The Pythagorean interest in music is supposed to have started when Pythagoras, passing a blacksmith's forge, listened to the harmonious tones produced by the impact of the hammer on the anvil. In the field of astronomy as well as in music and mathematics, Pythagoras led his followers toward notable advances. It is generally believed that they were the first to assert that the earth is a sphere suspended in space without support of any kind and that it revolves with all the other planets around a "central fire." Some scholars claim that the Pythagoreans knew the central luminary to be the sun but hesitated to make such an assertion lest they be persecuted. Such fears were probably justified. Anaxagoras, shortly after the day of the Pythagoreans, was banished from Athens because he had publicized his astronomical theories on the sun, which he described as a huge mass of burning metal. He had also written on eclipses, and had proposed a "nebular hypothesis" that anticipated the eighteenth-century cosmogony of Laplace. Such views came into conflict with the prevailing polytheistic religion of the Greeks, and one legend has it that only the intervention of Pericles saved the rationalistic astronomer from a death sentence.

To return to the Pythagorean theory of planetary behavior, Copernicus expressed the opinion that it contained the germ of his own heliocentric hypothesis. But the brotherhood forced the "all-comprising, all-bounding, never-tiring holy ten" into their cosmological scheme. The sun, moon, and five known planets totaled seven, the earth and the heaven of fixed stars two more. To obtain the mystic "holy ten" the Pythagoreans invented a "counter-earth" that, like the central fire, is invisible, because the side of earth on which we live always faces the other way.

To combine their cosmogony with their musical theory and their belief that nature is modeled on the natural numbers, the Pythagoreans assigned to the distances of the various planets from the central fire the same ratios that produced harmonious combinations in the musical scale. The planetary motion produces sublime music, Pythagoras said, inaudible to us because we are like the blacksmith and his assistants who cease to be aware of sounds which they hear constantly and cannot contrast with silence.

How romantic the personality that could see nature in such a light! The myth-makers, however, created the legend of a more conventional, personal romance. They related that Pythagoras fell in love with one of his young students, Theano. After their marriage, the couple might have lived happily ever after if the Society had not become involved in politics. But having regulated its astronomic theory so as not to fall afoul of religious bigotry, the brotherhood encountered another pitfall—the lust for power. The democratic populace of Crotona objected to the Pythagorean control of local affairs. The group was disbanded, and Pythagoras, accompanied by the loyal Theano, went into exile. Tragedians would have us believe that enemies followed him and slew Pythagoras in the very presence of his young wife. For us, such fact or fiction is unimportant; the Pythagorean legacy to mathematics gives the master an eternal role in that drama we call the "glory that was Greece."

Chapter 3

Mathematical Reasoning from Eudoxus to Lobachevsky

After the method and two main streams of mathematics had been launched by the Pythagoreans, Greek mathematical activity shifted away from cities in Italy. Athens and centers in Asia Minor then became important, but ultimately Hellenic scientific activity was concentrated in the metropolis of Alexandria. Here Euclid (*ca.* 300 B.C.), the most classic figure in mathematics, lived and worked. Archimedes, the greatest of all Greek mathematicians, was in constant touch with Alexandrian scientists.

In an address* before the Mathematical Association of America, Professor Rudolph E. Langer (1894–1968) described the historical and geographical setting of this famous city.

. . . On the southern shore of the eastern Mediterranean Sea, not far from the westernmost mouth of the great river Nile, a narrow ridge of limestone separates the sea from a lake named Mareotis. Not far offshore and lying like a breakwater parallel with it, is a long narrow island called Pharos. In the year 331 B.C. Alexander the Great saw in this spot unusual potentialities for the site of a city. He conceived upon it a great city which should serve at once two missions which he had set himself, namely, the spread of Hellenic influence over the world, and the return of the ancient land of Egypt to a former greatness and glory.

Upon the death of Alexander, Egypt fell under the governorship of his general Ptolemy. There was much mutual good fortune in this turn of events. For while Egypt, a fabulously fertile

---

* Rudolph E. Langer, "Alexandria, Shrine of Mathematics," *American Mathematical Monthly*, Vol. 48, No. 2 (February 1941), pp. 109 ff.

country, meant power and almost limitless wealth for Ptolemy, he in turn proved himself worthy of it. The distinctive culture of the country, with traditions extending into the interminable past, had always fascinated the Hellenic mind, and Ptolemy was not unreceptive to this charm. His rule, first as governor and later as king, was guided by intelligence and statesmanship, by a fine natural artistic taste, and by an appreciation of the dignity and substantial worth of intellectual attainment. His dynasty was to rule the land, now for better, then for worse, over a period of two hundred and fifty years.

From early times in the history of the Greeks there had existed so-called philosophical schools, which were in reality communities of scholars. These schools were frequently organized as brotherhoods, dedicated, as in the cases of the Pythagoreans, to the cult of the Muses. Their housings, therefore, came quite generally to be known as *museums*. Ptolemy conceived the ambition to establish such a museum at Alexandria. He envisaged the city as a center of Greek culture, not merely as a trading post, and with large revenues at hand he thought to make association with his school attractive by the then novel means of granting salary stipends, as well as board and residence, to prominent scholars of his choice. Not unnaturally this plan was an immediate success, and at about the year 300 B.C. the Alexandrian Museum had become an actuality. It included in its membership intellectuals of all sorts—poets, philosophers, grammarians, mathematicians, astronomers, geographers, physicians, historians, artists, and many others. The mathematician in this initial galaxy was the immortal Euclid.

Ptolemy's constructiveness, which was manifested in his incorporation of the Alexandrian Museum, was matched again both in originality and grandeur by his founding of . . . the Alexandrian Library. . . . The Library was established almost simultaneously with the Museum and adjacent to it. . . .

Close to the harbor and connected by colonnades with the palaces stood the fine white buildings of the Great Library and of the Museum. Such were the environs in which the scholars of Alexandria lived. In a great basilica they ate their meals together, and had their dormitories and lecture halls. In groves of palms and under arcades adorned with classical sculptures they carried on their discussions with each other or with their students and disciples. Contemporary Alexandrian satire liked to depict them as costly birds fed and treasured in a golden cage.

It would be difficult to think of Euclid as a bird in a gilded cage, but one would like to believe that he enjoyed the natural beauty of Alexandria, its artistic wonders, its advanced culture, and all those happy features set forth in Professor Langer's address. None of the personal details of Euclid's life have come down to us, however, and we must limit ourselves to his mathematical activities. Because his name is usually identified with geometry, there is little realization that he contributed to other subjects as well. He wrote on astronomy, optics, and music; his greatest treatise, the *Elements*, contains not only geometry but considerable number theory (Chapter 21) and geometric algebra as well.

Even more important than the comprehensive content of Euclid's classic is its logical format, which has served as the prototype of all modern deductive systems constructed by the *axiomatic* or *postulational* method. Euclid must not be given all the credit for this standard pattern, however, since it seems to have evolved gradually, as we have already related, through the ideas of his Greek mathematical predecessors, among whom were Thales, Pythagoras, and Eudoxus (Chapter 2). The basic idea of the axiomatic method is that the initial content of geometry or any scientific subject should consist of a set of assumed propositions, called *axioms* or *postulates*, and that other propositions, called *theorems*, should be derived from the basic assumptions by applying the rules of deductive logic.

Since mathematics is the domain par excellence where facts are proved, it is often a shock to the uninitiated to learn that the fundamental postulates of a mathematical science are *unproved* propositions. To see why an argument or a debate or a "deductive system" must start with assumptions, let us suppose that in some mathematical science proof is demanded for a particular statement, which we shall call Proposition A. Now this proposition may be a logical consequence of propositions B, C, and D. Suppose next that one is asked to demonstrate these propositions and that they are collectively dependent on propositions we shall label E, F, G, H, I, J, K, and L. If proof is demanded once more, we shall have to demonstrate eight more propositions, and so on. If we continue to demand proof, we shall have an infinite sequence of backward steps in our reasoning, unless we decide to call a halt at some point and accept at least one proposition without proof.

A parent attempting to reason with a four-year-old is familiar with the threat of an infinite regression in logical argument. "Why must I go to sleep?" Johnny asks. "Because you need rest," says Dad. "*Why* do I need rest?" Johnny continues. "Because it will give you the strength to play games with your friends tomorrow." "*Why* should I play games with my friends tomorrow?" "Because a little boy needs exercise." "*Why* do I need exercise?" At this point, Dad says, "*Because!* And that's that! Go straight to bed and *no more questions!*"

Dad is declaring as *axiomatic* the proposition that a child requires exercise; that is, he is stating that Johnny must accept this proposition *without proof*. It is a necessity to stop at some point in a regressive argument and "lay down the law." Even if one does not attempt to answer an endless chain of "whys," there is a certain logical danger in permitting a *finite* sequence to become too lengthy. Let us imagine that Dad decides to argue a little longer. When Johnny asks "*Why* do I need exercise?", Dad may answer, "Because it provides healthy fatigue." "*Why* do I need healthy fatigue?" "Because it will make you *sleepy and ready to go to bed* right now." Dad is right back where he started. He has just involved himself in a "vicious circle" or he is "begging the question," since if we fuse all Dad's answers into one long chain, we find that Johnny must go to sleep because he must go to sleep.

Just as one gets into an endless chain of argument by trying to prove all propositions, so is there a similar difficulty in trying to define everything. In some of the older texts one may find a point defined as "that which has no dimensions," a line as "something with one dimension," and so on. Then, what, pray, is a dimension? And when you have defined that, we shall have more questions. So make your choice of a starting place. You will just have to leave some things undefined. In this way you will avoid the endless chain and also, as in the case of propositions, the danger of circularity. A dictionary may define frugality as economy and economy as frugality, but a mathematician must not do so. He must initiate a deductive science with *unproved* propositions about *undefined* terms.

If the scientific subject under construction in postulational-deductive fashion is to be practical, realistic, and purposeful, the axioms are usually selected so as to approximate or idealize actual experience. Thus Euclid may have been the founder of postulational thinking, but he did *not* conceive of his postulates as mere assumptions. Instead, he described them as "common notions." Later textbooks called them "self-evident truths" or "matters of empirical fact," and Euclid's axioms about "points," "lines," and so forth, do actually appear to tally with the drawings we make by the use of pencil and straight-edge. Also, histories of mathematics customarily suggest that the origins of geometry are to be found in the work of Babylonian and Egyptian surveyors, just as we have explained that the Pythagorean "theorem" was an early empirical discovery (Chapter 2). All that we have just stated gives the point of view of *applied mathematics*, which can be described roughly as consisting of those mathematical sciences which deal with situations in the real world, for example, statistics, physics, astronomy, biology, economics, psychology, etc., or deductive systems derived from portions of those subjects.

The attitude of modern *pure* or abstract mathematics is quite different from that just described. In it one has the right to choose the content of axioms somewhat arbitrarily, subject only to certain logical criteria which we shall explain presently. Then, in theory, a pure mathematician may found a deductive system by assuming what he pleases. He is unlikely to take advantage of such latitude, however, nor does he prepare a list of postulates out of a clear sky, with no special background or specific purpose. Such an aimless system could serve only as the basis for a mental exercise or as the set of rules for some esoteric game. Although his undefined terms are meaningless symbols as it were, and he is permitted to state whatever he wishes about them in his postulate system, he may actually be making assertions with which he is already familiar from other mathematical subjects, for example, statements about cardinal numbers (Chapter 1), algebraic x, y, z's, and the like. A common method of forming postulate systems, as we shall illustrate shortly, is to use a standard set of axioms, like those for ordinary algebra, or those for Euclidean geometry, and alter or omit one or more of the axioms.

But, one may say, if the pure mathematician is not required to furnish intuitive or experimental justification for his postulates, will these propositions be "true"? If not, will his theorems be valid? One answer customarily given to such questions is that *if* the postulates are true, and *if* the theorems are derived in accordance with the laws of logic, then the theorems are true. The theorems thus become *relative*, not absolute truths. A second answer is to say that in modern logic, "truth" has a different meaning from the usual one (Chapter 6). Since neither of these explanations may seem entirely satisfactory, we shall now present a third

point of view, one which focuses on the role of the undefined terms used in the axioms of a system.

In modern improvements of Euclid's postulate system,
"point" and "line" may be listed as undefined terms. Suppose that one includes among the axioms Euclid's postulate:
There exists one and only one "line" containing any two
"points." Although "point" and "line" are undefined or
meaningless, it is difficult to divorce the terms from their
usual connotations. It is of no use to declare that the "truth"
of the postulate is *not* a pertinent issue, for someone may
insist, "But the statement in question is obviously true." He
may change this judgment, however, if we replace the two
undefined terms by x and y, respectively, in order to
emphasize that they are meaningless, empty symbols. The
postulate becomes: There exists one and only one y that contains any two x's. Is this statement true or false? We cannot answer if x and y are "unknowns."

If the revised statement of the postulate were presented
to someone unacquainted with Euclidean geometry, he
would be unprejudiced, and if asked whether it is true or
false, would say he could not tell. Or in order to render a
verdict, he might seek to interpret x and y, that is, to assign specific meanings. Suppose he recalls that his three
children have formed a miniature club with committees as
follows: {James, Harold}, {James, Martha}, {Harold, Mar-
tha}. With this picture in mind, he decides to interpret x
as meaning any one of his children and y as representing
any one of the three committees. Then the postulate is
converted into the statement: There exists one and only
one committee that contains any two children. Thus he is
able to pronounce the postulate true for his *particular*
interpretation.

On the other hand, his wife, who is preparing to do some
shopping, is thinking of a "system" consisting of various
coins and the purses in which they can be placed. She interprets x as "coin" and y as "purse." She transforms the
postulate into the statement: There exists one and only one
purse that contains any two coins. She pronounces the
postulate false for her interpretation by indicating that there
are several coins inside a change purse which is contained
in a larger purse. Thus, for pairs of these coins it is *not*
true that there is only one purse containing them. Or she
may have placed two coins on a table. For these coins it is
not true that there exists a purse containing them.

The illustrations above are meant to indicate that one cannot judge the truth of an abstract postulate containing undefined terms. Such an axiom becomes true or false only for specific, concrete interpretations of these terms. For a pure or abstract science the postulates are like rules in a game. No one judges chess rules to be either "true" or "false." One merely observes these rules in playing the game.

Clarification of the issue of "truth" is not the only advantage in conceiving of the undefined terms of a deductive system as mere symbols akin to the x, y, z's of ordinary algebra. In that subject, letters are usually considered to be *variables*, that is, to represent many different numbers simultaneously, as in statements like $x^2 - y^2 = (x + y)(x - y)$, which is true when x and y are replaced by *any* of the numbers used in common algebra. This suggests that the undefined x's and y's of postulate systems also be conceived as variables with a potential for many valid interpretations. Thus, if the statement of some postulate should assert that

$$x \text{ is a believer in } y$$

then it may be true that "Mr. Smith is a believer in Zen-Buddhism" but this is not necessarily the only valid interpretation. Or if x, y, and z are undefined terms in a postulate,

$$z = x + y$$

then the following and many more specific statements are valid interpretations:

$$5 = 2 + 3$$
$$\frac{5}{6} = \frac{1}{2} + \frac{1}{3}$$
$$(-9) = (-6) + (-3)$$
$$10\sqrt{3} = 8\sqrt{3} + 2\sqrt{3}$$

In fact, if, in the postulate $z = x + y$, the symbols $+$ and $=$ are also undefined, we might offer "and/or" as an interpretation for $+$ and "is equivalent to" as a meaning for $=$. Then, interpreting x, y, and z in terms of requirements for the Ph.D., one might arrive at a true statement: Russian is equivalent to German and/or French.

In summary, then, the use of undefined terms or empty

symbols in the postulates of a deductive system* has the advantages of all abstract formulation, namely economy and generality. A single concept or statement or proof, even an entire deductive system, may simultaneously fit numerous different situations. A small example of this fact occurred in connection with positional systems of notation, where arithmetic statements in any one system provided the abstract form for procedures in all other systems, including computer systems. In the same way, some abstract deductive system may have valid interpretations as a plane geometry, a hemispherical geometry, an algebra of number pairs, or a science that is not our idea of either a geometry or an algebra. Although the specific content of these subjects would vary, they would all have the same logical pattern, namely, the abstract postulates about x, y, z's and the theorems deduced from those postulates.

Thus, by using undefined terms or meaningless symbols in the postulates of a pure science, one accomplishes a double purpose by avoiding issues of "truth" and at the same time furnishing the potential for numerous valid interpretations. But if a pure mathematician need not be concerned with "truth," is he limited in any other way in setting up a postulate system? The answer is to be found in the logical criteria to which allusion has already been made. Logic furnishes only one imperative, but there are several other standards which are desirable under certain conditions. The primary characteristic which logic demands of a postulate system is that it be *consistent*. This signifies that it must not be possible to deduce from the postulates a pair of theorems which contradict one another.

How can a mathematician tell whether or not a system of axioms meets the requirement of consistency? If, in the course of deductions, he arrives at two contradictory theorems, he can pronounce the axiom system *inconsistent*. He must then discard or repair it. But suppose that he has derived all the theorems which he requires for some particular purpose and has found no contradictory pair among them. Is he to conclude that the postulate system is

---

* Throughout the present chapter the following terms should be considered synonymous: deductive system, deductive science, mathematical system, mathematical science, pure science or theory, abstract theory. Each of these terms signifies an aggregate of the following ingredients: (1) undefined terms, (2) postulates involving the undefined terms, (3) definitions involving the undefined terms, (4) theorems deduced from the postulates.

consistent? Decidedly not, for if he were to continue to deduce theorems, whether or not he is interested in such new propositions, he might ultimately arrive at a theorem contradictory to one previously established, and therefore *inconsistency* would be the proper verdict. The procedure of deducing more and more theorems is evidently not a practicable one. Can we ever reach a point where we can state with certainty that no more theorems are deducible? We need *all* theorems before we can render a judgment of consistency. For this reason, mathematicians usually accept the following working criterion for consistency: A set of postulates is said to be consistent if there exists an interpretation of the undefined terms which converts all the postulates into true statements.

Certain subtle logical issues form the rationale behind the working criterion for consistency, and we shall not go into them at this point. We shall, however, indicate the logical consequences of accepting the criterion. In order to avoid verbosity in explaining these logical fine points, we shall employ special vocabulary. In the first place, we shall consider *only* those interpretations of the undefined terms which convert the postulates into true statements. In mathematical logic the result of such interpretation, that is, the concrete set of true statements, is called a "model" of the abstract postulate system. Since the postulates are transformed into true statements of the model, all theorems deduced from the postulates must also be true statements of the model. Thus the abstract deductive system, consisting of postulates and theorems, is said to be transformed by interpretation from an *abstract theory* into a *concrete theory*. The word "model" is sometimes used to apply to the entire concrete theory (and not merely to its postulates) and sometimes to the relation of the concrete theory to the abstract theory. Since "model" is a favorite word of mathematicians, they use it with still other shades of meaning.*

* For example, one usage appears to reverse things by taking the abstract system as the model of the concrete one (see Chapters 10–14). In that case, a mathematical or abstract model is described as a deductive system in which axioms and undefined terms represent certain aspects of the observed realities. See Carl B. Allendoerfer, "The Narrow Mathematician," *American Mathematical Monthly*, Vol. 69, No. 6 (June–July 1962), pp. 462 ff.

To straddle both points of view, and to provide proofs of consistency, another description of a model makes it the interpretation of one mathematical theory with the assistance of another. See Nicolas Bourbaki, *Éléments d'histoire des mathématiques*, Hermann, Paris, 1960, p. 35.

To return to the working criterion of consistency, suppose that it is to be applied to some abstract postulate system. This requires that a "model" of the system be found, that is, an interpretation of the undefined terms which converts every postulate into a true statement. If a mathematician has abstracted the postulates from experimental situations, he will have a model at hand. All he has to do is reverse the process of abstraction which led to his assumptions and offer the original empirical propositions as the model. The applied mathematician might accept such a proof of consistency without any qualms. But others would become involved once more in that troublesome issue of "truth." Empirical propositions have no absolute validity, limited as they are by our senses and observational tools. Statistical inductions based on numerous careful repetitions of an experiment may have a high probability of being general truths, but they are still hypotheses, and future evidence may show them to be false.

Suppose, therefore, that empirical models are not to be accepted as proofs of the consistency of a postulate system. What other type of model is permissible? It is customary to find a model in some branch of mathematics that is already well established. When a pure mathematician seeks such a model, he may, in the fashion already described for the applied mathematician, return to the *source* of his postulate system. Whereas the applied mathematician uses empirical sources, the pure mathematician selects propositions (either axioms or theorems) from some well-established mathematical theory. Then part (or all) of that theory provides the model which demonstrates the consistency of his postulate system. Later we shall see that parts of Euclidean geometry, a long-established mathematical theory, are used in models establishing the consistency of different *non*-Euclidean geometries. Again, if we wished to demonstrate the consistency of a postulate system for a one-dimensional geometry of "points," we might proceed as in Chapter 2, and interpret the undefined "point" as a *real number*. If our postulates are thereby converted into accepted postulates or valid theorems about real numbers, we have demonstrated the consistency of our geometric system. In fact, if the same idea is extended to two-dimensional geometry, it turns out that Cartesian analytic (algebraic) geometry is the model that demonstrates the consistency of Euclidean geometry. (Although Descartes lived much later than Euclid, the arithmetic and algebraic foundations of the Cartesian subject are more secure, as it were.)

This sort of consistency proof, although accepted, merely displaces the problem of consistency from one mathematical theory to another. It leads to the inquiry: In the theory furnishing the model, is the underlying postulate system consistent? Its consistency is essential, for otherwise it may imply contradictory theorems, and some theorem used in the model (and hence considered "true") may be contradicted by an as-yet-undeduced theorem of the well-established subject. This makes the usual proof of consistency *relative*, not *absolute*. Such a proof shows that *if* the theory furnishing the model is consistent, then the model establishes the consistency of the postulate system which it interprets. All such considerations and still other difficulties into which we have not entered have provoked the comment: There is, in fact, *no* way of demonstrating the consistency of a system (Chapter 29). If such a judgment is too drastic, it is evident, nevertheless, that consistency proofs form a delicate logical issue. It is true, moreover, that some of the greatest minds of the recent era have carried on profound research related to the problem, and have indicated the difficulty of obtaining an absolute species of consistency proof. Kurt Gödel (page 93) has, in fact, shown the *impossibility* of such a proof for a comprehensive, formal (completely abstract) system (Chapter 29).

Consistency is the only essential property of a set of axioms, but a pure mathematician may ask for other qualities in certain postulate systems. With economy always in mind, he inquires: Have I assumed too much? Could I dispense with one or two axioms? Whereas an orator may achieve emphasis by describing a man as honest, upright, reliable, and so on, such redundancy does not appeal to the mathematician. Even concealed repetition seems to the mathematician a blemish which destroys the perfection of a set of axioms. Therefore he may require his postulates to be mutually *independent*. This means that no postulate of the system may be a logical consequence of other postulates. If it were deducible from the other axioms, then it could be stated as a theorem and there would be no need to assume it. If, paraphrasing Lewis Carroll, we assume that

(1) All babies are illogical,

(2) Illogical people cannot manage crocodiles,

then we need not also assume that

(3) Babies cannot manage crocodiles,

since proposition (3) is a logical consequence of (1) and (2), or is *dependent* on these propositions.

Let us emphasize again that independence is not an essential attribute of a set of postulates but is only called for by an ideal of logical perfection. It may be advisable, for psychological or pedagogical reasons, to use postulates that are not mutually independent. Readers may recall, from school geometry, that various propositions related to the congruence of triangles were *postulated* (after an experimental proof). These propositions are actually deducible from Euclid's postulates, in other words, are *theorems* of his geometry. But the proofs are exceedingly difficult for the beginning student, and hence textbooks add the propositions to the axiom set, which, as a result, fails to possess the quality of *independence*. This and other examples up to this point have all been negative in that they have exhibited systems lacking independence. We shall temporarily postpone positive illustrations because they involve an explanation of how independence is customarily established. The independence proof which will eventually be cited involves the most dramatic incident in the history of axiomatics, the turning point from the classic to the modern. It was Nicholas Lobachevsky (1792–1856), a great Russian mathematician, who was responsible for this revolutionary turn in mathematical events.

By contrast with assuming too much in founding a mathematical science and thereby failing to have independent postulates, there is the question of whether one can assume too little. A postulate system may be *incomplete* in that additional assumptions are required in order to prove certain theorems. As an example, the reader may recall, from school days, a "proof" that purported to deduce the proposition: Every triangle is isosceles. The demonstration involves the drawing of various auxiliary lines, and the proof is ultimately termed "fallacious" because the drawing is "careless" and the positions of various points and lines are incorrect. If there are any faults in the proof, however, they must be attributed to Euclid, since there are no postulates in his system which require points and lines to take the allegedly correct positions. Put otherwise, there is nothing in his system to rule out the "faulty" diagram. What this means is that one cannot deduce from his postulates either of the following contradictory statements: (1) Every triangle is isosceles. (2) Not every triangle is isosceles. This illustrates that Euclid's postulate system is *incomplete*. It also suggests a possible definition for completeness: A postulate system is called *complete* if it is possible to deduce from it either a proof of any proposition about elements of the system (undefined and defined entities) or a proof of the negation of that proposition.

Categoricalness is another attribute which may be sought for certain postulate systems, because it limits their models to a sort of uniformity (similar to that of the *isomorphic* arithmetic systems of Chapter 1), and in this way insures that the single abstract theory arising from the postulates will provide the total pattern for *all* applied theories which interpret it. A postulate system is *categorical* if, in every pair of models of the system, elements are in one-to-one correspondence, and all relations among elements are preserved.

In defining the properties of postulate systems and in explaining how these can be established, the role of the model or interpretation has appeared repeatedly. This gives the impression that specific, concrete subject matter is used only as a preliminary to formulating the axioms of an abstract theory, or for purposes of testing the consistency and other attributes of these axioms. But this is not the case. After the theorems of the pure theory have been deduced, they are often reinterpreted to check with the sources that inspired the postulate system, or to make "predictions" in some physical model of the system, or to provide proofs of theorems in concrete mathematical models, etc. The process will be illustrated later on when we discuss relativity. Einstein abstracted his axioms from observations made by physicists, deduced his abstract theory, reinterpreted it in terms of "planetary orbits," "Doppler effects," etc. so that certain theorems became "predictions." The fact that the latter were confirmed by observation shows that the abstract theory of relativity has a "real" model.

And now let us return to Euclid, who, with his illustrious Greek predecessors, founded the axiomatic method. We appear to have presented only negative aspects of his postulate system by pointing out that it was incomplete, and that Euclid himself did not realize that he had constructed a *pure* science, not limited to surveyors' "points" and "lines" or founded on "common notions." More satisfactory postulate systems for Euclidean geometry were devised by a number of mathematical leaders of the recent era. Among these there is a postulate system due to David Hilbert (1862–1943) and another formulated by Oswald Veblen (1880–1960). Both men will appear frequently as *dramatis personae* in our story because their discoveries were not limited to geometry or to the logical aspects of founding mathematical theories.

But how and when did the mathematical world first come to realize that Euclid's notion of postulates was inadequate, and that his set of axioms required repair? The most famous axiom in mathematical history, namely, *Euclid's parallel postulate*, will provide the answer. This axiom can be stated in many equivalent forms. If we define two "lines" that lie in the same "plane" but never meet as parallel, a statement equivalent to Euclid's parallel postulate is: *Through a point P outside a line l there is one and only one line parallel to l.*

Euclid's attitude toward the parallel postulate differed from his opinion of the other axioms. Although he considered the latter to be "common notions," he did not find the parallel postulate "self-evident." Because substantial empirical justification was lacking, he realized, in this one case only, that he was making an assumption. Since he dared not *assume* the parallel postulate, he tried to prove it, that is, to deduce it from the other axioms. In doing this, he established a precedent for centuries to come (twenty-one of them) for, until the day of Lobachevsky, mathematicians were constantly struggling for proofs of the parallel postulate. None of the Russian's predecessors considered the possibility that the postulate is *not* deducible from Euclid's other axioms. To use twentieth-century terminology, the parallel postulate may possibly be *independent* of the other Euclidean axioms.

If one is to show that a given postulate is independent of the other axioms of a system, he must demonstrate that it cannot possibly be a theorem deduced from those axioms by logical methods. The procedure for accomplishing such a demonstration today is strongly reminiscent of the technique for establishing consistency by the use of a model (interpretation) in which postulates and theorems of an abstract deductive system are converted into true statements of the model. Let us then suppose that we have already provided such a model to demonstrate the consistency of some deductive system. But, as we have seen, there can be many different ways of interpreting the undefined terms of a system. With this fact in mind, let us proceed further by removing the postulate whose independence is under scrutiny and then seeking models for the residual set of axioms. In any such model those axioms will be converted into true statements, and so will any theorems deducible from them. Now if we can exhibit a model for the residual axioms such that the deleted postulate is converted into a *false* statement, then that postulate cannot possibly be a theorem deducible from those axioms, for otherwise it would be true in the model. In summary, then, in a consistent postulate system, any given postulate can be proved to be independent of the other axioms of the system by exhibiting an interpretation in which the given postulate is false and the other postulates are true.

Lobachevsky's ideas included the above procedure. Specifically, he removed the parallel postulate from Euclid's list, and substituted a postulate equivalent to the following assumption: *In a plane, through a point outside a line l, there are an infinite number of lines which do not intersect l.* Then, on the basis of the revised postulate system, he constructed his *non*-Euclidean geometry. That Lobachevsky's geometry is (relatively) consistent was demonstrated by the Italian geometer Eugenio Beltrami (1835–1900), who used a model, namely, the "pseudosphere" (page 92). But more important for our present purpose is the fact that geometry on the "pseudosphere" provides an interpretation in which Euclid's parallel postulate is *false*, while his other axioms are *true*. Therefore the parallel postulate *cannot* possibly be a theorem deducible from those axioms, but is independent of them. That is why the twenty-one centuries of search for a proof of the parallel postulate had proved fruitless.

Thus Lobachevsky's geometry solved the problem of the parallel postulate for all time. But much more than that was accomplished by his bold procedure. It showed that postulates ought not to be conceived as "self-evident" truths, since it seems possible to replace a particular axiom by a radically different one without producing logical nonsense.

Because one may do this, an axiom is a somewhat arbitrary statement, neither self-evident nor something to be proved. In other words, it is, as constantly emphasized, a mere assumption. Therefore, in the creation of Lobachevskian geometry and its implications, we have the modern point of view in a nutshell. After Lobachevsky's initial step, mathematicians were led to a reconsideration of the nature of postulates and eventually to the point of view we have set forth in this chapter.

Credit should also be given to Janos Bolyai (1802–1860), a Hungarian mathematician, who worked out the notion of non-Euclidean geometry simultaneously with Lobachevsky, but independently. Since Lobachevsky's publication antedated Bolyai's, it is customary to name Lobachevsky as the creator of the concept. Gauss, the great mathematical giant of the nineteenth century, is said by some to have discovered results similar to those of Lobachevsky and Bolyai before either, but to have lacked the courage to publish facts so startling. As a matter of fact, Girolamo Saccheri (1667–1733), an Italian priest, had attempted a proof of Euclid's parallel postulate in 1733, in the course of which he actually discovered Lobachevskian geometry without being aware of it. Thus the way was well paved for Lobachevsky or Bolyai or Gauss.

After Lobachevsky had constructed his own particular brand of logical non-Euclidean geometry, the German mathematician Bernhard Riemann (1826–1866) constructed another. Riemann subsituted for Euclid's parallel postulate the assumption. *Through a point P outside a line l there is no line parallel to it; that is, every pair of lines in a plane must intersect.* When the term *non-Euclidean geometry* is used in mathematical literature, the geometries of Lobachevsky and Riemann are always meant, although the term can well be applied generically to any geometry that denies one or more of Euclid's axioms.

Lest the assumption of Lobachevsky and Bolyai seem too bizarre for the practical man, let us ask him to picture the infinite number of parallels to a line through an outside point as a sheaf so thin that it is not distinguishable from a single line. Riemann's postulate is easier to imagine, for may not two lines that seem to be parallel meet at an infinite distance? If this interpretation of the two non-Euclidean geometries is too much for the reader to swallow, let us offer another. We know that the modern point of view does not require us to interpret "point," "line," etc. in the ordinary way. We must first explain a preliminary concept or two. One of Euclid's axioms is: *A straight line segment is the shortest distance between two points.* That is the assumption for a *plane* surface, but what, then, is the shortest distance between two points on a spherical, cylindrical, or ellipsoidal (egg-shaped) surface? You can find out experimentally by stretching a string taut between two points of the surface. On a spherical surface, the shortest distance is a *great-circle arc*, the path followed by navigators in seeking shortest routes. It is a portion of a circle cut from the sphere by a geometric plane passing through the center of the sphere. Any plane section of a sphere will produce a circle, but only a plane through the center will produce a great circle. The shortest paths on other surfaces will be curves of various types. The mathematical name usually assigned to a shortest route is *geodesic*.

Since the geodesic for a plane is a line, this suggests interpreting the undefined term "line" as geodesic. Let us then consider Riemann's axiom first and interpret it in this way: *Through a given point P outside a geodesic l there is no geodesic which does not meet l.* If we picture a *spherical* surface, this axiom will satisfy the demands of common sense. All geodesics (great circles) on a sphere must meet one another, for their planes all go through the center of the sphere and must cut one another (Figure 3.1). In order to satisfy other postulates of Riemann's geometry, it is better, in fact, to use a *hemisphere*. Thus, on a hemisphere, geodesics (great circles) will meet in one point only. Then part of Euclidean geometry, namely, geometry on a hemisphere, is a model for Riemann's non-Euclidean geometry.

Let us next give Lobachevsky's axiom the interpretation:

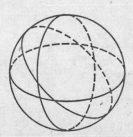

Figure 3.1   **Geodesics (great circles) on a sphere**

Through a given point P outside a geodesic l there are an infinite number of geodesics which do not intersect l. In 1868 Beltrami showed that there is a surface on which this makes sense (Figure 3.2). The diagram pictures a *tractrix*, whose revolution about its axis forms a sort of double-trumpet surface, Beltrami's "pseudosphere," so named by analogy with the sphere of Riemann's geometry. Then part of Euclidean geometry, namely, geometry on the pseudosphere, is a model for Lobachevsky's non-Euclidean geometry.

Having discussed the geometries of Euclid, Lobachevsky, and Riemann, one might ask: Which one of the three is the geometry of everyday life? Which one fits observed data best, involves the least computation and the simplest

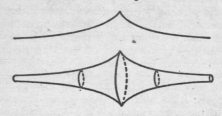

Figure 3.2   Tractrix and pseudosphere

mathematics? As far as agreement with the result of experiment is concerned, the surprising fact is that all three geometries are equally good in the small finite domain of ordinary existence. In Euclidean geometry there is the oft-quoted theorem, *The sum of the angles of any triangle is 180°.* The corresponding theorem of Lobachevskian geometry demonstrates that this angle sum is less than 180°, whereas Riemann's geometry holds that the sum is greater than 180°. In an attempt to ascertain which is the "true" theorem, Gauss performed an experiment in which a huge triangle with vertices on three mountain peaks in Germany was measured, and after that stellar measurements were brought into play. Even if it made no practical difference which geometry was the true one for small figures, it was felt that it might make some difference if the sides of a triangle were so huge that it would take centuries for light, traveling 186,000 miles a second, to traverse them. All experiments failed to bring about a decisive conclusion. The sum of the angles observed was always so close to 180° that the excess or deficiency in each case could have been readily caused by the unavoidable imperfection in the measuring techniques. Even if the three geometries fit experimental facts equally well, they are not equally simple for computational purposes. For ordinary everyday measurement on earth the Euclidean system has the easiest formulas, and hence we use it, not because it is the absolute and only truth, but because it is more readily applicable.

Presently we shall give considerable space to a biography of Lobachevsky because we consider him such a very important figure in the development of pure mathematics. Not only did his non-Euclidean geometry initiate the tradition of axiomatics, which is the essence of formal mathematical thinking, but it also led to patterns for establishing *consistency* and *independence* which are imitated in the most important *current* issues associated with the foundations of all mathematics.

To illustrate this fact, we must point out that although we have treated the notion of a postulate system, we have not as yet considered the logical apparatus by which theorems are to be deduced from the basic axioms. That question will be discussed in Chapter 6. However, we have indicated almost from our first page that the concept of *set* is basic in mathematics. Chapter 6 will emphasize the algebra of finite sets, but infinite aggregates will be discussed much later (Chapter 24), and credit will be given to Georg Cantor for developing the theory of such sets. Set theory is an essential part of the logical foundation of pure mathematics, and hence it has been provided with a formal postulate system by Cantor's successors.

Now just as the parallel postulate was a thorn in the side of mathematicians prior to Lobachevsky (because they were attempting to deduce it as a *theorem* from the other Euclidean postulates, when in fact it was consistent with, but *independent* of, those postulates), there is a similar situation in abstract set theory. In that subject there is an assumption called the *axiom of choice* which is essential to logical reasoning in many branches of mathematics but which some mathematicians for special reasons (Chapter 24) find hard to accept. The first step in making it palatable to them occurred in 1938 when Kurt Gödel, one of the foremost leaders in the study of the foundations of mathematics, showed that there is nothing inconsistent about assuming the fact in question. He proved that the troublesome postulate is *consistent* with the other postulates of pure set theory. Gödel gave a relative consistency proof, that is, he used a model or interpretation (thereby imitating the use of the pseudosphere as a model for establishing the consistency of Lobachevskian geometry).

Gödel took care of the consistency question, but what about the *independence* of the bothersome axiom of choice, the issue completely analogous to the problem of the parallel postulate? That has been handled only since 1963, in the work of the young American mathematician Paul J. Cohen, a living Lobachevsky, who has presented us with a consistent *non-Cantorian* set theory in which he uses one or another form of the *negation* of the Cantorian axiom. Gödel had previously done this within a certain special class of sets, the "constructible sets," as he called them. But Cohen did not limit himself to such sets. By using models (exceedingly subtle in nature in contrast with such elementary pictures as the sphere and pseudosphere of the non-Euclidean geometries), he established independence from the other axioms for the axiom of choice and, in fact, for another challenging postulate (which Cantor and his immediate successors hoped to deduce as a theorem), called the *continuum hypothesis* (Chapter 24).

At a meeting of the International Congress of Mathematicians, held in Moscow in August 1966, Cohen was awarded a Field Medal in recognition of all his achievements in attacking major unsolved problems in the foundations of mathematics. He had previously received the Bôcher Prize of the American Mathematical Society in 1963 and part of the special RCA award for scientific research.

To return to Lobachevsky, the man who started the sort of thinking Cohen is now carrying on at a much more advanced level, we have seen that two millennia of mathematical history formed a prologue to his bold replacement of the parallel postulate. But what sequence of events in Lobachevsky's own intellectual life led to that revolutionary step? Although the man in the street may picture Archimedes or Einstein or Cohen arriving at a theory as the result of a sudden brilliant inspiration, the inspired moment, if it exists, is just the culmination of a lengthy sequence of considerations on the part of the scientist, and this is subsequent to all the thought contributed by his predecessors. What was the course of the creative process with Lobachevsky? To answer, we must reveal some events from his personal life.

The year 1956, the centenary of Lobachevsky's death, was the occasion for special lectures to commemorate the fact that his discovery marked a turning point in mathematical history. Under the auspices of the University of Paris, one of the memorial addresses was delivered by Sophie Piccard, Professor of Mathematics at the University of Neuchâtel, Switzerland. Her lecture on Lobachevsky was delivered on December 1, 1956, at the Palais de la Découverte, one of the principal science museums of Paris. Professor Piccard was born in Russia, where she attended a lycée and later the University of Smolensk. Her understanding of Russian as well as her mathematical scholarship enabled her to draw on some hitherto untapped sources and the memorial address was an excellent popular account of Lobachevsky's work. What follows is a condensation of the memorial address* freely translated from the French by the present author.

Little is known about the first years of Lobachevsky's life. Only recently have the date and place of his birth been established with certainty. He was born on November 20, 1792, at Nijny-Novgorod. (This date of birth is the one ascertained only recently. It is approximately a year earlier than that which was formerly given by historians.) His father, who was of Polish descent, worked for the government as a surveyor. Shortly after his son was born, he became ill and lost his position, with the result that his wife, Praskovia Alexandrovna, and his children spent the ensuing years in dire poverty. After almost a decade of illness, Lobachevsky's father died and in 1802 his mother requested the admission of her three sons, Alexander (aged eleven), Nicholas (aged nine), and Alexis (aged seven), as scholarship students in the "Premier Gymnase" of Kazan.

Situated on a small tributary of the Volga, Kazan, at the beginning of the nineteenth century, was a city of 25,000 inhabitants, about one-fourth of whom were Tatars. Extremely picturesque in appearance with its Tatar quarter and its numerous churches built on hills separated by deep ravines, it had unpaved clay roads that became massive mud puddles after every small shower and from which rose columns of dust when the weather was dry. Although it was an important commercial center of western Russia, it offered little in the way of cultural opportunity. The *gymnasium***

---

* S. Piccard, *Lobatchevsky, grand mathématicien russe. Sa vie, son oeuvre.* Conférences du Palais de la Découverte, Université de Paris, Série D, No. 47.
** A *gymnasium* (German) or *lycée* (French) is a pre-university school on the continent of Europe. Its course of study corresponds to the education provided by the American junior and senior high schools plus the first two years of college, and the students range from ten to eighteen in age.

attended by Lobachevsky had been founded in 1798 by members of the nobility for the education of their children as well as those of commoners; it offered a four-year course in preparation for civil service and military careers, and its program made heavy demands on the students.

In 1804 Emperor Alexander I signed a law founding a university at Kazan. The following year this university was opened without buildings, equipment, or professors, and was at first merely an annex of the *gymnasium* whose principal, Iakovkine, became University Director and whose teachers became the faculty of the higher institution. In 1805, in an attempt to recruit students, Iakovkine appealed to parents of the students in the *gymnasium* to have their children continue their education by attending the University of Kazan. Free tuition and board were available for indigent pupils, provided they promised to devote six years after graduation to teaching. Lobachevsky's mother was persuaded to consent to this scholarship offer for her three sons, and thus the boys left the *gymnasium* and entered the University of Kazan. Nicholas was admitted in February 1807, at the age of fourteen, having completed his *gymnasium* studies brilliantly a month earlier.

During his first year at the university he was taught mathematics by two student teachers who knew less than their pupils, but in 1808 he had the good fortune to study with Johann Martin Bartels (1769–1836), who had been Gauss's teacher. Thus young Lobachevsky embarked on the reading of research papers as well as scientific works in Latin, German, and French. At this time he decided to specialize in pure science instead of preparing for a career in medicine, which had been his earlier ambition. His reading suggested problems for which he gave remarkably original solutions.

The atmosphere at Kazan was a very serious one. In spite of this earnest setup, or perhaps because of it, Lobachevsky became involved in some student pranks. Having spent five years as a boarding student at the *gymnasium*, where iron discipline reigned, he indulged in a brief breath of freedom at the university. He had the audacity to go to parties which university boarding students were expressly forbidden to attend. Once he prepared a rocket which another student set off in the courtyard of the university. His major blunder, however, was his sarcastic manner toward Kondyrev, the confidant of the principal, Iakovkine. Kondyrev, unpleasant in personality and grotesque in appearance, was only five years older than Lobachevsky. It was his responsibility to supervise the students and to report their conduct to the principal. Kondyrev avenged himself by submitting very bad reports on Lobachevsky, even to the extent of accusing him of atheism, a charge which was not at all justified but which might have had tragic consequences for Lobachevsky. The principal wanted to have him dismissed from the university, and only the energetic intervention of the professors from Germany, who did not wish to lose their best student, permitted him to complete his studies. On July 10, 1811, Nicholas Lobachevsky was called before the council of the school and was upbraided for his bad conduct. He had to apologize, admit his guilt, and promise to reform. Only after he had put all this in writing was he granted the master's degree.

Thus, in 1811, at the age of nineteen, he ended his student days at Kazan. He remained at the university, however, in order to receive Bartels' guidance, and at once read two of the greatest mathematical works ever written: Gauss's *Disquisitiones Arithmeticae* and Laplace's *Mécanique Céleste*. These treatises, which have become classics, were less than a decade old at the time; they inspired Lobachevsky's *Theory of the Elliptical Movement of Celestial Bodies* (1812) and his *Concerning the Solution to the Algebraic Equation of the Type* $x^n - 1 = 0$ (1813). The first of these papers has not come down to us, but Bartels' report stated that his protégé's study indicated a mastery of Laplace's exceedingly difficult *Celestial Mechanics* and enriched the same subject with original ideas that could be produced only by a remarkable mathematical talent.

Lobachevsky studied the great masters—Gauss, Cauchy, etc.—but strangely, Euler, that prolific genius who had lived in St. Petersburg, scarcely influenced the young Russian mathematician. In 1814 Bartels was influential in obtaining an adjunct professorship for Lobachevsky, and although this was equivalent in rank to an assistant professorship, the young man had to teach arithmetic, algebra, and other elementary mathematics courses because students entering the university had no background whatsoever in mathematics.

Lobachevsky did not resort to textbooks in teaching these elementary courses, but conscientiously prepared his own lecture notes, which he willingly lent to students. Virtue was its own reward, for it appears that pedagogic considerations led to his interest in the theory of parallels. Like his predecessors, he tried to prove Euclid's parallel postulate and presented such a proof in his geometry course of 1815, as the notes of one of his students, P. Temnikov, indicate. The demonstration was ingenious but inevitably erroneous, as Lobachevsky himself soon realized.

The year 1816 brought a promotion to associate professor for the young teacher, but unhappy days ensued for him and his associates. About this time Alexander I came under the influence of men who claimed that the universities were centers of atheism and revolutionary activity, and hence should be shut down one and all. In 1819 the dull-witted Magnitzky was assigned to investigate the setup at Kazan. He promptly recommended that the university be closed, but Alexander did not accept this suggestion. Instead he ordered the malevolent Magnitzky to institute reforms. The latter lost no time in setting about the task; he dismissed seven professors including Iakovkine; he established a chair of Greek Orthodox theology; he laid down the law on methods of instruction, insisting that they be religious and completely autocratic; he "purified" the library, and burned all the books he condemned; he instituted monastic discipline for the students. One result of this terror was that all the outstanding foreign scholars felt insecure and departed from the University of Kazan.

Lobachevsky was ill and had missed the first round of Magnitzky's activities. But when Bartels left in 1820 and Lobachevsky was appointed in 1821 to succeed his friend in the chair of pure mathematics, as well as in the direction of the entire physicomathematical section, Magnitzky summoned him to St. Petersburg and kept him busy there for almost a year with tasks that were either dull or distasteful—for example, preparing statistical data on Kazan, directing the acquisition of library books and laboratory equipment, finally, examining the lecture notes of the natural science professors at St. Petersburg, Raupach and Herrmann, to see if these men of German origin were not subversive. Lobachevsky rendered a mild, noncommittal report but never forgave Magnitzky for burdening him with such an ugly mission.

Starting in 1822, when Lobachevsky was teaching ten courses, more and more duties were assigned to him. He was placed in charge of the university library, and then made chairman of the committee on the construction of university buildings. Next he was asked to help in the establishment of a scholarly scientific periodical for the physico-mathematical section of the university, and then to supervise the founding of an astronomical observatory. Little by little he became the central figure of the university. He was an indefatigable worker, a man of action who enthusiastically undertook all tasks that were entrusted to him, straightforward, just, poised, calm, and a keen diplomat. He knew how to get the whole university council to reach unanimous agreement. He was warmly loved and venerated by the students.

Since he did not flatter Magnitzky, however, the latter considered him subversive and eventually had him watched, along with other suspects. Thus it came about in 1823, when Lobachevsky submitted the manuscript of his *Geometry* for publication at government expense, that Fuss, the permanent secretary of the St. Petersburg Academy, criticized the work severely. He even objected to Lobachevsky's use of the metric system, because it was "created by the French Revolution"! The result was that the *Geometry* was not published during Lobachevsky's lifetime, was mislaid, then found in 1898, and printed for the first time in 1909.

When Nicholas I became czar, Magnitzky was removed from his position, and his duties at Kazan were taken over by General Jeltoukhine on February 21, 1826. Two days later there occurred an event of major importance in the history of modern mathematics: Lobachevsky presented before the physico-mathematical section of the University of Kazan a report written in French and entitled *A Brief Statement of the Principles of Geometry with a Rigorous Demonstration of the Theorem of Parallels*.

He asked the opinion of his colleagues on the merit of this work. They submitted it to a committee of three professors, whose respective subjects were astronomy, chemistry, and applied mathematics. No one of the three was able to understand the report, and the group was unanimous in its disapproval. Nevertheless Lobachevsky included the same material in a larger work, the *Elements of Geometry*, published in 1829. This treatise contained the foundations of his new geometry, but neither this nor any of Lobachevsky's subsequent works was appreciated in Russia. On the contrary, he was severely and unjustly criticized, even by the St. Petersburg Academy. He was not discouraged, however, and from 1825 to 1838 wrote additional papers including his great treatise, *New Elements of Geometry with the Complete Theory of Parallels*. Because he was accused of lack of clarity, he decided to write a short expository work on the more elementary aspects of his new geometry, and this was published as a pamphlet in Berlin in 1840. Although it was extremely lucid, a veritable mathematical masterpiece, which was to rouse the scientific world a quarter of a century later, Lobachevsky became the butt of German criticism of a type similar to that offered in his native land.

Fortunately, his personal life was happy during this period of professional frustration. In 1832 he had married Varvara Moiseieva, a wealthy young woman of property. They had several children, of whom Lobachevsky was most fond. He purchased an estate on the Volga, near Kazan, where he spent his vacations, such as they were. He would rise at 7 A.M., permit himself an hour's walk, and then start a day of work. He was an enthusiastic gardener and built a beautiful park covered with Siberian cedar trees. The Lobachevskys were hospitable, and among their many guests there were always half a dozen needy students on holiday.

From 1827 to 1846 Lobachevsky was rector of the university, but in 1846 was not reelected. After thirty years of service to the university, he was forced to leave and was assigned by the minister of public instruction to the position of "adjunct superintendent" of the school district of Kazan. His chair in pure mathematics was taken over by his pupil Popov, and Simonov, the professor of astronomy, replaced him as rector of the university. Lobachevsky did not get along well with his superior, the superintendent of the school district, a General Molostvov. The mathematician's heart was not in his new work. His interest was in the university, which to this day maintains both the external appearance and the internal policies which he gave to it.

His last years were unhappy ones not only on account of his removal from academic activities but also because of the death of his son Alexei, the image of his father, who had been his student

and excellent in mathematics. The youth died of tuberculosis at
the age of nineteen. Added to these sorrows were grave financial
difficulties resulting from Lobachevsky's loss of his job at the
university. Next came arteriosclerosis, blindness, and the loss of
his position as adjunct superintendent. Nothing deterred him,
however, in his complete devotion to science. In 1855 he decided
to contribute a paper to the collection commemorating the fiftieth
anniversary of the founding of the University of Kazan, but his
blindness made it necessary to dictate it to his pupils. This
memoir, Lobachevsky's last, was called *Pangeometry*.

He died in February 1856, just thirty years after he had presented the concept of his new geometry to the physico-mathematical section of the university. When Professor Boulitch delivered a glowing eulogy, he was denounced as a freethinker and
removed from his position. Such was the tragic close to the life
of a mathematician whose genius revolutionized the pattern of
all scientific thought.

The present chapter has treated postulational reasoning,
Hellenic style, along with Lobachevsky's discovery that
there is one grave imperfection in the Euclidean point of
view, namely, the failure to realize that the fundamental
axioms in any mathematical science are assumptions. The
matter at issue is the nature of the foundation of a branch
of mathematics or any abstract theory. Euclidean geometry
(in modern dress) has been cited as an example of such a
theory, but arithmetic or algebra can also be constructed on
the basis of postulates containing undefined terms. Thus,
in contrast with the informal, heuristic presentation of our
previous chapter, Giuseppe Peano (1858–1932), one of the
first and foremost contributors to modern axiomatics,
based his pure, logical theory of the natural numbers on the
following five postulates, in which "natural number" and
"successor" are undefined terms:

(1) 1 is a natural number.
(2) Every natural number has a successor which is a
    natural number, and this successor is unique.
(3) No two natural numbers have the same successor.
(4) 1 is not the successor of any natural number.
(5) Principle of finite induction: Any property that be-
    longs to 1, and also to the successor of any natural
    number that has the property, belongs to all natural
    numbers.

If the reader will examine the first four of these axioms,
he will see that they are satisfied by the "counting numbers"

—1, 2, 3, 4, . . . of elementary arithmetic, although Peano's use of "natural number" as an undefined term leaves the way open for other interpretations. The fifth of Peano's postulates is a subtler assumption, which has its roots in what algebra textbooks call the method of mathematical induction. At any rate, from his five simple assumptions, Peano deduced, in rigorous fashion, theorems concerning the behavior of the natural numbers. The importance of Peano's formal foundation for the arithmetic of the natural numbers will become apparent only much later in our story. But we have already seen how and why, even for the purposes of Euclidean geometry, it became necessary to extend the natural aggregate so as to include other types of number. Still further number extensions will be presented in our next chapter, along with the postulate systems governing the arithmetic of the new numbers.

Chapter 4

Algebra from Hypatia to Hamilton

"His Excellency, the Prefect of Alexandria." The announcement was made by a young slave to the group of half a dozen men seated in one of the lecture rooms of the museum.

A minute later, a striking-looking young man made his appearance. He was attired in elegant senatorial robes; elaborate metallic and jeweled ornaments hung from his neck, and a heavy odor of Oriental perfume surrounded him.

"Welcome, honored Orestes. Hypatia will rejoice to see you back in Alexandria and present at her lectures once more." Theon, the oldest of the group, was the first to speak. His pale, drawn face and his simple philosopher's robe contrasted sharply with the splendid attire of the young Roman prefect.

Palladas the poet, Wulff the Goth, Petrus the Christian, Hesychius the Jew, Kalliphonos the astronomer, and Euoptius, the emissary of Synesius of Cyrene, greeted Orestes in turn. All were fellow students in the classes of that leader of Alexandrian thought, Hypatia, daughter of Theon.

The prefect told of his travels, while the others spoke of affairs at home. A sudden silence fell on the group when the door of the adjoining room opened, and Hypatia mounted the tribune. All eyes were focused on the figure of the young woman who was about to address the group. She was clad in a loosely flowing Ionic robe, whose simplicity was relieved by the touches of color in the purple stripes marking Roman citizenship, the gold-embroidered sandals, and the wide gold band of the headdress.

"In honor of Your Excellency's return, and in order that you may know what we have discussed in your absence, my good father, Theon, has consented to read a brief summary of this month's lectures." Hypatia descended from the platform and motioned to Theon to take her place.

He began to read: "The primeval Being, the One, is the source of life, the only real existence, and the supreme Good, All things are brought forth by it. All things are divine, being reflections of the One." Theon read on and on. Orestes, attentive at first, was ultimately distracted by the restlessness of others in the group.

Barely waiting for Theon to complete his summary, the astronomer Kalliphonos voiced his criticism: "In this document Theon has failed to mention my objections to our abject subscription to the doctrine of Plotinus. Even if you yourself cannot agree with any other point of view, Hypatia, you should devote some lectures to the thought of Democritus, Epicurus, Lucretius. My fellow students are entitled to hear at least once the words of those who believe in the virtue of the material world. Give us the chance to be eclectic. We must have the right to choose from all philosophies."

"Then you shall be the one to present such a point of view." Hypatia's countenance had become suffused with color and her eyes were flashing. "I cannot teach what I do not believe. Still I am willing to have my followers exposed to opinions which differ from my own."

The Christian Petrus had seemed impatient during the conversation between Kalliphonos and Hypatia. He gave the speakers no opportunity to prolong the discussion, but voiced his own complaint. "Theon has not recorded my opinion, either—that we ought to discuss the philosophy of the religion which Orestes and I have embraced. Let us see whether our fellow students will choose Lucretius or Plotinus after they hear the teachings of Jesus Christ."

Hypatia trembled visibly as she answered, "Petrus, you also shall have the right to speak. I can see where the beliefs of Lucretius are in contrast with ours. But those of the Christians—never! Do we not, like you, teach that charity is stronger than the sword, that man must lose his life to gain his life, that self-sacrifice is the highest virtue? Do we not believe in the mortification of the flesh for the immortality of the soul? Let those who see greater beauty in the Christian creed embrace the cross. But do not force us to desert the faith which seems to us the equivalent of your Christian philosophy."

A troubled look came over the face of Orestes. As he rose to speak, the dignity of the Roman governor seemed to replace the youthfulness of the dandy. "These riddles of 'Who am I? What am I?'—shall we, here, try to settle them, when they are as old as thought? Never! We shall quibble from now until the end of time, if once we get started. Why not spend these precious hours in which Hypatia shares her wisdom with us, on pure mathematical questions whose abstract nature will prevent quarrels, and whose logical format will be indisputable? I recall that last year when Synesius visited us, we had a series of lectures on the *Arithmetica* of Diophantus. I think that I personally would enjoy a review and a continuation of this mathematical work."

The tension was relieved. Hypatia smiled once more. "Why, just this last week, Synesius sent an epistle through Euoptius, requesting further information on the construction of an astrolabe and also on those very questions of Diophantus to which your excellency alludes. I can read from the response I am sending to our good friend, the Bishop of Cyrene."

For an hour or longer Hypatia spoke, explaining the techniques of Diophantus for the solution of indeterminate problems of various types. She told of the novel Diophantine symbolism which would facilitate expression and resolution of such problems. Her students interrupted every now and then to suggest particular answers. Then she would indicate that general formulas were Diophantus' objective and that he had obtained them for some of the more elementary types. She promised that she would devote future meetings to the "quadratic" problems which Diophantus had solved most ingeniously. With this, Hypatia concluded her lecture. Then there was the inevitable after-class discussion mingled with a bit of social gossip. When it was all over, Orestes still remained.

With a glance through the window to make sure that all the others were on their way, he turned to Hypatia. "As usual I feel intellectually stimulated by your brilliant lecture. But you know very well that I come not to hear these arguments of materialism versus idealism, nor even to study the work of Diophantus, but rather to seek the guidance of the best brain in Alexandria concerning affairs of state. I come once more about the same problem. My absence from Alexandria has not improved matters."

"And what is the nature of this problem?" Hypatia questioned.

"You know well enough Cyril is ever the same. Although he is Bishop of Alexandria, his conscience does not deter him from stirring up trouble. What stand am I to take in these latest riots?"

"That of justice tempered with mercy." Hypatia's voice resounded through the lecture room.

"A fine abstract doctrine, dear teacher, for your lectures, but an impractical cliché outside the classroom. You must modify or elaborate it." Orestes paused as if awaiting some further suggestion from Hypatia. But she remained silent. After a moment or two, Orestes seemed both anxious and hesitant to make another request. "And, Hypatia . . . ," he started slowly, "I am tempted to repeat an oft-spoken plea. May I once again entreat you to embrace Christianity as a practical safeguard? At this very moment Petrus is probably in Cyril's study, reporting on your lecture and my presence here. By this evening there will be new whisperings everywhere. Cyril will see to that. The words 'heathen' and 'sorceress' will circulate freely on the tongues of the ignorant. General opinion does not favor this free association of men and women to which you are accustomed. Come then, accept my counsel in exchange for your own. Then you will be safe from the bishop's persecution, and free to carry on your researches with peace of mind."

A long silence followed Orestes' speech. Hypatia then turned her head, and her dark expressive eyes met those of the young prefect. "Charmingly put, my practical Roman. I wish that I could agree with you, but, good friend, I can only reiterate what I have said several times before. I cannot compromise with my beliefs, my ideals, my devotion to a particular philosophy."

The prefect was still undeterred, and renewed his plea. "Hypatia, if I can make no other appeal to you, let me plead for those very ideals and activities which you cherish. Loyal follower of Plotinus, your very life is in danger. With Cyril as bishop, what chance will there be for you to pursue studies or lectures in safety?"

The rejoinder came quickly. "Shall I, a disciple of Plotinus, delay the joyous reunion of my soul with the highest

Spirit? Christianity should have taught you, too, Orestes, not to fear death."

"Forgive me, dearest Hypatia, if I have been too emphatic with regard to your welfare. You must not blame me."

And so it was that Orestes gave up this battle as lost.

Orestes' warning was prophetic. Not long after it was delivered, Hypatia was barbarously murdered by the Nitrian monks and a fanatical Christian mob. She was torn from her chariot, dragged to the Caesareum, a Christian church, stripped naked, slashed to death with oyster shells, and finally burned piecemeal. In the eloquent, beautiful, and brilliant high priestess of mathematics and philosophy, the bigoted could see nothing but a pagan influence on the prefect of Alexandria.

After Hypatia's martyrdom, Hellenic mathematics came to an end, and we are fortunate that the mathematical tradition was kept alive in India. The great Alexandrian library had been burned by Roman soldiers before Hypatia's day, and during her lifetime the only remaining library, in the temple of Serapis, was sacked by an Alexandrian mob. This will give some idea of what Alexandria was like in 400 A.D. at the time when Hypatia lectured there on Neoplatonic philosophy and Diophantine algebra.

Tradition labels Hypatia the first woman mathematician in history, but almost nothing is known with certainty about either her original contributions or her expository treatises, since all her scientific writings are lost. She received her mathematical training from her father, Theon, who is usually credited with the revised and improved version of Euclid's *Elements* that is in use to this very day. In addition, he wrote other valuable commentaries, and so did his daughter. Texts on the *Conics* of Apollonius, the *Almagest* of Ptolemy, the *Arithmetica* of Diophantus are all attributed to Hypatia. But the customary belief is that her mathematical activity was mainly in the field of *algebra* and that is why we began this chapter with her story.

We are now going to discuss certain important aspects of the evolution of algebra from the earliest Babylonian era to the middle of the nineteenth century. In this chapter and in the next, we shall see that what was developed during almost four millennia was mainly the methodology of solving equations of a certain kind, that this entailed an extension of the real number system so that "imaginary"

and "complex" numbers would be included, and that further
extension produced a turning point in algebra akin to and
contemporary with Lobachevsky's revolution in geometry.
Then, ultimately, algebra became something very different.

In modern times, one of the most potent creators of the
new "abstract algebra" was Hypatia's modern counterpart,
Emmy Noether (1882–1935), the greatest woman mathematician in history. She, too, was a martyr of sorts. Fleeing to
the United States to escape Hitler's persecution, her health
failed, and she did not long survive her arrival on our
shores.

To return to Hypatia, it was Diophantus, the greatest
algebraist of antiquity, who inspired her. He, too, lived and
worked in Alexandria, but his nationality and exact dates are
unknown. At present some historians claim that he lived
during the first century of the Christian era, about the time
of Nero, whereas others cling to the previous opinion,
which placed him around 250 A.D. Diophantus' work is his
monument, and the only clue to his personal life is found in
the following problem from the Palatine or *Greek An-
thology*, a compilation of numerical epigrams assembled in
the sixth century.

God granted him youth for a sixth part of his life, and adding
a twelfth part to this, He clothed his cheeks with down; He lit
him the light of wedlock after a seventh part, and five years after
his marriage He granted him a son. Alas! lateborn wretched
child; after attaining the measure of half his father's life, cruel
Fate overtook him, thus leaving to Diophantus during the last
four years of his life only such consolation as the science of numbers can offer.

A reader who has studied school algebra might use the
literal symbol x to represent Diophantus' age, and then put
the epigram into symbolic form, thus:

$$\frac{1}{6}x + \frac{1}{12}x + \frac{1}{7}x + 5 + \frac{1}{2}x + 4 = x$$

$$\frac{75}{84}x + 9 = x$$

$$9 = \frac{9}{84}x$$

$$84 = x$$

Diophantus lived to be eighty-four, and had married at thirty-three. His son was born when the father was thirty-eight and lived to the age of forty-two.

Modern literal algebraic symbolism was used in the equation above, and will be employed throughout this chapter. But such symbolism, launched to some extent by Diophantus, was not in vogue before the sixteenth century, when François Viète (1540–1603), better known by his Latin pen name Vieta, was the first to use letters to represent unknowns. Before the day of Diophantus algebra was *rhetorical*, that is, results were obtained by means of verbal argument, without abbreviations or symbols of any kind. One could, in fact, provide formulas, solve equations, and carry out algebraic procedures even if one were to write *number* or *numero* or *Zahl* or *res* (the Latin for the word "thing" —a customary usage even as late as the sixteenth century) instead of using x or y or z. But it would make reasoning difficult. Therefore one of Diophantus' major contributions was the "syncopation" of algebra.

Syncopated algebra, as it is called, is more a case of shorthand than completely abstract symbolism, but it is a marked step in the right direction. At any rate, Diophantus was the first mathematician in history to provide any sort of substitute for lengthy verbal expression. He was given to the initial-letter type of shorthand. Instead of our proverbial x, he used a symbol that resulted from the fusion of α (alpha) and ρ (rho), the first two letters of *arithmos* ($\alpha\rho\nu\theta\mu\text{os}$), the Greek word for number. Our x^2 and x^3 were Δ^v and K^v from *dunamis* ($\delta\nu\nu\alpha\mu\iota\text{s}$), meaning power, and *kubos* ($\kappa\nu\beta\text{os}$), the word for cube.

The degree of influence of Babylonian algebra on the pre-Diophantine geometric algebra of the Greeks, on Diophantus himself, and on algebra in India, is now evaluated as considerable. This may have been brought about through trade relations and, in rather negative fashion, by the frequent foreign invasions of India during the early centuries when Hindu algebra was being developed by Aryabhata the Elder (475–550 A.D.), Aryabhata the Younger (dates uncertain), Brahmagupta (*ca.* 628), Mahavira (*ca.* 850), and Bhaskara (1114–1185). These men, like Diophantus, contributed to the theory of indeterminate equations. They even used a syncopated symbolism akin to that of Diophantus, but they were more imaginative and more thorough. Thus Bhaskara wrote:

In those examples where occur two, three, or more unknown quantities, colors should be used to represent them. As assumed by previous teachers, there are: *yavat-tavat* (so much as), *kalaka* (black), *nilaka* (blue), *pitaka* (yellow), *lohitaka* (red), *haritaka* (green), *svetaka* (white), *cirtaka* (variegated), *kapilaka* (tawny), *pingalaka* (reddish-brown), *dhumraka* (smoke-colored), *patalaka* (pink), *savalaka* (spotted), *syamalaka* (blackish), *mecaka* (dark blue), etc.[*]

Another Hindu text lists a few more colors, and also adds a set of *flavors*. Bhaskara used still further types of abbreviation in symbolizing unknowns. Ultimately only initial syllables were used—*ya, ka, ni*, etc. For a known number there was *ru* (from *rupa*), and for a product there was *bha* (from *bhavuta*), written after the factors. Addition was indicated by juxtaposition, and subtraction by placing a dot over the subtrahend. Thus

$$ru \ 9 \ ya \ ka \ ni \ 7 \ bha \ ru \ \dot{5}$$

(transliterated from the Sanskrit) corresponds to our

$$9 + 7xyz - 5$$

Using their syncopated symbolism, the Indian algebraists achieved great heights in indeterminate analysis, but their discoveries never reached the western world and all their profound efforts were duplicated at a later date by the Europeans Pierre de Fermat (1601–1665), John Wallis (1616–1703), Lord William Brouncker (1620–1684), Leonhard Euler (1707–1783), the first and the last being among the greatest names in the whole history of mathematics.

To illustrate an exceedingly elementary indeterminate problem, let us consider the modern issue of making change for coins. Suppose that a quarter is presented with a request for dimes and pennies in exchange (at least one coin of each kind). This can be expressed by the equation.

$$10x + y = 25$$

where x represents the number of dimes and y the number of pennies. The problem is indeterminate because, as the reader will see, there are *two* solutions, namely, $x = 1$, $y = 15$ and $x = 2$, $y = 5$. If one were *not* talking about

[*] B. Datta and A. N. Singh, *History of Hindu Mathematics*, Motilal Banarsi Das, Lahore, 1935, Vol. 1, p. 18.

dimes and pennies, the abstract equation would have an infinite number of other numerical solutions like $x = \frac{1}{2}$, $y = 20$, $x = 3$, $y = -5$, etc. Diophantus and his Hindu kindred spirits considered both determinate and indeterminate equations. In the latter the unknowns were *always* considered to be natural numbers only, as in the case of our question about dimes and pennies.

The restriction that permits "syncopated" or modern symbols to be replaced only by natural numbers, or the greater freedom that might allow a *ya* or a *ka* or an *x* to represent any real number, is an essential feature of what we call algebra. The x, y, z's need not symbolize unknowns in some practical or recreational problem, but may be interpreted as *variables*, with a specified *replacement set* or *domain*. These concepts are useful not only in solving problems where unknowns may be natural or integral or rational or real numbers, etc., but also in making *general* statements about all members of such sets of numbers, for example, the commutative law, $x + y = y + x$, or the "identity," $(x + y)^2 = x^2 + 2xy + y^2$, where in the two illustrations the domain of both variables, x and y, is the real number aggregate. For this reason, traditional algebra is often described as *generalized arithmetic*. In arithmetic, statements refer only to *constants*, the names of specific things, for example, "three" or IV or 7 or $10 - 2$, etc. In algebraic statements, both constants and variables may be involved.

Since, as we have said in previous chapters, many fundamental concepts of mathematics can be explained in terms of the *basic* notion of a *set* of things, *variable* and *constant* may also be defined in that way. A *constant*, then, is a symbol which names a *specific* member of some set, and a *variable* is a symbol which, in a particular context, may be replaced by *any* member of some set, called the *domain* or *replacement set* of the variable.

Variables and constants are analogous to the pronouns and proper nouns of ordinary speech. If I assert, "*He* is my cousin," I might as well say, "*x* is my cousin." Either "he" or *x* is a variable which is open to replacement by the name of any living male. Any such name, for example, Henry Jones, is a *constant*. Although one is free to replace the variable by an enormous number of different constants, not all replacements will lead to *true* statements. Perhaps in all the wide world I have only two male cousins, Henry Jones and Peter Smith. Mathematical custom would name the assertion containing the variable an *open sentence*. The aggregate {Henry Jones, Peter Smith} would be called the *truth set* or *solution set* of the sentence.

The statements "Michael Brown is my cousin" (in the above example), and "$5 = 2 + 3$" (in arithmetic) are said to express *propositions*. Here as well as elsewhere in mathematics and logic (Chapter 6), an idea that can be pronounced either true or false is called a *proposition*. Logicians calls a declarative sentence expressing a proposition a *statement*. This makes a statement a sort of constant that names an idea, namely, the corresponding proposition. Although logicians distinguish between statement and proposition, numeral and number, any constant and the *value* it names, we shall *not* do so in this book. We have indicated here and in previous chapters the distinction between a name and the object named. Belaboring the point makes for pedantic expression but, for the record, we indicate once more that a unique object may have many names. A certain cardinal number may be named "three," "drei," III, 3, $1 + 2$, $1 + 1 + 1$, $8 - 5$, etc. The same proposition is asserted by "If two sides of a triangle are equal, the angles opposite are equal" and "The base angles of an isosceles triangle are equal." For those who know mathematical tradition, *Pons Asinorum* (Bridge of Asses) is still another name for the proposition (because the original proof in Euclid was so difficult that many students could not "cross over" to pass beyond it).

To review some of the things we have said, let us suppose that x is a variable whose domain is the set, {1, 2, 3, 4, 5}. Then "$x < 4$" is a declarative sentence (read as "x is less than 4") but it is *not* a statement because it does not express a proposition, an idea that can be pronounced either true or false. Because the sentence has the *form* of a statement, however, it would sometimes be described as a *statement form* or *propositional form*. But since the sentence presents an "open question" and the variable x is open to replacement by any value in its domain, it is customary to describe "$x < 4$" as an *open sentence*. Replacement of x by the five values in its domain would lead to five propositions, only three of which would be true. Those values of x which lead to true statements are said to constitute the *truth set* or *solution set* of the open sentence, "$x < 4$." It is readily seen that the truth set is {1, 2, 3}, a *subset of the domain*.

For other illustrations, suppose that the domain of each

of the two variables x and y is $\{1, 2, 3, 4, 5\}$. Then the following are open sentences:

$$x > 2$$
$$x + 1 = 3$$
$$x^2 < 5$$
$$x - y = 2$$
$$x + y = 4 \quad \text{and} \quad x - y = 2$$

The reader can verify, by replacing x in the first three sentences by each of the five values in the domain, that the solution sets of those three open sentences are $\{3, 4, 5\}$, $\{2\}$, and $\{1, 2\}$, respectively. In the remaining sentences one must replace both x and y by values in the domain. The truth set for the fourth sentence is $\{(3, 1), (4, 2), (5, 3)\}$. The fifth sentence, which is *compound*, has the solution set $\{(3, 1)\}$. We observe that only the second and fifth sentences are *determinate*.

If the domain of both x and y is still the same aggregate, $\{1, 2, 3, 4, 5\}$, the following open sentences have solution sets that are special in nature:

(1) $x + 3 = 1$
(2) $3x = 2$
(3) $x + y = 1$
(4) $x + 4x = 5x$
(5) $x \leq 5$ (read "x is equal to or less than 5")
(6) $x + y > 1$

It will be seen that the truth set of the first three sentences is $\emptyset = \{\ \}$, the empty or null set (Chapter 1). On the other hand, sentences (4) and (5) have the entire domain as solution set. Sentence (6) has a solution set containing the *twenty-five* ordered pairs, $\{(1, 1), (1, 2), \ldots, (1, 5), (2, 1), \ldots, (2, 5), \ldots, (5, 1), \ldots, (5, 5)\}$.

We have suggested that all sentences containing variables must be considered *open*. But this is not the case since, for example, the last six sentences can be "closed," that is, converted into statements of propositions if each sentence is prefixed by a suitable *quantifier*. Thus sentences (4) and (5) might be prefixed by "For all x," and sentence (6) might be prefixed by "For all x and for all y." In that case the quantified (4), (5), and (6) would be *true* propositions. If (1) and (2) are prefixed by "For some x," and (3) is prefixed by "For some x and some y," the results are statements of *false* propositions. Thus only sentences containing *unquantified* variables are open.

Our six special sentences as well as the equation $10x + y = 25$, discussed earlier, show that the number of solutions and, in fact, the extremes of possibility or impossibility of solution are dependent on the domain of each variable occurring in a sentence. The relation of the solution set to the domain of variables is closely associated with the history of algebra. Thus when Hellenic mathematicians considered $x^2 = 1$ and $x^2 = 2$, they gave $\{1\}$ and $\{\sqrt{2}\}$ as the respective solution sets. In effect, they limited the domain of x to the *positive* real numbers. In the extended domain of *all* real numbers, the solution sets would be $\{+1, -1\}$ and $\{+\sqrt{2}, -\sqrt{2}\}$. We remark, in passing, that not only Diophantus but all European mathematicians prior to the Renaissance would have balked at including negative numbers in the domain of variables (and hence in a solution set).

But there came a time in the evolution of algebra in India when the "law of signs" for the multiplication of directed (positive and negative) real numbers was known and applied. In fact, quoting Neugebauer as our authority once more, we can state that Babylonian astronomical texts of the third century B.C. made explicit use of the rule: The product of numbers with like signs is positive, while the product of those with unlike signs is negative. Perhaps, somehow, Indian awareness of the law can be traced to Babylonian sources. At any rate, Bhaskara intended to make use of the rule when he raised the following question: What (real) number, multiplied by itself (squared) is equal to -1? In modern terminology, Bhaskara sought the solution set for $x^2 = -1$, where the domain of x is the aggregate of real numbers.

Having posed the problem, Bhaskara labeled it "impossible" to solve, and so did all algebraists, oriental and occidental, before the sixteenth century. Bhaskara argued that any real number is either positive or negative, and when squared, that is, multiplied by itself, will yield a *positive* result by virtue of the "law of signs." In modern terminology, the solution set of $x^2 = -1$ in the real domain is $\emptyset = \{\ \}$, the empty set.

But once again appropriate enlargement of the domain of a variable can make the impossible possible, and the Hindu algebraists, although they did not recognize this fact, had themselves engendered the mechanism that would, so to speak, do the trick. They had solved some equations by a procedure which they called *vilomogati*, usually translated as *inversion*. We shall not explain this method but merely relate that Brahmagupta had given a general rule for it in which square root was recognized as the operation *inverse* to squaring (multiplying a number by itself). Therefore *vilomogati* (inverting or working backwards) required that the solution set of $x^2 = a$ (where a is *any number*) must be $\{+\sqrt{a}, -\sqrt{a}\}$. In the case of $x^2 = 1$ and $x^2 = 2$, Brahmagupta's rule would lead straight to the answers already given. For $x^2 = -1$, the rule would give the solution set, $\{+\sqrt{-1}, -\sqrt{-1}\}$. But the solution set is *meaningless* in the real domain, and Bhaskara was unable to resolve the crisis by finding a suitable extension of the domain.

That task awaited the sixteenth century Italian mathematician Rafael Bombelli (born *ca.* 1530). He elevated $\sqrt{-1}$ to the rank of a "number," and defined arithmetic operations on $\sqrt{-1}$, $\sqrt{-2}$, $\sqrt{-3}$, $\sqrt[4]{-1}$, $\sqrt[6]{-2/5}$, $-\sqrt{-1}$, $-\sqrt{-2}$, etc. and all even roots of negative numbers. He stated that such symbols represent *imaginary* numbers, a derogatory term on a par with those other descriptions, irrational and negative.

Today we still carry out arithmetic with imaginary numbers by using Bombelli's rules, but we have simplified his notation somewhat. We employ the symbol i for $\sqrt{-1}$ and consider it to be the imaginary unit. If we choose an inch as the unit of length, all other lengths are real multiples of that unit. Analogously, all imaginary numbers are real multiples of the unit i. Thus $\sqrt{-25}$ is interpreted to mean $\sqrt{25} \cdot \sqrt{-1} = 5i$, and other examples of imaginaries are $\frac{1}{3}i$, $i\sqrt{2}$, $-i\sqrt[3]{5}$, etc.

Bombelli adjoined the imaginaries to the reals and then defined arithmetic operations on the united set. To have a well-defined addition operation, that is, to have *closure* with respect to that operation, the sum of a real number like 3 and an imaginary like $2i$ must be meaningful. In other words, $3 + 2i$ must be a "number." All such sums, for example, $\frac{1}{2} - i$, $-1 + i\sqrt{3}$, $\sqrt[5]{2} - \frac{1}{2}i$, etc., are described as *complex numbers*. In general, a *complex number* is defined by the formula, $a + bi$, where a and b are any real numbers.

Then a real number is a special kind of complex number for which $b = 0$, and an imaginary is the special type for which $a = 0$. In other words, the aggregate of all complex numbers contains the set of real numbers and the set of imaginaries as two proper subsets.

At this point, certain questions seem natural: Are there any more kinds of numbers? Can the complex numbers be embedded in some larger system? We shall answer both these questions presently but, for the moment, it will suffice to state that the problems of classical algebra do *not* require any further types of number. Let us explain why.

In traditional algebra the fundamental expression containing variables was the polynomial, which, equated to zero, gave a polynomial equation, whose solution set was sought. Thus $x^2 + 7x - \sqrt{5}$ and $5x^4 - \frac{1}{2}x^3 + (3 - 1)x + i\sqrt[3]{2}$ are polynomials in the variable x, with coefficients that are complex numbers. The degree of a polynomial in x is that of the highest power of x in the polynomial. Thus the illustrative polynomials have degrees 2 and 4, respectively.

In our next chapter we shall consider some of the specific methodology for obtaining solutions of polynomial equations of degrees 2, 3, and 4. But in the present chapter we are concerned only with the *domain* of the variable x which appears in the polynomial equation. If we choose Bombelli's set of complex numbers as the domain of x, will there always be a solution set other than $\emptyset$, the empty set, for the polynomial equation

$$a_0 x^n + a_1 x^{n-1} + \cdots + a_n = 0$$

where n is a natural number and the coefficients are in the complex set? This question was answered in the affirmative when the great Carl Friedrich Gauss (1777–1855) proved the *fundamental theorem of algebra:* A polynomial equation with complex coefficients has at least one solution in the complex domain.

Gauss's proof of the fundamental theorem was very advanced in nature. But once the basic proposition was established, it was easy to deduce from it the corollary: Every nth-degree polynomial equation with complex coefficients has at most n distinct solutions in the complex domain.

Gauss's theorem and corollary spelled the end of one road in classical algebra, namely, the path of number extension. Since the complex numbers will guarantee one or more solutions for polynomial equations with complex coefficients, why seek new species of number? But classical algebra is not all of mathematics, and hence efforts to generalize the number concept continued. That story will now lead us from the old algebra to the new, from the type of question considered by Hypatia to that created by Emmy Noether.

The history of mathematics indicates that when new numbers are created, they are not accepted with alacrity. The Pythagoreans rejected the irrationals even though they had concrete examples in the form of lengths. Ultimately it was a good abstract theory, namely that of Eudoxus, which gained recognition for the incommensurables. With negatives, the situation was reversed. They made their appearance in algebraic equations but were, for the most part, rejected until such time as they were interpreted as business debts, and operations with them were conceived to be bookkeeping procedures. History repeated itself with the imaginaries and the complex numbers. They achieved full status only in the nineteenth century, when, on the one hand, they were accorded superior theoretical treatment and, on the other, were given concrete interpretation as geometric and physical entities.

An elegant abstract formulation of the algebra of complex numbers and one whose generalization had tremendous impact on all of modern mathematics is due to William Rowan Hamilton (1805–1865), the greatest of Ireland's men of science. Hamilton, like many child prodigies, excelled in languages at an early age. He mastered Latin, Greek, and Hebrew by the age of five, French and Italian before he was eight, Arabic, Persian, Sanskrit, and half a dozen other Oriental languages by the age of thirteen. At the tender age of seventeen he was pronounced the first mathematician of the day. In his adult years he made colossal contributions to mathematics and mathematical physics. In this chapter we shall see how he launched the new era in algebra. Later on we shall indicate that he played a similar role in theoretical physics.

For Hamilton a complex number was just an *ordered pair of real numbers*. Thus $2 + 3i$ was $(2, 3)$ and $3 + 2i$ was $(3, 2)$. A real number like 5, that is, $5 + 0i$, was $(5, 0)$. An imaginary like $4i$, that is, $0 + 4i$, was $(0, 4)$. Hamilton defined addition of the real number pairs and showed that this operation had the properties of closure, commutativity, and associativity. At school the reader learned to add $2 + 3i$

and $-5 + 4i$ by "adding real and imaginary parts separately" to give the sum $-3 + 7i$. In terms of Hamilton's definition, this would become

$$(2, 3) + (-5, 4) = (-3, 7)$$

or, more generally,

$$(a, b) + (c, d) = (a + c, b + d)$$

The sum is always meaningful because $a + c$ and $b + d$ are real sums and real addition has closure. Moreover

$$(a, b) + (c, d) = (c, d) + (a, b)$$

because $a + c = c + a$ and $b + d = d + b$. Thus the commutativity of complex addition follows from the same property of real addition, and it is similar with associativity.

To understand Hamilton's definition of multiplication of complex numbers, we first consider the viewpoint of school algebra, where one is told that since $\sqrt{2} \cdot \sqrt{2} = 2$, it seems logical to define $\sqrt{-1} \cdot \sqrt{-1}$ as -1, that is, $i \cdot i = -1$. With $i^2 = -1$, and the assumption of distributivity, one can multiply any two complex numbers. Thus

$$(a + bi)(c + di) = ac + bci + adi + bdi^2 = ac - bd + (ad + bc)i$$

Instead of the elementary rationale, there is Hamilton's definition, which states that, for two ordered pairs of real numbers,

$$(a, b) \times (c, d) = (ac - bd, ad + bc)$$

From this definition one can deduce (instead of assuming) the closure and associativity of complex multiplication, and its distributivity with respect to complex addition. Once again arithmetic laws for complex numbers can be derived from those for real numbers. Here is just another indication that the latter system is mathematical bedrock.

What Hamilton sought to do next was to generalize his idea of ordered pairs of real numbers, and to consider the possibility of *hypercomplex numbers* which would contain the real and complex systems as proper subsets just as the complex aggregate contains the reals and the imaginaries.

Various modes of generalization will suggest themselves to the reader. Should one think of triples, quadruples, quintuples, etc. of real numbers? Or should one retain the idea of ordered pair, but generalize the nature of the numbers paired, for example, by considering the set of ordered pairs of ordinary complex numbers, $(a + bi, c + di)$? In the latter case, $a + bi$ is the same as Hamilton's (a, b) and $(c + di)$ the same as (c, d). Therefore Hamilton employed the *quadruple* of real numbers (a, b, c, d) instead of the complex pair. Either formulation employs *four* real numbers and hence Hamilton called the hypercomplex numbers he created *quaternions*.

A set of pairs or quadruples is structureless unless one or more operations and/or relations on the set are defined. If one desires an "arithmetic" of hypercomplex numbers in which "numbers" and operations are akin to those in ordinary arithmetic, he must define an addition and a multiplication which obey the customary fundamental laws (closure, commutativity, associativity, distributivity). Now here is where Hamilton made an epochal discovery! After *fifteen years* of thought on the subject, he found that he could *not* formulate a quaternion algebra in which the hypercomplex numbers would simultaneously satisfy both the traditional arithmetic laws and the requirements of a physical science of space. Finally, in 1843, he released a revolutionary but logically consistent algebra in which the commutative law of multiplication was abandoned. Multiplication was defined in such a way that $q_1 \times q_2$ is *not* equal to $q_2 \times q_1$, where q_1 and q_2 are any two quaternions, (a_1, b_1, c_1, d_1), and (a_2, b_2, c_2, d_2).

Hamilton, as we have indicated, considered himself primarily a *physicist*, and not a pure mathematician. If we are to understand the motivation for his definition of quaternion multiplication, we must examine a physical interpretation of quaternions. Before doing that, we shall build up a suitable background for generalization by illustrating concrete geometric and physical counterparts for those more elementary entities, Bombelli's *complex numbers*.

In 1797 a geometric interpretation of complex numbers was given by Caspar Wessel (1745–1818), a Norwegian surveyor. Then in 1806 the Swiss-French mathematician Jean Robert Argand (1768–1822) arrived independently at the same interpretation. The Wessel-Argand representation generalizes the use of coordinates on a number line. In a previous chapter, a one-to-one correspondence was established between the aggregate of real numbers and the points of a straight line. In similar fashion, one can match real number *pairs*, that is, *complex numbers*, with the points of a plane. Thus the complex number $3 + 4i$ has the Hamiltonian interpretation $(3, 4)$ which corresponds to the point whose *Cartesian coordinates* (Chapter 7) are 3 and 4, respectively (Figure 4.1). If the plane is considered as a rectangular network of streets and avenues, then (3, 4) corresponds to the corner where "street 3" meets "avenue 4." Some real and imaginary numbers (conceived as real number pairs) are represented by points in the diagram of Figure 4.1. It will be seen that the real numbers correspond to the points of real number line (Chapter 2), usually called the X-axis, the imaginaries to points of a second number line, the Y-axis. In this picture of the imaginary numbers, the American mathematician Arnold Dresden (1882–1954) saw a way of removing the stigma of their name. He sug-

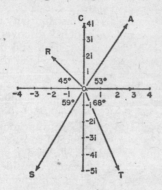

Figure 4.1

gested that they be called *normal* numbers because the term "normal" is synonomous with *perpendicular*. Thus, imaginaries are *normal* because their picture, the Y-axis, is perpendicular or *normal* to the X-axis of real numbers.

We have stressed the fact that new number types did not seem to gain general acceptance until the abstract or pure number symbols were given interpretations in the real world. The Wessel graphic representation lends itself to such an interpretation of the complex numbers. By a slight addition to the Wessel diagram (Figure 4.1) one can picture any complex number as a *directed line segment* or plane *vector*. Thus the complex number 3 + 4i can be pictured as the arrow OA in Figure 4.1, the *directed line segment* whose initial point is (0, 0) and whose terminal point is (3, 4). The term "vector" is derived from the Latin word *vectus*, which means carried. If one is *carried* from (0, 0) to

(3, 4) by car or plane (where a unit is one hundred miles), the journey can be pictured by the vector *OA* in Figure 4.1.

The vector interpretation of a complex number was designed for application to physics. For the physicist a vector is an entity that has both magnitude and direction, for example, a displacement, a force, a velocity, an acceleration. Specifically he may cite an *upward* force of 3 lb., a velocity of 20 mi. per hr. *southwest*, a *downward* acceleration of 32 ft. per sec. per sec.

For another way of representing a vector, let us find the *length* (size) and *direction* of *OA* in Figure 4.1. By the Pythagorean theorem,

$$\mathbf{r}^2 = 9 + 16 = 25$$
$$\mathbf{r} = 5$$

Physicists might say that 3 and 4 are the components of the vector in the horizontal and vertical directions, respectively. Or they might say that the *resultant* of two component motions is 5 ft. per sec. in a direction that can be found by protractor to be 53° approximately (or more precisely by trigonometry). Thus, a force or velocity can be described by a vector, an entity having both *size* (5 lb. or 5 ft. per sec.) and *direction* (53°). The description (3, 4) or $3 + 4i$ is called the *rectangular* form of this vector or complex number, and (5, 53°) is called the *polar* form (Chapter 7). Rectangular and polar representations of other vectors in Figure 4.1 can readily be obtained.

The geometric vectors representing complex numbers are called *centered* or *bound* vectors because they all initiate at *O*, the origin. In physics, however, vectors are *free* since they may start at any point. Thus the geometric vector represented by $3 + 4i$ or (3, 4) or (5, 53°) describes simultaneously an infinite number of vectors, for example, all forces of 5 lb. acting at an angle of 53° with the horizontal, but applied at different points in a plane.

Since a plane vector is just a real number pair, plane vectors can be added by Hamilton's definition,

$$(a, b) + (c, d) = (a + c, b + d)$$

To obtain the geometric analogue, two plane vectors (complex numbers) and their sum or resultant are pictured in Figure 4.2. This diagram suggests what the physicist calls the *parallelogram law* for the addition of plane vectors. To him a resultant means the combined effect of two forces or

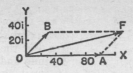

Figure 4.2

velocities or accelerations, etc. The triangle of Figure 4.2 is just half of a parallelogram in which the vector representing the first force or velocity is one side *OA*, the vector representing the second force or velocity forms the adjacent side *OB*, and the resultant or sum is the diagonal *OF*.

Physical forces, motions, etc. are not confined to a plane, but may occur in space. Hence the abstract idealization of such "3-dimensional" physical vectors should be an ordered *triple* of real numbers, like (3, 4, 12), say. To picture a physical analogue for this particular triple, let us imagine that a particle at point *O* in Figure 4.3 is moved 3 ft. east, then 4 ft. north, then 12 ft. up to position *P*. Its total displacement from point *O*, measured "as the crow flies," can be described by the directed line segment or vector *OP* in Figure 4.3. This is the vector (3, 4, 12), which is the *resultant* of the *component* displacements in the three directions, "east," "north," "up." The vector *OP* is described by the ordered triple (3, 4, 12) but it could be described by another ordered number triple in which the numbers are its length or magnitude, 13, and two angles giving its direction. Thus, by protractor or trigonometry (as in the case of $3 + 4i$), angle $COA = 53°$ (approximately). This angle gives the direction of *OC* in Figure 4.3. Then *OC* and *OZ* determine the plane in which vector *OP* lies, and again experimental measurement would give the angle between *OP* and the Z-axis as 23° (approximately). Hence vector *OP* can also be described as the number triple (13, 53°, 23°).

If, in Figure 4.3, the particle at point *P* were subsequently to be moved 5 ft. east, 2 ft. north, 6 ft. up, this displacement would correspond to the *vector* (5, 2, 6). Obviously the final displacement from *O* would be the vector $(3 + 5, 4 + 2, 12 + 6) = (8, 6, 18)$. This suggests that Hamilton's rule for addition of complex numbers or two-dimensional vectors can be extended to vectors in space so that the latter, like the former, are added by summing their respective components.

Today mathematicians generalize the vector concept so

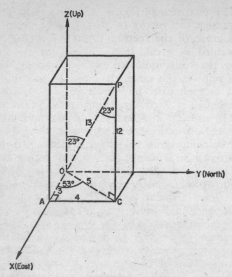

Figure 4.3

that an abstract vector can have any number of components. Thus $(3, -5, 0, -2/7, 6)$ is a vector of order 5, or a "5-dimensional" vector. Later on we shall be able to furnish significant concrete interpretations of such vectors.

If "structure" is to be provided for sets of vectors, it will be necessary to define arithmetic operations on them. Since physical vectors in space (3-dimensional vectors) do not seem essentially different from plane vectors, it is not surprising that one can define addition for them and in fact for all higher-dimensional vectors merely by extending Hamilton's definition for the plane. Hence

$$(a_1, a_2, \ldots , a_n) + (b_1, b_2, \ldots , b_n)$$
$$= (a_1 + b_1, a_2 + b_2, \ldots , a_n + b_n)$$

The sum of two vectors is a vector whose components are equal to the sums of the components of the addends, respectively.

One can also define an operation on vectors (of all dimensions) which we shall, for the moment, call a change of scale. To illustrate it, consider the displacement vector

(3, 4, 12) pictured in Figure 4.3. The same graph might well represent the vector (6, 8, 24), whose components are twice as great, or the vector (1, 4/3, 4), whose components are one-third as great. It would be merely a matter of changing the scale indicated on the drawing. Even if the diagram remains the same, the physical meaning would be different in each case. In Figure 4.3 the *resultant* velocity *OP* was equal to 13 ft. in the direction indicated (by the angles 53° and 23°). When components are multiplied by 2 or 1/3, the direction would be the same but the magnitude of the resultant would be 26 feet or 13/3 feet, respectively. In other words, if *V* is the original vector, the two changes in scale lead to the vectors 2*V* and 1/3 *V*, respectively. The change in scale is thus tantamount to *multiplying a vector by an ordinary number*, and is accomplished by *multiplying each* component of the vector by this number.

This rule for multiplying a vector by a number has been illustrated for positive rational numbers only. It has more general validity, however, but the description as a change in scale may not seem appropriate if one multiplies the vector by zero, in which case it is converted into a null or zero vector. Again, to multiply the vector by a negative number would require a change of scale that reverses the signs of numbers on the *X*-, *Y*-, and *Z*-axes of a diagram like Figure 4.3. In such cases, an alternative interpretation of the multiplication is possible, where instead of changing the scale one changes the vector. Then multiplying it by a positive number would *stretch* or *contract* it, according to whether this number is greater than or less than one, and multiplication by a negative would not only stretch or contract it, but would also reverse the direction of the vector. For the use of alternative viewpoints, see the discussion of "alias" or "alibi" in Chapter 17.

The reader may find the description of multiplication of a vector by a number confusing if the vector is also considered a sort of "number" albeit a complex or *hypercomplex* number. Therefore physicists apply the term *scalar* to the single "ordinary number," like 2 or 1/3, which effects the change in scale. Then what we have been talking about is the multiplication of a vector by a *scalar*, that is, multiplication of a complex or hypercomplex number by a single "ordinary number."

We have dwelt on the *addition* of vectors of *any* dimension and have given Hamilton's definition for the multipli-

cation of plane vectors, but we have not discussed the
geometry or physics of that multiplication. We have nowhere defined the multiplication of vectors of dimension 3
(or of any higher dimension). The reader must not be
confused by our discussion of "scalar multiplication," a
term which we could not avoid since it is used so frequently in the literature of mathematics and physics. As far
as vectors are concerned, scalar multiplication is a *unary*
operation because it is carried out on *one vector only*. It is
a change of scale in the components of that one vector or,
in the alternative interpretation, a stretching or shrinking
of that vector.

Now to consider a *binary* operation, how can one define
the multiplication of two 3-dimensional vectors, that is,

$$(a_1, a_2, a_3) \times (b_1, b_2, b_3)$$

where the letters represent real numbers? That was the
question which Hamilton kept asking himself during the
fifteen years from 1828 to 1843. The reason the issue presented great difficulty was that no matter what "common
sense" definition Hamilton attempted, he could not get the
resulting vector "multiplication" to satisfy certain essential
criteria as well as all the fundamental laws of ordinary
algebra. In the course of his reasoning he decided to embed
the 3-dimensional vectors in the set of quaternions, that is,
to consider those vectors as the ordered *quadruples* (0, b,
c, d). Then if quaternion multiplication is defined, it will
apply to those special quaternions which are 3-dimensional
vectors.

But if quaternions are to include the real numbers, now
defined as (a, 0, 0, 0), and the complex numbers (plane
vectors), now defined as (a, b, 0, 0), quaternion multiplication must be so defined that it will reduce to real and complex multiplication for the special quaternions just illustrated. This factor, plus the needs of space physics, plus the
fundamental laws of algebra, gave Hamilton a very exacting
set of conditions. Day after day, week after week, year after
year, he would sit for hours in his study, forgetting about
meals, brooding, struggling and striving to formulate the
elusive definition. If he appeared at the breakfast table, his
wife and son would immediately inquire, "Have you succeeded in multiplying quaternions yet?"

Finally, and most unwillingly, Hamilton recognized what

to do. He could satisfy some of the most important requirements of physics and algebra by defining a *noncommutative* multiplication. His action in doing so was analogous to Lobachevsky's procedure in abandoning Euclid's parallel postulate and substituting a different axiom.

Full details of Hamilton's quaternion algebra will appear in a later chapter. Here we shall merely explain his definition of multiplication. Now, a plane vector has the alternative forms (a, b) and $a + bi$, where the latter form is the sum of real multiples of the "units," 1 and i. If $b = 0$, one obtains the real numbers, a, and if $a = 0$, one has the imaginaries, bi. Similarly a quaternion can be expressed as an ordered quadruple of real numbers or as a hypercomplex number, $a + bi + cj + dk$, where the latter form is the sum of real multiples of the "units," 1, i, j, and k. If $b = c = d = 0$, one obtains the real numbers. If $c = d = 0$, one has the complex numbers. If $a = 0$, one has the 3-*dimensional vectors*, $bi + cj + dk$.

For agreement with complex multiplication, it is necessary to have $i^2 = -1$. Hamilton considered the units j and k to be akin to i and therefore defined $j^2 = -1$ and $k^2 = -1$. Suppose that one is to carry out the quaternion multiplication

$$(1 + i - j + k)\,(3 - i + j - k)$$

Then application of the distributive law will lead to a product containing terms like ij, ji, jk, kj, etc. If quaternion multiplication is to be *closed*, all such terms must be defined to be of the form $a + bi + cj + dk$. Hamilton accomplished this by providing the following multiplication table.

	1	i	j	k
1	1	i	j	k
i	i	-1	k	$-j$
j	j	$-k$	-1	i
k	k	j	$-i$	-1

He had poured so much of his mind and heart and soul into quaternion multiplication that one day, when he was out walking with his wife, he felt impelled to carve the above tabulation on the stone of a bridge near Dublin.

In the table, the quaternion expression for the product ij can be found in "row i" and "column j." Thus, $ij = k$.

Reading the entry at the intersection of "row j" and "column i" reveals that $ji = -k$. Here is our first example of the noncommutativity of quaternion multiplication. The product ji is not equal to ij. In fact, $ji = -ij$. The reader can consult the table to verify that $ik = -ki$, $kj = -jk$. Also, by using the table he can carry out some simple quaternion multiplications like $(2 - k)(i + j) = 3i + j$ and $(i + j)(2 - k) = i + 3j$ to show that reversing the order of quaternion factors can lead to two completely different products.

Again, it is easy to show that if the domain of the variable x is the set of quaternions, then the polynomial equation

$$x^2 + 1 = 0$$

has a solution set containing the quaternions $\pm i$, $\pm j$, $\pm k$, $\frac{1}{2}\sqrt{2}j + \frac{1}{2}\sqrt{2}k$, and an infinite number of other solutions. The corollary to the fundamental theorem of classical algebra permits a maximum of *two complex solutions*, and those are the answers $\pm i$. But infinitely many *hypercomplex* solutions exist.

More of the physics of Hamilton's quaternions will be discussed later (Chapter 28). Pure mathematicians, however, were less interested in applications than in extending his ideas further—to other types of hypercomplex number, and in examining the effects of relinquishing algebraic postulates other than the commutative law of multiplication. For example, the British mathematician Arthur Cayley (1821–1895), generalizing Hamilton's notion of pairing, considered hypercomplex numbers that are *ordered pairs of quaternions*, or ordered "8-tuples" of real numbers. Cayley defined a multiplication of these hypercomplex numbers that was neither commutative nor associative, thus abandoning another fundamental law of common algebra.

It should also be mentioned that in 1844, just a year after Hamilton published the details of his quaternion algebra, the German geometer Hermann Grassmann (1809–1877) formulated a far more general concept of algebras of hypercomplex numbers of all orders (Chapter 28). Grassmann's algebras have a multiplication that is noncommutative. In fact, Hamilton's quaternions became just one special algebra among the many Grassmann species.

Because Hamilton holds chronological priority in the creation of nontraditional algebras, he is often considered the founder of modern "abstract algebra." That term applies not only to hypercomplex number algebras like those of Hamilton, Cayley, and Grassmann, but to all systems where postulates differ from the rules of the game of classical algebra, by being either less or more restrictive. But it is not this feature that makes the new algebra "abstract," but rather the fact that it is conceived from the axiomatic point of view discussed in our previous chapter, and suggested right from the start of this book in all our discussions of the fundamental properties of arithmetic operations. But the idea of treating algebra as a pure postulational-deductive science did not really begin until the period just before Hamilton. Then it was gradually developed by members of the British algebraic school, namely, George Peacock (1791–1858), Duncan Farquharson Gregory (1813–1844), Augustus De Morgan (1806–1871), and George Boole (1815–1864).

The modern abstract point of view requires a pure science, whether it is an "algebra" or a "geometry" or something else, to be founded on postulates (assumptions) about undefined elements, which are *not* necessarily "numbers" or "points" but *abstractions*, potentially capable of varied interpretations consistent with the basic assumptions. With this in mind, we can gain some idea of the variety of modern algebraic systems or "structures" if we "purify" the postulates for common algebra, and play what we shall call Hamilton's game* of relinquishing some postulates, or replacing them by different ones. In the previous chapter we saw that Lobachevsky played a more restricted "game" in changing only one postulate of Euclidean geometry.

One might begin with systems in which S, a set of undefined elements, is given, as well as two binary operations on these elements, $\oplus$ and $\otimes$. These symbols are used to suggest some kinship with ordinary addition and multiplication, although in different concrete realizations the interpretations might be considerably different from the usual ones. Then our postulate set can include those "laws" or "properties" we have mentioned so frequently; that is, we can assume closure, commutativity, and associativity for both $\oplus$ and $\otimes$, and also distributivity of $\otimes$ with respect to $\oplus$. We have seven postulates thus far. To make sure our

---

* This must not be confused with the "Hamiltonian game" discussed in books on mathematical recreations and described in Chapter 25 of the present work.

fundamental set contains elements akin to *zero* and *one*, the additive and multiplicative "identities," we shall use the symbols Z and *I*, and make two more assumptions:

(1) S contains an element Z such that $a \oplus Z = a$, if *a* is *any* element in S.

(2) S contains an element *I* (different from Z) such that $a \otimes I = a$, if *a* is *any* element of S.

Then to avoid the necessity for introducing "subtraction" and "division" operations, we introduce additive and multiplicative inverses by postulating:

(3) For each element *a* in S, there exists an element $\bar{a}$ in S such that $a \oplus \bar{a} = Z$.

(4) If *a* is any element of S with the exception of Z, there exists an element a^{-1} such that $a \otimes a^{-1} = I$.

Any system satisfying the eleven postulates of common algebra is called a *field*. Because it is associated with common algebra, the field is the most familiar of algebraic structures. Thus the rationals or the reals or the complex numbers each constitute a field if the binary operations are ordinary addition and multiplication. The reader might try his hand at showing that the set of all numbers of the form $a + b\sqrt{2}$, where *a* and *b* are rational, is a field under $+$ and $\times$. But the postulates for a field are not categorical (Chapter 3); there are fields where the fundamental set S is *finite* and, in addition, $\oplus$ and $\otimes$ are *not* ordinary addition and multiplication. Such finite fields are called *Galois fields*, in honor of Évariste Galois (1811–1832), who first studied their properties and who, as the next chapter will indicate, accomplished the liberation of algebra in a way essentially different from Hamilton's.

If, playing Hamilton's game, we delete one or more of the postulates for a field, we shall arrive at a system that is less restricted or more general. If, for example, we remove (2) and (4) above, the nine remaining axioms define what algebraists today call a *commutative ring*. If, further, the commutativity of multiplication is relinquished, a more general type of ring results. We shall illustrate such more general rings later and shall also indicate the nature of certain special *subrings* studied by Emmy Noether, to which Dedekind had given the subtle and beautiful name *ideals*.

Returning to familiar territory, let us examine the system

consisting of the integers, $\{\ldots, -3, -2, -1, 0, +1, +2, +3, \ldots\}$, and the binary operations of ordinary addition and multiplication which, as we can see, satisfy all the field postulates except (4), the assumption of multiplicative inverses within the integral set. Thus the system is *not* a field, because only $+1$ and -1 have multiplicative inverses that are integers. Therefore one cannot carry out, within the set of integers, the Babylonian scheme of substituting a suitable product for any quotient of number pairs in the set. But we know that there are integral answers for some quotients like $12 \div 3$, $30 \div 5$, etc. Putting this fact into algebraic form, $3a = 12$ or $3 \times a = 3 \times 4$ yields $a = 4$, and if c is any integer except zero, $ca = cb$ yields $a = b$ by a process of *cancellation*. Then the addition and multiplication of integers obey the first ten field postulates and a postulate permitting cancellation.

Therefore, playing Hamilton's game, we define an abstract system consisting of a set S and binary operations $\oplus$ and $\otimes$ which are governed by the first ten field postulates and the

Cancellation Law: If $c \otimes a = c \otimes b$, where a, b, and c are any members of the set S such that $c \neq Z$ (the "zero"), then $a = b$.

Such a structure is called an *integral domain* (because of its kinship to the integers).

One can make more drastic deletions from the field postulates, for example, by removing one of the binary operations and all the postulates which refer to that operation. Suppose that we remove $\oplus$ and limit ourselves to $\otimes$. Also, in true Hamiltonian spirit, let us abandon the commutative postulate for $\otimes$. What is left is a set S, with an operation $\otimes$ satisfying closure, associativity, and the postulates we have labeled (2) and (4), namely, existence within S of a multiplicative identity (*unit element*) and multiplicative inverses. (Because commutativity has been relinquished, the statements for these postulates must be enlarged to include $I \otimes a = a$ and $a^{-1} \otimes a = I$.) Any system with a single binary operation satisfying the four specified postulates is called a *group*. The group concept is of inestimable importance in modern mathematics and physics, so much so that the great Henri Poincaré (1854–1912), whose ideas will be discussed at many points of our book, once brashly said,

"The theory of groups is *all* of mathematics." At any rate, we shall be alluding to groups in so many later chapters that we shall not give specific references at this point.

We remark that there are *commutative groups* in which ⊗ satisfies the commutative law. Such groups are described as *abelian* in honor of the Norwegian Niels Henrik Abel (1802–1829). The fact that the adjective is not capitalized is testimony of the frequency of its occurrence in mathematical literature. If, instead of adding a fifth postulate to the four group postulates, we were to relinquish (2) and (4), we would be defining a *semigroup*, a system consisting of a set S and a single binary operation which satisfies closure and associativity. If one also abandons associativity, the system becomes a *groupoid*.

If Hamilton had never succeeded in multiplying 3-dimensional vectors, he would still have been able to add them and perform *scalar* multiplication on them, and the same would have been true for vectors of higher dimension. Moreover, the operations would have satisfied the traditional properties. Thus there is a theory of *vector spaces*, which are systems with two fundamental sets, V (the vectors) and F (a field of scalars), with a vector addition and scalar multiplication satisfying the same postulates as those for physical vectors and scalars. If a third operation is defined on a vector space, namely, a *vector multiplication* (which may possibly be neither commutative nor associative), one arrives at an *algebra* in the spirit of Hamilton or Grassmann or their successors.

After our brief excursion into modern abstract algebra, let us now recall that this new area of mathematical thought is just the ultimate outgrowth of the number extensions of ordinary algebra. Even if abstract algebra is all-embracing and is probably the favorite speciality of pure mathematicians today, classical algebra is still of practical importance. Therefore our next chapter will recapitulate slightly, and then examine both the practical procedures and the additional generalizations associated with the solution of polynomial equations.

Chapter 5

Equations, Human and Inhuman

To make good the promise of the previous chapter, we shall now consider the evolution and nature of techniques for solving polynomial equations. Throughout our discussion it will be assumed, unless a statement to the contrary is made, that wherever constants a, b, c, etc. are mentioned, they specify numbers in the complex domain and also that the replacement set for all variables x, y, z, etc. is the same complex domain. There will be no quaternions, Cayley numbers, or other "hypercomplex" entities in this chapter.

Since decipherment of cuneiform tablets is providing increasing evidence that all mathematics started with the Babylonians, who, in addition, had a particular penchant for algebra, one would expect to hear that they contributed to the methodology of solving polynomial equations. They did, in fact, evolve formulas for the solution of first- and second-degree equations, apply some truly advanced ideas to cubic (third-degree) equations, and solve some systems of equations in two unknowns. They even found solutions in the real domain for *eighth*-degree equations like

$$x^8 - 17x^4 + 16 = 0$$

and we shall subsequently examine their procedure for doing so.

Sometimes one can guess or estimate solutions, and such hunches can always be checked by substitution for the variable. For example, it is easy to verify that $x = +1$ and $x = -1$ are solutions of the above equation. Are there other solutions? The corollary to the fundamental theorem of algebra (Chapter 4) tells us that there may possibly be as many as eight distinct solutions. Perhaps some readers can guess the other roots of the above equation. But, in general, how can we guess or estimate answers, with the vastly infinite real number continuum (Chapter 2) from which to make a possible selection and the much greater *embarras de choix* if one makes guesses that are complex numbers, that is, *pairs* of real numbers? In most equations, to track down solutions without specific clues or standardized procedures would be infinitely worse than searching for the proverbial needle in the haystack!

But to descend from the sublime to the elementary, it would seem logical to begin by solving equations of *first* degree. In the case of such equations, for example, $2x - 1 = 0$ or $3x + 2 = 0$, it is easy to guess and check the solutions $x = 1/2$, $x = -2/3$, respectively.

One can readily generalize such results to obtain a formula for solving *all* polynomial equations of the first degree. If b is any constant in the complex domain and a is any such constant except zero, then

$$ax - b = 0$$

has the solution

$$x = \frac{b}{a}$$

This is verified by the substitution

$$a \cdot \frac{b}{a} - b = b - b = 0$$

Moreover, the solution $x = b/a$ is *unique*, that is, the complete solution set for the above equation is $\{b/a\}$. This is true by virtue of the corollary to the fundamental theorem of algebra. That corollary states that a polynomial equation of first degree cannot have more than one root. Finally, as examples of how our formula can be applied, we state that the solutions of $5x + 3 = 0$, $3x - 2\sqrt{7} = 0$, $\frac{1}{2}x + 3i - 4 = 0$ are respectively $-3/5$, $2\sqrt{7}/3$, $8 - 6i$.

If all polynomial equations of first degree can be solved simply by formula, the reader may well wonder why so much time is given to first-degree equations in school algebra. To see what may be involved, consider the following problem, which the Hindu Mahavira (*ca.* 850 A.D.) addressed to his students: Of a basket of mangoes, the king took 1/6, the queen 1/5 of the remainder, and the three oldest princes 1/4, 1/3, and 1/2 of the successive remainders. There were then only three mangoes left for the youngest member of the royal family. Tell me, all you who are clever in such problems, how many mangoes there were in the basket.

We see that in such problems, practical or fanciful, the first step, which may not be easy, is to express the question in algebraic form. If we let x represent the unknown number of mangoes, then $1/6\ x$ will represent the number taken by the king, and $5/6\ x$ the remaining number. But the queen takes 1/5 of this remainder or $1/5 \cdot 5/6\ x = 1/6\ x$, and after her share (and the king's) have been removed, only $4/6\ x$ mangoes remain. The first prince takes $1/4 \cdot 4/6\ x = 1/6\ x$. It is readily seen that the other princes also take $1/6\ x$ each. Totaling the five shares, we find that $5/6\ x$ mangoes have been removed, leaving only $1/6\ x$ for the youngest member of the royal family. Therefore

$$\frac{1}{6}x = 3$$

We can now guess that $x = 18$ mangoes.

But suppose that a verbal problem leads to a first-degree equation like

$$7x - 2 = 4x - 11$$

Then it may not be so easy to guess the solution. If one wishes to solve by formula, it will be necessary to deduce from the given statement an equation in the standard form

$$ax - b = 0$$

Until recently there was a tendency to mechanize the deductive process in algebra by using certain rules concerning "transposition and collecting similar terms." In fact, the word "algebra" derives from just such procedures carried on, of all places, at the court of Harun-al-Rashid, Caliph of the Arabian Nights. This Moslem ruler and his son Al-Mamun encouraged scientific activity. In the royal entourage there was the mathematician Al-Khowarizmi, who wrote a text called *al-jabr w'almuqabalah*, meaning transposition and condensation of terms in an equation. The abbreviated title, *al-jabr*, became our *algebra*.

Instead of using mechanical *al-jabr w'almuqabalah*, let us

see how one can deduce the transformation of $7x - 2 = 4x - 11$ into the "canonical form," $ax - b = 0$. The idea is to obtain *zero* in the right member of the equation, and we shall do this by adding 11 to both sides (to eliminate -11 on the right) and then adding $-4x$ (in order to eliminate $4x$). This is permissible because the given equation states that $7x - 2$ and $4x - 11$ are symbols for the same number. Hence if we add $11 - 4x$ to that number, there will be a unique sum (by the closure property of addition of real numbers) even though the two members of the equation lead to different expressions for that sum. Hence, adding 11 first, we have

$$(7x - 2) + 11 = (4x - 11) + 11$$

By virtue of the associative law of addition the above equation can be expressed as

$$7x + (-2 + 11) = 4x + (-11 + 11)$$

or

$$7x + 9 = 4x$$

Adding $-4x$ to each member (or adding each member to $-4x$, which is the same thing in accordance with the commutative law of addition),

$$-4x + (7x + 9) = -4x + 4x$$

Once more the associative law permits a change in the left member to yield

$$(-4x + 7x) + 9 = -4x + 4x$$

or

$$3x + 9 = 0$$

which is a first-degree equation in "canonical form."

The early mathematicians in general, as well as students and laymen throughout the ages, have been as much interested in recreational problems as in the practical uses of algebra. Nevertheless, at an early era, some algebraic equations arose from more serious issues. Second-degree or *quadratic* equations played an important role in even the simplest questions of buying and selling in ancient Babylonia. This was the result of the Mesopotamian method of quoting prices, which was the reverse of our own. Our authority in the matter is the eminent Dutch scholar, Professor E. M. Bruins.

We would quote the price of ground or "pearled" barley as 20 cents per package, while the Babylonians spoke of 5 sacks of barley per shekel. We point to the package first and then give a certain amount of money, the number of cents depending on the particular item. In Mesopotamia the purchaser indicated the money first and then received a certain amount of merchandise, depending on the amount of money offered. As a result, when *exact* answers were required for some elementary questions of profit and loss, this called for the solution of quadratic equations.

Thus, suppose that experience had taught a Babylonian merchant that he could dispose of 120 sacks of barley at market time. Then he might have asked himself, "What can I afford to pay the farmer for barley if I am to profit 10 shekels on 120 sacks with a difference of 2 sacks per shekel between cost and selling price?"

Using modern algebraic symbolism, let

x = the "cost," that is, the number of sacks received by the merchant for each shekel he gave the farmer

$x - 2$ = the "selling price," the number of sacks received by a customer in the market for each shekel he gave the merchant

$\dfrac{120}{x}$ = the number of shekels spent by the merchant

$\dfrac{120}{x - 2}$ = the number of shekels spent by the customers and received by the merchant

Then the fact that receipts are to exceed expenditures by 10 shekels can be put in the form of the equation

$$\frac{120}{x - 2} - \frac{120}{x} = 10$$

Having simplified this by various algebraic manipulations, we arrive at the quadratic equation

$$x^2 - 2x - 24 = 0$$

Algebraists, starting with the Babylonians, developed a formula for solving quadratic equations, and subsequently we shall see how such a formula can be derived and applied. But in the above equation one can proceed simply by expressing it as

$$(x - 6)(x + 4) = 0$$

This form asserts that the product of two (unknown) numbers, $x - 6$ and $x + 4$, is zero.

If we were asked to illustrate a zero product using *known* numbers, we might cite $0 \cdot \frac{1}{5}$, $-2 \cdot 0$, $0 \cdot \sqrt{-3}$, $0 \cdot 0$, etc. These examples illustrate a law governing the arithmetic of real and complex numbers: The product of two numbers is zero if and only if at least one of these numbers is zero.

Therefore at least one of the above unknown numbers must be zero, that is,

$$x - 6 = 0 \quad \text{or} \quad x + 4 = 0$$

and

$$x = 6 \quad \text{or} \quad x = -4$$

Both 6 and -4 are solutions because they will check when substituted in the quadratic equation. But only the positive answer $x = 6$ would be meaningful in the Babylonian merchant's problem because x stood for the number of sacks of barley he obtained in exchange for each shekel he gave to the farmer. The solution $x = 6$ says that he did receive 6 sacks per shekel, and since he acquired 120 sacks in all, he must have spent 20 shekels. For every shekel, his customers received $x - 2 = 4$ sacks. Hence the customers' expenditures, or the merchant's receipts, would have been 30 shekels, and the latter's profit would have been 10 shekels.

The method of solution of a quadratic by factoring and equating factors to zero is due to Thomas Harriot (1560–1621), who, as a young man, had been a member of one of Sir Walter Raleigh's expeditions to Virginia. After Harriot had completed an extensive geodetic survey in the new land, he returned to England and gave his scientific efforts to algebra and astronomy.

Both before Harriot's time and after it, algebraists actually used his method and, in fact, applied it to polynomial equations of higher degree. Thus, by Gauss's day, there was the following theoretic result, a corollary to his fundamental theorem (page 115): *A polynomial of the nth degree with complex coefficients is factorable uniquely as follows:*

$$c(x - r_1)(x - r_2) \ldots (x - r_n)$$

where c, r_1, r_2, $\ldots$, r_n are complex numbers.

Formerly this corollary was often stated in the form: Any polynomial equation of the nth degree with complex coefficients has n complex solutions. This form of the proposition is sometimes confusing, however, since the n solutions may not all be distinct. Thus a cubic polynomial may be factorable as

$$(x-2)(x-2)(x-2)$$

and the corresponding cubic equation,

$$(x-2)(x-2)(x-2) = 0$$

has as solutions

$$x = 2 \qquad x = 2 \qquad x = 2$$

The cubic polynomial does satisfy the first statement of the corollary, since there are three factors. However, these factors are all the same, and hence the equation has only one solution. Therefore we have, in the previous chapter, stated the corollary in the alternative form: *Every nth degree polynomial equation with complex coefficients has at most n distinct solutions in the complex domain.*

But to return to Harriot's technique, it would not be readily applicable to quadratic equations in general. For example, the reader might find it difficult to factor the left member of $x^2 + 2x - 4 = 0$. To solve such equations, other methods are preferable. The cuneiform textbook tablets gave verbal instructions that are equivalent to the quadratic formula of today's algebra. We do not know how the Babylonians arrived at this formula, but it is generally believed that they derived it by the method of *completing the square*, which was also used by Greek and Arab mathematicians. To illustrate this technique, we consider the equation that would be difficult to solve by Harriot's method.

The quadratic $x^2 + 2x = 4$ signified to the Greeks that the area of a certain figure was 4 square units. That figure was pictured (Figure 5.1) as composed of a square with unknown side x (and area x^2), and two rectangles, each with length x and width 1 unit. The area of each rectangle is x square units. Hence the area of the entire figure is $x^2 + 2x$. Now to complete the figure so as to form a square, the shaded area must be added to it. This shaded area is a square whose side is 1 unit, and whose area is 1 square unit. Then the area of the completed square is $4 + 1 = 5$ square

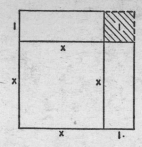

Figure 5.1

units. Thus, when 1 is added to each member of the original quadratic equation, the result is

$$x^2 + 2x + 1 = 5$$

Referring to Figure 5.1 once more, the side of the completed square is $x + 1$, and therefore its area is $(x + 1)^2$, making

$$(x + 1)^2 = 5$$

If the area of the large square is 5 square units, its side must have the irrational length $\sqrt{5}$ linear units and therefore

$$x + 1 = \sqrt{5}$$
$$x = \sqrt{5} - 1$$

The answer just obtained is the only one that Greek and Arab algebraists would have given. But when negative numbers were understood and, in addition, solution was no longer dependent on geometric pictures, there was the alternative,

$$x + 1 = -\sqrt{5}$$

and

$$x = -\sqrt{5} - 1$$

The second solution is both *negative* and *irrational*.

Further liberation from geometry is called for if one is to solve the quadratic equation $x^2 + 4x = -5$. One can, of course, be helped by making a diagram (Figure 5.2). But the figure is merely an auxiliary scheme, since no physical or geometric square can have a total area measuring -5

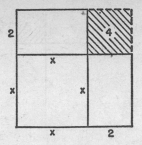

Figure 5.2

square units. But, in the abstract algebraic sense, one can "complete the square" to obtain

$$(x + 2)^2 = -5 + 4$$

or

$$(x + 2)^2 = -1$$

Therefore

$$x + 2 = \sqrt{-1} = i \qquad x + 2 = -\sqrt{-1} = -i$$

and

$$x = -2 + i \qquad\qquad x = -2 - i$$

The solutions are *complex numbers*.

Although the later Babylonians had some understanding of negative numbers, they never considered imaginary or complex numbers. But they apparently completed the square in the *general* equation

$$x^2 + Bx + C = 0$$

In other words, they carried out algebraic manipulation equivalent to

$$x^2 + Bx = -C$$
$$x^2 + Bx + \frac{B^2}{4} = \frac{B^2}{4} - C$$
$$\left(x + \frac{B}{2}\right)^2 = \left(\frac{B}{2}\right)^2 - C$$
$$x = -\frac{B}{2} \pm \sqrt{\left(\frac{B}{2}\right)^2 - C}$$

This is a formula for solving all quadratic equations. If the given equation is $2x^2 - 2x - 1 = 0$, one need merely divide both sides by 2 in order to obtain $x^2 - x - 1/2 = 0$, to which the Babylonian formula is applicable. But if one desires a formula for solving

$$ax^2 + bx + c = 0$$

where $a \neq 0$, he can divide by a to obtain

$$x^2 + \frac{b}{a}x + \frac{c}{a} = 0$$

Then substituting b/a for B and c/a for C in the Babylonian solution yields the quadratic formula that appears in most of our modern elementary texts, namely,

$$x = \frac{-b \pm \sqrt{b^2 - 4ac}}{2a}$$

With the Greeks and those continuing their tradition, problems in algebra involved unknown lengths, areas, and volumes—our x, x^2, x^3. There were no geometric pictures for x^4, x^5, x^6, etc. But the Babylonians were not limited by diagrams and were therefore not afraid to consider the eighth-degree equation cited at the beginning of this chapter. What they did was reduce the problem of solving

$$x^8 - 17x^4 + 16 = 0$$

to the more elementary question of solving a quadratic. By the substitution, $x^4 = z$ (and hence $x^8 = z^2$), the above equation is transformed into

$$z^2 - 17z + 16 = 0$$

We use Harriot's method and obtain

$$(z - 1)(z - 16) = 0$$
$$z = 1 \qquad z = 16$$

or

$$x^4 = 1 \qquad x^4 = 16$$

What the Babylonians did was to cascade quadratics, that is, repeat the previous type of transformation, by setting $w = x^2$, whence

$$w^2 = 1 \qquad w^2 = 16$$

Therefore

$$w = +1 \qquad w = -1 \qquad w = +4 \qquad w = -4$$

which means

$$x^2 = +1 \qquad x^2 = -1 \qquad x^2 = +4 \qquad x^2 = -4$$

Finally there are the *eight* roots

$$x = 1, -1, \quad i, -i, \quad 2, -2, \quad 2i, -2i, \qquad \text{where } i = \sqrt{-1}$$

(The Babylonians would not have recognized the imaginary solutions.)

Our illustration was an exceptionally simple instance, produced *ad hoc*, as were all the Babylonian eighth-degree equations. We shall see that, in general, eighth-degree equations *cannot* be solved in the elementary sense. In fact, most polynomial equations of degree higher than four cannot be solved in finite terms. What we mean is that there are no answers expressible in terms of the coefficients of the equation if one is limited to a *finite* number of additions, subtractions, multiplications, divisions, and root extractions performed on the coefficients. But we are getting ahead of our story, for what we have just stated was not given a complete and rigorous proof until the nineteenth century, when the young genius Évariste Galois furnished a profound and elegant demonstration (Chapter 16).

Solving an "easy" eighth-degree equation is just a matter of cascading quadratics, as we have just seen. But what issues arise between second- and eighth-degree equations? What about third-degree or cubic equations, since they are next in rank after quadratics? Great algebraists as they were, the Babylonians were naturally interested in the question. Their tablets show many cubic equations of a specialized type illustrated by

$$x^3 + x^2 = 80$$
$$x^3 + x^2 = 12$$
$$x^3 + x^2 = 1100$$
$$x^3 + x^2 = 36$$

If these problems are verbalized, the statement of all of them is seen to be the same except for the final word: Find a number such that if its cube is added to its square, the sum is—(80 or 12 or 1100, etc., as the case may be).

The Babylonians had tables of squares and cubes and merely combined them to form tables of $x^3 + x^2$, thus:

Number	$x^3 + x^2$
1	2
2	12
3	36
4	80
5	150
6	252
.	.
.	.
.	.
10	1100

Then the answers to the illustrative cubics can be read directly from the table and found to be 4, 2, 10, 3, respectively. But suppose that the problem assigned is

$$x^3 + x^2 = 10$$

Evidently 10 is not in the table of values of $x^3 + x^2$, but since 10 is smaller than 12 (the value of $x^3 + x^2$ for $x = 2$), therefore a number slightly below 2 will solve $x^3 + x^2 = 10$. We might use "linear interpolation" to read between the lines of the table, and say that since 10 is 8/10 of the way from 2 to 12, we estimate crudely that the corresponding value of x will be 8/10 of the way from 1 to 2, or $x = 1.8$. Since the Babylonians carried out interpolative processes freely in their other tables—square root, interest, astronomical data, etc., it is conjectured that they probably did so in the tables of $x^3 + x^2$. Now 1.8 is only an estimate. If we substitute 1.8 for x, then $x^3 + x^2 = 9.1$ approximately. If we had the exact answer, the sum would be 10, not 9.1. Hence 1.8 is too small an estimate. If we try a slightly larger approximation, $x = 1.9$, then $x^3 + x^2 = 10.5$, which is closer to 10 than 9.1. The true value of x lies between 1.8 and 1.9 but if we are approximating to the nearest tenth, $x = 1.9$ might seem to be a better approximation than $x = 1.8$.

To see how a simple practical problem may lead to a cubic equation, consider that an open rectangular box with a square base is to be constructed from 27 sq. in. of cardboard and is to have a volume of 13.5 cu. in. Let

$$x = \text{the length of the base edge}$$

$$\frac{13.5}{x^2} = \text{the height of the box (height} \times \text{length} \times \text{width} =$$
$$13.5, \text{and therefore height} \times x \times x = 13.5)$$

$$(x)\left(\frac{13.5}{x^2}\right) = \text{the area of one lateral face of the box}$$

The fact that the total surface consisting of the square base and the four lateral faces measures 27 sq. in. leads to the equation

$$x^2 + 4\left(\frac{13.5}{x}\right) = 27$$

or

$$x^3 - 27x + 54 = 0$$

It is easy to obtain the root $x = 3$ by trial. Substitution in the equation will verify this answer. Therefore the dimensions of the box should be 3 in., 3 in., 1.5 in. When Harriot's method is applied to the above cubic, it is expressed as

$$(x + 6)(x - 3)(x - 3) = 0$$

and hence there are two distinct answers, namely, $x = -6$ and $x = 3$. The negative root is not a suitable answer, however, for the box problem.

The above illustration was selected to indicate that geometric problems where volume is involved may lead to cubic equations. However, the need to solve cubics is not limited to such issues. There are many situations in modern applied mathematics where such equations must be solved. To give a single example: In physical chemistry, Van der Waals' equation for the specific volume, x, of carbon dioxide, when the numerical value of the pressure is 70 atmospheres and the absolute temperature is 300° C, is as follows:

$$7x^3 - 64x^2 + 224x - 260 = 0$$

The reader can check by substitution that $x = 2.3$ is an approximate root of this equation.

Neugebauer believes that the Babylonians went far beyond the elementary phase of cubics, but other scholars in the field do not agree. It is possible, if one knows sufficient algebra, to perform a manipulative stunt that will transform *any* cubic into the "canonical" form

$$x^3 + x^2 = k$$

Then the Babylonian tables, if extended sufficiently, can be used to obtain exactly or approximately any positive roots that such an equation may have. For example, with the cubic

$$4y^3 + 20y^2 + 33y - 22 = 0$$

the substitution $y = 1/2\ x - 3/2$ will transform the equation into

$$4 \left(\frac{1}{2}x - \frac{3}{2} \right)^3 + 20 \left(\frac{1}{2}x - \frac{3}{2} \right)^2 + 33 \left(\frac{1}{2}x - \frac{3}{2} \right) - 22 = 0$$

When this is simplified, it becomes

$$x^3 + x^2 = 80$$

and the tables indicate that $x = 4$ is an answer. Then

$$y = \frac{1}{2}x - \frac{3}{2} = \frac{1}{2}(4) - \frac{3}{2} = \frac{1}{2}$$

should be an answer to the equation in y. A substitution of $y = 1/2$ in that equation will verify that this is so.

But the facts involved in deciding what transformation will bring a general cubic to the above canonical form were first developed, as far as we know, in the sixteenth century A.D. The Babylonian mathematicians may have used sheer intuition and ingenuity, but if they possessed the necessary theoretical knowledge, their mastery of algebra was even more incredible than that revealed in the cuneiform tablets deciphered to date.

If we solve a cubic by modern methods, it is easier to transform it to the standard form

$$x^3 + ax + b = 0$$

where the x^2 term is absent (not the x term as in the preceding normal form). Before we examine how this is accomplished, however, let us discuss some of the early history of cubic equations.

Among Greek mathematicians who solved special cubic equations by the use of geometric algebra, there were Menaechmus (*ca.* 350 B.C.), tutor to Alexander the Great, and Archimedes (287–212 B.C.), whose name is known to all. The Persian poet, mathematician, and astronomer, Omar

Khayyám (*ca.* 1100) is the next name in the story of cubics. Although he used geometric algebra and never arrived at a general cubic formula, Omar bin Ibrahim al-Khayyami created techniques of solution for thirteen types of third-degree equation. For this and the applied mathematics by which he devised a calendar superior to our own, Omar is considered to be one of the most original of the Moslem mathematicians. As for the algebra of cubics, his ideas were among the greatest contributions between the fifth and sixteenth centuries.

The geometric methods of Menaechmus, Archimedes, and Omar are still valuable for special problems, and we shall examine some of them in a subsequent chapter. What mathematics demands, however, is a technique that will solve any and all cubics. The algebraic activity of Italian mathematicians in the sixteenth century provided such a method and produced the formula

$$x = \sqrt[3]{-\frac{1}{2}b + \sqrt{R}} + \sqrt[3]{-\frac{1}{2}b - \sqrt{R}} \text{ where } R = \left(\frac{b}{2}\right)^2 + \left(\frac{a}{3}\right)^3$$

for the solution of

$$x^3 + ax + b = 0$$

where a and b are any *real* numbers. Earlier in this chapter it was shown how a general cubic can be transformed into the Babylonian "canonical form." It is even simpler to change a general cubic to the standard form above, which is the one needed before the general formula can be applied. For example, in the complete cubic

$$y^3 - 3y^2 - 2y - 2 = 0$$

the substitution $y = x + 1$ will transform the equation into

$$(x + 1)^3 - 3(x + 1)^2 - 2(x + 1) - 2 = 0$$

When this is simplified, it becomes

$$x^3 - 5x - 6 = 0$$

Then if -5 is substituted for a and -6 for b in the cubic formula, the root

$$x = \sqrt[3]{3 + \sqrt{\frac{118}{27}}} + \sqrt[3]{3 - \sqrt{\frac{118}{27}}}$$

is obtained. Because $y = x + 1$, a root of the original cubic can be found merely by adding 1 to the answer for x. There are two other roots for either cubic and a modification of the above formula will produce these. Since the slight change in formula involves imaginary numbers and may appear difficult to a reader who is not well acquainted with their manipulation, we shall not indicate the procedure here. The appearance of the exact value for x is rather formidable, but the whole point is that this root is *exact*, and not an approximation interpolated in a table or read from a graph. While the pure mathematician desires precise formulation, a practical worker might still prefer a good approximation, and he could obtain this by substituting values obtained from a table of square roots and cube roots in the above formula. If a reader wishes to try this, his answer should be $x = 2.7$ (to the nearest tenth) and hence $y = 3.7$, answers which can be checked by substitution in the equations above.

A strange fact will now appear—namely, when a cubic is specially easy in the sense that its three roots are all *real* and distinct, the general formula leads to an "irreducible" result. This is one of the reasons why a geometric approach may be more revealing and why we shall return to it again in a later chapter. When all is said and done, modern physicists, engineers, statisticians, and applied mathematicians in all fields usually solve all but the simplest cubic equations by *graphic* methods or "algorithms" equivalent to such methods. In American textbooks the two most favored algorithms are due to Newton and William George Horner (1786–1837). Although Horner does not have status as a mathematician, his name has become well known through its association with school mathematics. He was a teacher at Bath, England, when he discovered his algorithm. We now know that a similar method had been used in China and that Paolo Ruffini (1765–1822) had formulated virtually the same technique around 1804. But Horner discovered it independently, presented it in a paper to the Royal Society in 1819, and had full details published (of all places!) in the *Ladies' Diary* for 1838.

The geometric spirit of the Greeks continues in modern (approximate) methods of equation-solving, but the analytic geometry of Fermat and Descartes (Chapter 7) has made it possible to provide geometric pictures not only for cubics, but also for equations of higher degree, and even for "tran-

scendental" (nonalgebraic) equations. Therefore, as far as
concepts and practicality are concerned, nothing novel has
been added to the approximate geometric solution of cubics
since the days of Omar.

But the achievement of the general cubic formula, from
which a general formula for fourth-degree (quartic or bi-
quadratic) equations soon followed, was more than a mile-
stone in algebra. It spelled *finis* to the classic period in that
subject, although mathematicians were not to realize until
the late eighteenth and early nineteenth century that it was
futile to search for formulas that would solve algebraic
equations of degree higher than the fourth. The reason for
this will appear in Chapter 16. To return to the cubic formula, if R is negative, then $\sqrt{R}$ will be imaginary. There is
no objection to this except that in the theory of equations it
is proved that R will be negative when the cubic has *three
real roots* that are distinct. In this "easy" case, the general
formula furnishes the answer in terms of the cube roots of
imaginary numbers, and there is no simple algebraic method
for extracting such cube roots. For example, one can readily
verify that −6 is a root of

$$x^3 - 63x - 162 = 0$$

Yet the general formula furnishes the answer

$$x = \sqrt[3]{81 + \sqrt{-2700}} + \sqrt[3]{81 - \sqrt{-2700}}$$

If one is a good guesser and is apt at the manipulation of imaginaries,
one can actually find the cube roots and thus obtain

$$x = (-3 + \sqrt{-12}) + (-3 - \sqrt{-12}) = -6$$

For this and other reasons the formula is a pure mathematical triumph but, as we have said, other methods are needed
in applied situations. Thus, if one were really able to guess
−6 (and special propositions of the theory of equations
would assist his guess), he could complete the task of solution by using Harriot's method of factoring. He might consider his guess, $x = -6$, as if it were the result of equating
the factor $x + 6$ to zero. Then, dividing the above cubic
polynomial by $x + 6$ to obtain the quotient $x^2 - 6x - 27 =
(x - 9)(x + 3)$, he would say that $x - 9 = 0$ or $x + 3 = 0$,
and the remaining roots are $x = 9$, $x = -3$.

It is difficult to assign credit for the cubic formula to any
particular one of the sixteenth-century Italian algebraists.

From their own writings, which are not considered reliable since each author was so biased in his own favor, one gathers the following approximation of the truth: Around 1535 a mathematics contest was proposed by Antonio Mario Fior of Bologna. Each contestant was to deposit a certain stake with a notary, and whoever could solve the problems in a collection of thirty propounded by his opponent was to get the stakes, thirty days being allowed for the solution of the questions proposed. Fior had learned to solve a special type of cubic from his teacher, Scipione del Ferro (1465–1526). It is believed that Del Ferro may have obtained his method from Arab sources. Fior's opponent in the contest was a Venetian mathematics professor, Niccolo Fontana (1500–1557), commonly known as Tartaglia, a nickname meaning "stammerer" but nevertheless adopted by Fontana, whose impediment was due to an injury suffered during the French sack of Brescia, his native town. Tartaglia suspected that the questions would all be cubics, and so developed a formula for solving cubic equations. He answered all the questions put to him, and in return gave Fior questions on cubics of a type the latter could not handle. Thus Tartaglia won the contest and composed some verses to commemorate his victory. Each stanza described a step in the derivation of the general formula for solving cubics. In his *Quesiti et invenzioni diverse* (1546), dedicated to Henry VIII of England, Tartaglia recorded these particular verses, stating, "If this poem is not very good, I don't care. It helps me to remember the rule."

Tartaglia's happiness, however, was to be short-lived. He planned to keep his method secret, but another Italian mathematician, Girolamo Cardano (1501–1576) (Cardan), professor of medicine at Milan and author of the algebraic masterpiece *Ars Magna* (1545), wheedled the mnemonic poem out of his stammering friend. Having secured the facts, which he promised to keep secret, Cardano nevertheless included in the *Ars Magna* Tartaglia's method for solving a cubic. He gave full credit to Tartaglia, but in many modern texts the method is still referred to as "Cardan's Solution of the Cubic."

The cubic equation incident was only one of many that reveal why Cardano is considered the "bad boy of mathematics." That his career was no path of ease or virtue is set forth in his *Book of My Life*, written at the age of seventy-four, a sort of Rousseau's *Confessions*. Though the book lacks the literary and philosophic qualities of the latter, it is equally lusty, in the true spirit of the Italian sixteenth-century scene. To place Cardano in the correct historic epoch, we need only state that he was a contemporary of Benvenuto Cellini. The extravagance of Cardano's autobiography might be attributed to senility except that it is known that his lifelong behavior lacked balance. On the one hand, he holds a high rank in the history of medicine and he was truly the leading algebraist of his era. His mathematical creativeness is only now being fully recognized. For example, he was one of the founding fathers of modern probability theory (Chapter 13). On the other hand, he was an astrologer, a gambler, and a man of dubious ethical principles. Perhaps he was slated for neurosis from birth, since he was the illegitimate son of a professor of jurisprudence and medicine in Milan.

According to Cardano's own account, his later life was as unhappy as his early years. He relates that his older son was deaf and hunchbacked but, worst of all, had a psychopathic personality which led him to poison his worthless wife, a crime for which he was put to death. The younger son of the great mathematician was also a ne'er-do-well of violent type. His daughter, Cardano comments, was no trouble except in the matter of dowry. After all his efforts in providing this sum and getting her married, he complains, she disappointed him by failing to provide grandchildren.

Although Cardano derived no joy from his own children, he took great pleasure in the accomplishments of his favorite pupil, Lodovico Ferrari (1522–1565), who discovered a general method for solving any *quartic* equation. Cardano published Ferrari's formula for the quartic, along with Tartaglia's for the cubic, in the famous *Ars Magna*. These formulas can be considered, as we have said, the terminal performance in classic algebra.

In the present chapter we have considered polynomial equations involving a single unknown number. But in the previous chapter we solved some equations in two unknowns. The solution was not always determinate; that is, mere specification of the domains of the variables was not sufficient to fix a unique solution (pair of values satisfying the equation) or even a *finite* number of solutions. If a polynomial equation contains several unknowns, a finite solution set will require further limitations on the variables, for example, additional equations or reduction of the domains to subsets of the original replacement sets. The effect of such conditions and also graphic methods of solving systems of simultaneous equations will be discussed in a later chapter, but we remark that in many cases algebraic techniques make possible the elimination of all but one of the unknowns and provide a polynomial equation for that single variable so that the whole problem is reduced to the classical issue of solving a polynomial equation.

In the previous chapter we mentioned the name of Évariste Galois in connection with finite fields, and later we shall discuss Galois' theorem of 1831. We shall see how it put an end to traditional algebra, Italian style, where one provides a neat formula in terms of coefficients, which is applicable to all polynomial equations of a certain degree. For two hundred years prior to 1826, when Abel dealt the first deathblow to such equation-solving, algebraists tried in vain to solve the general equation of the fifth degree,

$$ax^5 + bx^4 + cx^3 + dx^2 + ex + f = 0$$

In the year named, Abel showed that even though Gauss guaranteed a solution when coefficients are real or complex, it is *impossible* to express this solution using only a *finite* number of rational operations and root extractions on the coefficients a, b, c, d, e. Galois gave a more elegant proof of the same fact, but then established a general theorem indicating the impossibility of finite algebraic formulation of solutions for polynomial equations of *all* degrees greater than 4.

Galois' great theorem states: *A polynomial equation is solvable if and only if its group is solvable.* This theorem, whose date is 1831, mentions the term "group," which is due to Galois himself, and refers to specialized types like the "group of an equation" and a "solvable group." Now all this was mentioned a dozen years in advance of the date when Hamilton's quaternions launched the "game" which, by deletion of one or more of the postulates for a field, leads to the various modern abstract algebraic structures, including the group. The idea (if not standard name) of a group structure had, in fact, started in the eighteenth century and had been developed by a number of mathematicians before Galois. His great discovery began the new era in two ways very different from Hamilton's initiation of new algebraic systems by changing the rules of the traditional game. In the first place, Galois put an end to equation-solving and, secondly, his work provided motivation for a general abstract approach in which the elements of an algebraic system are *not* necessarily numbers. Galois, and Augustin-Louis Cauchy (1789–1837) before him, studied finite groups whose elements are *mappings* (Chapter 16) with a finite domain.

As a final comment, we remark that Galois' theorem did *not* shut the door to *nonalgebraic* solutions requiring an "infinite" number of operations on the coefficients of a polynomial equation. But just what does "infinite" mean, in an exact mathematical sense? From the point of view of common sense, it would seem that one could, at best, approximate a solution requiring an infinite number of steps by taking a great many of these steps so as to get closer and closer to some ideal goal. This requires concepts from *analysis*, the area of mathematics which is associated with the "infinite" real continuum and "infinite" processes in general. Some of those concepts were treated in Chapter 2, and others will be developed later in our story.

Chapter 6

A Universal Language

"The human race, considered in relation to its own welfare, seems comparable to a battalion that marches in confusion in the darkness, without a leader, without order, without any signal or command to regulate its march, and without any attempt on the part of individuals to take cognizance of one another. Instead of joining hands to guide ourselves and make sure of the road, we humans run hither and yon, and merely interfere with one another."

The simile is not part of some current plea for world federation or increased activity on the part of the United Nations, but a thought recorded almost three hundred years ago by Leibniz, who believed that the panacea for the lack of human cooperation lay in the formulation of a universal language (*characteristica universalis*) and an algebra of reasoning (*calculus ratiocinator*). To people today this suggestion for the solution of man's woes must appear over-optimistic, just as it did to Voltaire, whose *Candide* satirized Leibniz' "Everything is for the best in this best of all possible worlds." Nevertheless, Leibniz did initiate a "universal language," namely, a form of *symbolic logic*.

The illustrious creator of that "Esperanto" was always one to give credit where credit was due, and hence he pointed out that the Catalan mystic Ramón Lully (1235–1315) had anticipated his idea to some extent. Lully's *Ars Magna* contained formulas so utterly mystic as to be completely unintelligible, but it also presented tabulations resembling the multiplication table for quaternions (page 125) except that the entries were not quaternion "units" but instead ideographs representing the primitive concepts which Lully planned to combine in order to express all other ideas and to solve all problems of science, religion, and philosophy.

It is true that Leibniz' motivation was similar to that of Lully. But Leibniz provided a lucid formulation of his universal tool, so that later logicians were able to develop and improve his creation. If twentieth-century philosophers are not as sanguine as Leibniz, they feel nevertheless that part of his dream has been realized, for a universal *scientific* language, mathematical logic, has been devised, and there is every hope that the future will witness its further progress, the solution of its unresolved problems, and its application to all situations calling for scientific thought.

Such a program for logic can be considered the ultimate outgrowth of an essay, *De arte combinatoria*, written by Leibniz in 1666, when he was "barely out of school" (*vix egressus ex Ephebis*), to use his own words. In that year he laid the foundation for "a general technique by which all reasoning can be reduced to mere calculation." "This method," Leibniz wrote, "should serve at the same time as a sort of universal language, whose symbols and special vocabulary can direct reasoning in such a way that errors, except those of fact, will be like mistakes in computation, merely a result of failure to apply the rules correctly." In later writings Leibniz enlarged on these ideas, stating that "the method should be an Ariadne's thread, a medium that will guide the mind in the fashion that geometric lines guide the eye." He explained that the language of logic should be ideographic, each symbol representing a simple concept, but should differ from languages like Chinese by combining symbols in order to compound ideas, instead of having a vast number of different characters corresponding to different things. Thus while it may require a lifetime for a foreigner to master Chinese completely, any one should be able to perfect himself in the *characteristica universalis* in a few weeks. Leibniz himself provided only a sketchy outline of his proposed language, but said that leading scientists ought to study the question, and select the "alphabet of human thought," the catalogue of the simplest ideas and associated symbols, and then rewrite all of science in terms of this standard alphabet.

Leibniz' idea was regarded as nothing more than a dreamer's fantasy until the time of Giuseppe Peano (1858–1932), who actually did devise one species of scientific Esperanto. Then, in 1894, with a number of collaborators, he started on the rest of Leibniz' program. The result was the five-volume *Formulaire de Mathématiques* (1895–1905), in which all of mathematics was rewritten in terms of the Peano language. The Italian logician continued to propagandize the *Formulaire* during the rest of his life. Maria Cinquini-Cibrario, an Italian analyst and one of the few women mathematicians of our day (or any day), started her own career by serving as an assistant to the aging Peano, and for any one who would like to see a sample of the Peano language, there is one of Professor Cinquini-Cibrario's early papers, *Proposizioni universali a particolari e definizione di limite.**

Some of Peano's symbols will appear in the present chapter, but we do not plan to expose the reader to the rigors of his *Formulaire*. Instead, we shall show how Leibniz' great ideas experienced a rebirth in the writings of George Boole and Augustus De Morgan, logicians whose names have been mentioned as contributors to the task of placing traditional algebra on a sound postulational foundation. Boole's *Laws of Thought* (1854) was written in apparent ignorance of Leibniz' ideas on the same subject. In a sense, Boole's unawareness of the work of his predecessor was fortunate, because his own formulation was so much simpler and clearer. He became the "re-founder" of symbolic logic, and all subsequent contributions to the subject go back to his 1854 treatise. Some of the outstanding mathematical logicians after Boole were the American Charles Saunders Peirce (1839–1914) and the Germans Ernst Schroeder (1841–1902) and Gottlob Frege (1848–1925). The ideas of Frege and Peano were carried further in the *Principia Mathematica* (1910–1913) of Bertrand Russell and Alfred North Whitehead (1861–1947), a treatise often pronounced the greatest twentieth-century contribution to both a universal scientific language and an algebra of reasoning.

Symbolic logic, in the opinion of Russell, consists (like ancient Gaul) of three parts—the algebra of classes, the propositional calculus, and the calculus of relations. In the present chapter, the first two of these branches will be considered as two species of "Boolean algebra." We shall also touch on the question of logical relations, but shall postpone amplification to our next chapter.

It must be emphasized that we shall be treating only

---

* See *Atti della Reale Accademia delle Scienze di Torino*, Vol. 44 (1929).

certain selected aspects of symbolic logic, mainly because a complete, rigorous presentation would baffle the general reader, but also because we wish the present chapter to be properly contiguous with the chapters immediately preceding. We have just completed a discussion of how symbols were manipulated mechanically for the purposes of classical algebra. Now Boole's conception will make it possible to proceed in somewhat analogous fashion with literal symbols which are capable of far more general and more important interpretations than the x, y, z's of common algebra. Again, in discussing the formal aspects of a "Boolean algebra," that is, its axiomatic foundation, we shall be continuing the discussion of algebraic structures, a topic initiated in Chapter 4. In one sense, the present introduction to symbolic logic might have formed an immediate sequel to Chapter 3, where a pure mathematical science was seen to be based on a postulate system from which the theorems of the science are deduced. But just how is the process of deduction to be carried out? Evidently, in addition to the fundamental axioms, there must be agreement at the outset on acceptable logical laws and rules of proof. Such principles become additional postulates, as it were, although they may be theorems of another science, namely, some type of logic—the classic Aristotelian variety or some modern system of symbolic logic.

Boole, as we have said, was a member of the British algebraic school that gradually "purified" common algebra so that emphasis was placed not so much on the results of operations (addition, multiplication) as on their *formal properties* such as commutativity, associativity, distributivity. Thus algebra became a pure science where the x, y, z's are abstractions and need not necessarily be interpreted as representing numbers. This point of view gave Boole his opportunity. In his *Laws of Thought* he stated that he would "exhibit logic, in its practical aspect, as a system of processes carried on by the aid of symbols having a definite interpretation, and subject to laws founded upon that interpretation alone. But at the same time these laws are identical in form with the laws of the symbols of algebra, with a single addition, that is, the symbols of logic are further subject to a special law." In other words, Boole was able to assume commutativity, associativity, distributivity for his "logical addition" and "logical multiplication," and thereby reduce certain types of reasoning to the sort of algebraic manipulation one carries out in school algebra.

Having given a capsule description of Boole's contribution, let us now expand our brief outline. We shall gradually develop the concepts and laws of the algebra of classes in informal, intuitive fashion, prior to formulating a postulate system for a pure (abstract) Boolean algebra. Thus our procedure will be somewhat analogous to that of the ancient surveyors who provided the physical observations which were ultimately abstracted in the axioms of pure Euclidean geometry.

To review what has been said in earlier chapters, a *set* can be described as a *collection* of things that are called *elements* or *members* of the set. Some logicians use the term "class" in a somewhat different sense from the term "set," but we shall not do so, and in order to avoid constant repetition, any of the following words will be used as a synonym for set: class, collection, aggregate, ensemble.

In traditional arithmetic and algebra, one carries out various operations (+ and ×) within sets of numbers. In Boolean algebra one operates within sets of classes. We have already illustrated some sets of classes, for example, the aggregate of classes in a particular school, a collection of sets of china, the set of bunches of sticks which primitives used for counting. But it is possible that such sets of classes may not be suitable for a Boolean algebra because Boole's "logical addition" or "logical multiplication" may lack closure on the given collection.

To illustrate the last remark, we may as well reveal that we have in fact already performed "logical addition" without giving the operation that name. The *logical sum* of two sets is merely their *union* (page 48). Now if we unite two sets in one of the collections described in the previous paragraph, we may fail to obtain a set of the original collection. Thus, combining two sets of china will yield an enlarged set but not necessarily a set identical with one in the original collection, and a similar statement applies to the fusion of two classes in a school.

To avoid possible failure of closure, and also for other reasons that will appear presently, a Boolean algebra of classes starts by specifying a fundamental domain, that is, a *universal set* or *universe of discourse*. (This idea is due to De Morgan.) Then the collection of all *subsets* of the selected universe is an aggregate on which a *closed* "addition" and a closed "multiplication" can be defined. For purposes of illustration we proceed informally once again and select a small universe of discourse, namely, one made up of three men. Let I symbolize that universe, where

$$I = \{\text{Ames, Brown, Grant}\}$$

Then, recalling that a set X is said to be a subset of a set Y if and only if every member of X is also a member of Y, we see that $A = \{\text{Ames, Brown}\}$, $B = \{\text{Ames, Grant}\}$, $C = \{\text{Brown, Grant}\}$, $D = \{\text{Grant}\}$, etc. are subsets of I.

If we think of the subsets as committees, then, in addition to one-man and two-man committees, there will be a "committee of the whole," namely, I, which is an *improper* subset of itself, a *proper* subset of I being a subset that is not identical with I. At the other extreme, it is convenient for logical purposes to consider that $\emptyset = \{\ \ \}$, the empty (null) set, is a subset of any set, and hence is a subclass or "committee" of I.

If the universe of discourse selected should be the set of natural numbers, say, then finite subsets can be specified by roster, but the membership of an infinite subset could never be listed completely. In the latter case, one would have to define the subset by specifying some property common to its members and possessed by no other natural numbers. In that way one can define the subset of *even* natural numbers by stating that they are the natural numbers exactly divisible by 2. The symbol $\{2, 4, 6, \ldots\}$ is suggestive but it is *not* a list. The use of a defining property in place of a roster is also advisable for large finite subsets of any universe.

Since we are discussing *symbolic* logic and indicating similarities between Boolean and common algebra, let us now introduce the symbol $\subseteq$ for "is a subset of," and point out that its properties are similar to those of $\leq$ for numbers. In our illustrative three-member universe, $A \subseteq I$, which can be read either as "A is a subset of I" or as "A is *included in* I." In the same universe, $B \subseteq I$, $I \subseteq I$, etc. But we can also state that $A \subset I$, read either as "A is a *proper* subset of I" or as "A is *properly* included in I."

Just as $3 \leq 3$ (read as "3 is either equal to or less than 3") and $x \leq x$ (where x is any number), $X \subseteq X$ where X is any set, that is, every set is a subset of itself. One describes this characteristic by saying that $\leq$ and $\subset$ are *reflexive* relations, that is, relations which a thing can have to itself.

It will seem obvious to the reader that if $x \leqq y$ and $y \leqq z$, then $x \leqq z$, where x, y, and z are numbers. It may seem just as clear that a subset of a subset of a universal set is also a subset of that universe. In general, if X, Y, Z are any three sets such that $X \subseteq Y$ and $Y \subseteq Z$, then it is also true that $X \subseteq Z$. The property just considered is described by saying that $\leqq$ and $\subseteq$ are *transitive* relations.

If one states that two sets are equal, that is, $X = Y$, then the use of the "equals" sign is the same as that throughout mathematics. As already explained in Chapter 2, the sign $=$ means that the symbols on the two sides of the sign are both names for the *same* thing. When sets are defined by properties, it may sometimes be difficult to recognize that different properties define the *same* set, and in this connection a special attribute of $\subseteq$ may be helpful. If, in fact, X and Y do name the same set, that is, $X = Y$, then every member of X is a member of Y and vice versa, which signifies that $X \subseteq Y$ and $Y \subseteq X$. It is customary to postulate the converse fact (and apply it to test equality of sets): If $X \subseteq Y$ and $Y \subseteq X$, then $X = Y$.

But let us proceed to other concepts of Boolean algebra. In the universe of natural numbers,

$$I = \{1, 2, 3, 4, 5, 6, \ldots\}$$

there is the subset of *even* natural numbers, those exactly divisible by 2,

$$E = \{2, 4, 6, \ldots\}$$

and the subset of *odd* natural numbers, those not exactly divisible by 2,

$$O = \{1, 3, 5, \ldots\}$$

The subset O is the *complement* of the subset E in the sense that O contains all those members of the universe I which are not in E. We can also say that E is the complement of O.

In the small universe containing three members, $I = \{\text{Ames, Brown, Grant}\}$, the subset $D = \{\text{Grant}\}$ is the complement of the subset $A = \{\text{Ames, Brown}\}$. Modern symbolic logic uses A' or $\bar{A}$ as the symbol for "the complement of A." In the present instance, $D = A' = \bar{A}$. Also, if $B = \{\text{Ames, Grant}\}$, then $B' = \bar{B} = \{\text{Brown}\}$. If $C = \{\text{Brown, Grant}\}$, then $C' = \bar{C} = \{\text{Ames}\}$. Thus the subsets of any universal set occur in complementary pairs. In any universe of three elements, $I = \{\alpha, \beta, \gamma\}$, it is readily seen that there are eight and only *eight* subsets which can be symbolized as follows:

$$I = \{\alpha, \beta, \gamma\} \qquad \emptyset = \{\ \}$$
$$A = \{\alpha, \beta\} \qquad A' = \{\gamma\}$$
$$B = \{\alpha, \gamma\} \qquad B' = \{\beta\}$$
$$C = \{\beta, \gamma\} \qquad C' = \{\alpha\}$$

We observe that the universal set I and the null set $\emptyset$ are complementary, a fact obviously true in any universe. Also, in any universal set, if subset A' is the complement of subset A, it is also true that A is the complement of A'. Symbolically, $(A')' = A$, or $\bar{\bar{A}} = A$. The complement of the complement of a subset is the original subset.

In our miniature Boolean algebra there are eight subsets. These are the objects which will be "added" and "multiplied" presently. Since we already know that "logical addition" means union, a brief inspection of our list of eight subsets will indicate that uniting any pair of them will produce some subset of I. Hence "logical addition" is closed on the collection of eight subsets and we shall see shortly that the same is true of "logical multiplication." Therefore we shall be studying a *finite* algebra of eight objects, in strong contrast to traditional algebra, where the basic class of objects is usually infinite—the set of rational numbers or the set of real numbers or the complex aggregate. If an algebra of eight elements seems petite, let us remark that if one were to select a universe of two elements, $I = \{\alpha, \beta\}$, then there would be *four* subsets and a Boolean algebra of four objects. If one selects a universe containing a single element, $I = \{\alpha\}$, there would be only *two* subsets, namely I and $\emptyset$. We shall see that the *binary* Boolean algebra of two objects has exceedingly important interpretations. It is the smallest nontrivial Boolean algebra. To obtain a smaller algebra one would have to select $I = \{\ \}$, that is, $I = \emptyset$, and all procedures would lead to this vacuous set.

We have already carried out some arithmetic on the eight subsets of $I = \{\alpha, \beta, \gamma\}$, since forming the complement of a set can be considered a *unary* operation (on *one* set) or else a limited sort of subtraction where the minuend is always I but the subtrahend may be any subset. Since we have already explained that "logical addition" means *union*, let us now consider Boole's interpretation of $\otimes$.

Boole defined the *logical product* of two sets as their *intersection*, that is, as the aggregate of members common to both sets. Thus, referring to the subsets of $I = \{\alpha, \beta, \gamma\}$ (as listed on page 159), we can state that the logical product or intersection of $A = \{\alpha, \beta\}$ and $B = \{\alpha, \gamma\}$ is $C' = \{\alpha\}$, that is,

$$AB = A \otimes B = C'$$

Today we would use Peano's symbol for intersection, $\cap$, and symbolize the above multiplication as

$$A \cap B = C'$$

The reader can verify that $A \cap C = B'$, $A \cap I = A$, $A \cap A' = \emptyset$, etc. But the best way for him to obtain some practice with logical multiplication would be to check the products in the following multiplication table, where a product like $B \cap C$, for example, appears in row B and column C.

Multiplication Table for Subsets of $I = \{\alpha, \beta, \gamma\}$

$\otimes = \cap$	I	A	B	C	C'	B'	A'	$\emptyset$
I	I	A	B	C	C'	B'	A'	$\emptyset$
A	A	A	C'	B'	C'	B'	$\emptyset$	$\emptyset$
B	B	C'	B	A'	C'	$\emptyset$	A'	$\emptyset$
C	C	B'	A'	C	$\emptyset$	B'	A'	$\emptyset$
C'	C'	C'	C'	$\emptyset$	C'	$\emptyset$	$\emptyset$	$\emptyset$
B'	B'	B'	$\emptyset$	B'	$\emptyset$	B'	$\emptyset$	$\emptyset$
A'	A'	$\emptyset$	A'	A'	$\emptyset$	$\emptyset$	A'	$\emptyset$
$\emptyset$	$\emptyset$	$\emptyset$	$\emptyset$	$\emptyset$	$\emptyset$	$\emptyset$	$\emptyset$	$\emptyset$

Since every entry within the above table is one of the eight subsets of I, logical multiplication is *closed* on the collection of subsets. That logical multiplication will be closed on the subsets of *any* universal set results from the definition of that operation. For if X and Y are any two such subsets, then their intersection Z will contain the elements common to X and Y. Thus every element of Z is also a member of X, that is, $Z \subseteq X$. But $X \subseteq I$. Hence, by the transitivity of $\subseteq$, $Z \subseteq I$. In other words, the intersection (logical product) of two subsets of I must be a subset of I.

That logical multiplication is commutative and associative

in the present example can be verified by means of the table. That the properties of ∩ in the present instance also hold for subsets of any universal set can once again be demonstrated by applying the definition of logical multiplication.

But the previous multiplication table indicates other algebraic properties. For example, when $\emptyset$ and I are "factors," they act like the numbers 0 and 1, respectively, in ordinary algebra. Just as $a \times 0 = 0 \times a = 0$, and $a \times 1 = 1 \times a = a$, the table shows that $A \cap \emptyset = \emptyset \cap A = \emptyset$ and $A \cap I = I \cap A = A$, etc. On the other hand, our miniature Boolean algebra lacks the property that made possible the solution of polynomial equations by Harriot's method (Chapter 5). Whereas in common algebra the product of two numbers is equal to zero only if at least one of these numbers is zero, our multiplication table indicates that $B' \otimes C' = \emptyset$, $A' \otimes B' = \emptyset$, $A \otimes A' = \emptyset$, etc. It is possible for a logical product to be "null" without having either of its factors "null."

Again, there will *not* be perfect analogues in Boolean algebra for the "powers" of ordinary algebra, that is, for $a \times a = a^2$, $a \times a \times a = a^3$, etc. From our Boolean multiplication table,

$$A \otimes A = A$$
$$A \otimes A \otimes A = (A \otimes A) \otimes A = A \otimes A = A, \text{etc.}$$

and if we "multiplied" A by itself (or B by itself or C by itself) any number of times, the logical product would always yield the original set, as we can verify from the table, or obtain by reasoning that the intersection of any set with itself is that set. Logical multiplication is said to be *idempotent*, signifying that all "powers" of a set are the *same*, and hence there is no need for the exponential symbolism of common algebra. When Boole stated that "the symbols of logic are further subject to a special law" (page 155), he amplified his assertion by indicating that the special law is $AA = A$, that is, $A \cap A = A$, the *idempotent* law we have just illustrated.

The reader can readily develop most of the properties of "logical addition" after recalling that the *logical sum* or *union* of any two classes, X and Y, is the set of elements which belong to X or to Y or to both X and Y. Thus, in our illustrative universe, if the committee $A = \{$Ames, Brown$\}$ is united with the committee $B = \{$Ames, Grant$\}$, the committee of the whole, $I = \{$Ames, Brown, Grant$\}$ results. Both common sense and the definition of "union" permit the names in the union to be listed in any order and also cause Ames's name to be listed only once in the fused set. Symbolically,

$$A \oplus B = A \cup B = I$$

(The symbols $\cup$ and $\cap$ for union and intersection are due to Peano.) Using the definition of A, A', B, B', etc., on page 159, the reader can check the entries in the following addition table. He can use it to verify that closure, commutativity, and associativity are properties of logical addition in our miniature Boolean algebra and can also apply the definition of $\cup$ to show that the properties named will hold in general.

Addition Table for Subsets of $I = \{\alpha, \beta, \gamma\}$

$\oplus = \cup$	I	A	B	C	C'	B'	A'	$\emptyset$
I	I	I	I	I	I	I	I	I
A	I	A	I	I	A	A	I	A
B	I	I	B	I	B	I	B	B
C	I	I	I	C	I	C	C	C
C'	I	A	B	I	C'	A	B	C'
B'	I	A	I	C	A	B'	C	B'
A'	I	I	B	C	B	C	A'	A'
$\emptyset$	I	A	B	C	C'	B'	A'	$\emptyset$

The reader can also verify that just as $a + 0 = 0 + a = a$ in common algebra, $A \oplus \emptyset = \emptyset \oplus A = A$, $B \oplus \emptyset = \emptyset \oplus B = B$, etc. in the table. He can see that if X is any set, then $X \oplus \emptyset = \emptyset \oplus X = X$. Again, just as there is an idempotent law for logical multiplication, there is a similar law for logical addition. The table shows that

$$A \oplus A = A$$
$$A \oplus A \oplus A = (A \oplus A) \oplus A = A \oplus A = A, etc.$$

and if one "adds" A to itself any number of times, the logical sum will always be A. Boolean algebra has no need for the coefficient symbolism of common algebra.

In traditional algebra, multiplication is *distributive* with respect to addition, that is,

$$a(b + c) = ab + ac$$

where a, b, and c are any numbers whatsoever. That the analogous law holds in Boolean algebra, in other words, that

$$A(B \oplus C) = AB \oplus AC$$

or

$$A \cap (B \cup C) = (A \cap B) \cup (A \cap C)$$

is suggested by Figure 6.1, which exhibits one type of *Venn diagram*, named after the logician John Venn (1834–1883).

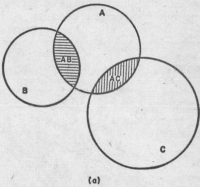

(a)

B and C have no common elements

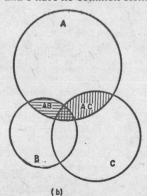

(b)

B and C overlap

Figure 6.1 · $A(B \oplus C) = AB \oplus AC$

But in Boolean algebra there is a second distributive law. It turns out that logical addition is distributive with respect to multiplication. The second distributive law can be obtained from the first by substituting $\oplus$ for $\otimes$ and $\otimes$ for $\oplus$, that is, $\cup$ for $\cap$ and $\cap$ for $\cup$ in the first law. Then

$$A \oplus BC = (A \oplus B)(A \oplus C)$$

or

$$A \cup (B \cap C) = (A \cup B) \cap (A \cup C)$$

That this law holds is suggested by the Venn diagram of Figure 6.2.

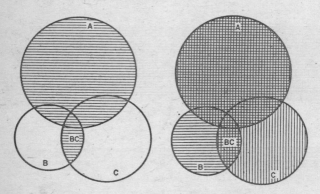

Figure 6.2 $A \oplus BC = (A \oplus B)\ (A \oplus C)$. The left member of the equation is represented by the shaded region in the first diagram. In the second diagram, horizontal shading represents $A \oplus B$, vertical $A \oplus C$. The doubly shaded region (intersection of the two sets) is the same as that shaded in the first diagram.

To see that the second distributive law does *not* apply to the ordinary addition and multiplication of numbers, let us show that it is *not* true that $a + bc = (a + b)(a + c)$ for all numerical values of a, b, and c. Thus if $a = 1$, $b = 2$, $c = 3$, the left member would have the value $1 + 2\cdot3 = 7$, and the right member would be equal to $(1 + 2)(1 + 3) = 12$.

Not only the second distributive law but also all theorems deduced from it fail to have counterparts in common algebra. Let us prove one such Boolean law by starting with the fact that

$$A = A \oplus \emptyset = A \oplus (\emptyset \otimes B)$$

Now, by virtue of the second distributive law, we can say that

$$A \oplus (\emptyset \otimes B) = (A \oplus \emptyset)(A \oplus B) = A(A \oplus B)$$

The result of all this is that the original set A is identical with $A(A \oplus B)$, or

$$A(A \oplus B) = A$$

that is,

$$A \cap (A \cup B) = A$$

which is called a *law of absorption* because (if B is not empty) the law states that the part common to class A and a larger class including A, namely, $A \oplus B$, is the first class. The larger class is "absorbed" into the smaller. In common algebra there is no such law of absorption. That, in general,

$$a(a + b) \neq a$$

when a and b are numbers, is indicated by the counter-example, $a = 2$, $b = 1$, which yields $a(a + b) = 2(2 + 1) = 6$. Now $6 \neq 2$.

The second distributive law was obtained from the first by replacing $\oplus$ by $\otimes$ and $\otimes$ by $\oplus$. That particular interchange of logical addition and logical multiplication illustrated a general *principle of duality* which asserts: In any Boolean law, the result of replacing $\oplus$ by $\otimes$, $\otimes$ by $\oplus$, $\emptyset$ by I, and I by $\emptyset$ is also a law.

Thus, applying the duality principle to the commutative law of logical addition, $A \oplus B = B \oplus A$, yields the corresponding law for logical multiplication, $A \otimes B = B \otimes A$, that is, $AB = BA$. Applying the same principle to the law of absorption, $A(A \oplus B) = A$, produces a *second law of absorption*, namely

$$A \oplus AB = A$$

which can also be proved to be true.

That there is a duality between logical sums and logical

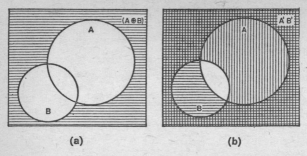

Figure 6.3 $(A \oplus B)' = A'B'$. **If the rectangle represents** I, **the universal set, the shaded region in (a) is identical with the doubly shaded region in (b), thus illustrating De Morgan's first law. Also, (b) illustrates De Morgan's second law.**

products is implicit in De Morgan's laws (Figure 6.3) which assert that

$$(A \oplus B)' = A'B' \text{ and } (AB)' = A' \oplus B'$$

The complement of a logical sum is equal to the product of the complements of the addends, and the complement of a logical product is equal to the sum of the complements of the factors. Application of the De Morgan laws enables one to convert any "sum" into a "product" and vice versa so that it would actually be possible to perform Boolean algebra by using only one of these operations (and complementation).

In order to summarize all that has been said thus far, the set of fundamental laws for a Boolean algebra of classes is listed below, where dual laws are paired. Some of these laws can be taken as *postulates* and the remainder derived from them as theorems, but it will be simpler for the reader to accept them all, in order to be able to advance to other issues of Boolean algebra. To indicate similarities with comon algebra, we have used juxtaposition of letters to indicate logical multiplication, and have used $\oplus$ instead of $\cup$. The letters A, B, C symbolize *any* subsets of *any* universe I.

Closure laws: $A \oplus B$ is a uniquely AB is a uniquely de-
                  defined subset of I fined subset of I
                  A' is a uniquely de-
                  fined subset of I

Commutative laws:	$A \oplus B = B \oplus A$	$AB = BA$
Associative laws:	$A \oplus (B \oplus C)$	$A(BC) = (AB)C$
	$= (A \oplus B) \oplus C$	
Distributive laws:	$A(B \oplus C)$	$A \oplus BC$
	$= AB \oplus AC$	$= (A \oplus B)(A \oplus C)$
Idempotent laws:	$A \oplus A = A$	$AA = A$
Complementation laws:	$A \oplus A' = I$	$AA' = \emptyset$
Laws of De Morgan:	$(A \oplus B)' = A'B'$	$(AB)' = A' \oplus B'$
Double complementation:	$(A')' = A$	
Laws involving $\emptyset$ and I:	$A \oplus I = I$	$A\emptyset = \emptyset$
	$A \oplus \emptyset = A$	$AI = A$
	$I' = \emptyset$	$\emptyset' = I$
Laws of absorption:	$A(A \oplus B) = A$	$A \oplus AB = A$

To give an especially simple, and hence somewhat artificial, instance of how some of the above laws can be
applied, consider the problem of two librarians who are
told to sort a pile of books just returned by borrowers.
The first librarian is told to collect all political works by
American authors and all books over 500 pages by foreign
authors. The second is told to take political works exceeding 500 pages and novels by Americans, provided they are
not political in nature. Will there be any books claimed by
both librarians? If

I is the class of books in the pile
A is the class of books by Americans
B is the class of books over 500 pages
P is the class of books of a political nature
N is the class of novels
A' is the class of books by foreign authors
B' is the class of books of 500 pages or less
P' is the class of nonpolitical works
N' is the class of books other than novels

then the first librarian will call for $AP \oplus A'B$ and the
second will claim $BP \oplus ANP'$.

Both will claim the intersection of these two sets, namely,
$(AP \oplus A'B)(BP \oplus ANP') = ABPP \oplus AANPP' \oplus A'BBP \oplus AA'BNP'$.

Since $PP = P$, $BB = B$, and because complementary classes

have no members in common, $PP' = \emptyset$ and $AA' = \emptyset$, therefore the set of books claimed reduces to $ABP \oplus A'BP$. This equals $BP(A \oplus A') = BPI = BP$ since the elements common to the universe and any class in it constitute the class itself. Hence both librarians will claim political books of over 500 pages.

We abstracted the fundamental laws for a Boolean algebra from the behavior of the subsets of a universal set. As we have stated, some of those laws can be treated as postulates (assumptions) and the remaining laws can be deduced as theorems. Now if we divorce the Boolean postulates and theorems from their original association with classes, that is, if we consider the symbols I, $\emptyset$, A, B, C, . . . , $\oplus$, $\otimes$, $'$, as *abstractions*, which need *not* be interpreted as sets, union, intersection, complementation, then we have the fundamental laws of a *pure* Boolean algebra. There are, in fact, many *essentially different* concrete interpretations of those laws, as the present chapter will show. That a postulate system for a Boolean algebra is *not* categorical (Chapter 3), that is, does *not* have all its interpretations isomorphic (abstractly identical) is indicated by the fact that there are Boolean algebras of 2 elements, 4 elements, 8 elements, 16 elements, etc., so that matching of elements would be impossible in such interpretations and *a fortiori* they could not be isomorphic. Nevertheless any manipulations we perform or theorems we deduce must apply to all Boolean algebras, in particular to the algebra of classes, and also to two other Boolean algebras which we shall consider, namely, the algebra of propositions, and the algebra of switching circuits.

One way of emphasizing two important points, namely, that Boolean algebra applies to things other than sets and that its structure differs from the *field* (Chapter 4) of common algebra, is to describe a Boolean algebra as a *lattice*, an abstract system created and studied by the American mathematician Garrett Birkhoff. He defines a *lattice* as a set of elements (of any kind), closed under two binary operations which are commutative, associative, idempotent, and which satisfy the two absorption laws. If, in addition, the two distributive laws hold, the system is called a *distributive lattice*. Then a Boolean algebra is a *special* kind of distributive lattice, the specialization being brought about by the laws governing I, $\emptyset$, and the unary operation of complementation. One reason pure mathematicians may prefer the term *Boolean lattice* to the traditional "Boolean algebra" is that an "algebra" in modern usage often refers to a structure like Hamilton's quaternion system where one has a "vector addition," a "vector multiplication," and a "scalar multiplication" (Chapter 4).

Having discussed the nature of a pure Boolean lattice, we shall proceed to further applications. The surprising fact is that the most important interpretations, from the point of view of logic, are related to the smallest nontrivial Boolean lattice, where operations are performed on *two objects* only. In the algebra of classes we obtained such a tiny Boolean lattice by selecting a universe containing a single element, namely, $I = \{\alpha\}$. Then the only subsets are $I = \{\alpha\}$ and $\emptyset = \{\ \}$. The reader will readily verify that the entire arithmetic of this binary Boolean lattice is governed by the following tables.

Addition			*Multiplication*			*Complementation*	
$\oplus = \cup$	$\emptyset$	I	$\otimes = \cap$	$\emptyset$	I	Set X	Complement X'
$\emptyset$	$\emptyset$	I	$\emptyset$	$\emptyset$	$\emptyset$	$\emptyset$	I
I	I	I	I	$\emptyset$	I	I	$\emptyset$

But these tables are associated with a binary algebra of classes. To "purify" them, let us avoid the class symbols, $\emptyset$ and I; but, recalling that those classes behave somewhat like the 0 and 1 of common algebra, let us use the latter symbols, *not* to represent numbers, but to stand for abstract elements (of any nature whatsoever) which obey laws abstracted from the above. Then for a pure binary Boolean algebra, we have the following tables.

Addition			*Multiplication*			*Complementation*	
$\oplus$	0	1	$\otimes$	0	1	x	x'
0	0	1	0	0	0	0	1
1	1	1	1	0	1	1	0

These tables emphasize that the operations of a binary Boolean lattice (algebra) are almost like those of common arithmetic. The sums and products, *with one exception*, are those that would result from performing ordinary addition and multiplication with numbers. The only exception is

$$1 \oplus 1 = 1$$

which involves the "idempotency" of Boolean addition and also the fact that I (in this case, 1) in a Boolean lattice is a sort of "upper bound." The Boolean law, $A \oplus I = I$, signifies that no matter what is added to I (in this case, 1), no "higher" entity can be obtained. Complementation is like subtraction from the number 1.

Before we relate the propositional calculus to the binary Boolean lattice, we shall backtrack slightly in order to explain, by concrete examples, why one should expect a parallelism between the laws of the algebra of classes and those of the algebra of propositions. We might say that the key to the situation lies in the method of specifying a subset of a universal class by means of a defining property.

If, for example, the universe of discourse is $I = \{0, 1, 2, 3, 4\}$, then the property of "being a perfect square" defines the subset $P = \{0, 1, 4\}$. If we use the technical terminology of the two previous chapters, we can assert that "x is a perfect square" is an *open sentence*, where I is the domain of the variable x. Here P is called the *truth set* of the open sentence. This open sentence can also be described as a *propositional form* because substitution of the elements of the domain yields statements expressing *propositions*, that is, ideas which can be pronounced either *true* or *false*. Here, in the very first example, we have a correspondence between a *set P* and a *propositional form*. We shall symbolize the latter by $p(x)$ to indicate that it is a "function of x," a concept which will be discussed at length in the next chapter. Anticipating that discussion, we shall now point out that to each value of x in the domain I there corresponds a unique proposition, so that the "function" consists of the five pairs:

x	$p(x)$
0	0 is a perfect square
.	.
.	.
3	3 is a perfect square
4	4 is a perfect square

In the same universe of discourse, let us consider the *propositional form* which negates $p = p(x)$, namely, "x is *not* a perfect square." In symbolic logic this form might by symbolized as "$\sim p$" (read as *not-P*) or in the present instance by "$\sim p(x)$." Its truth set is obviously $\{2, 3\}$. We observe that this truth set is P', the complement of $P = \{0, 1, 4\}$. Thus if P corresponds to p, it appears that P' corresponds to $\sim p$. If this is a general fact for all universes, then the unary operation of complementation ($'$) of sets will correspond to a unary operation on propositions, namely *negation* ($\sim$).

In the same universe, the propositional form,

$$q = q(x) : x < 3$$

has the truth set $Q = \{0, 1, 2\}$, as the reader can readily verify, so that set Q corresponds to form q. For the truth set of "p and q," that is, "$p(x)$ and $q(x)$," we must solve the *simultaneous* open sentences "x is a perfect square" and "$x < 3$." Direct substitution of the five values in I will lead to the truth set $\{0, 1\}$. But one could obtain this set by reasoning that values of x making *both* sentences true would have to belong to P, the truth set of $p(x)$, and also to Q, the truth set of $q(x)$. In other words, the solution set would have to be the intersection of P and Q, namely $P \cap Q$. We can verify that $P \cap Q = \{0, 1\}$. Thus "p and q," the *conjunction* of two propositional forms, symbolized by "$p \wedge q$," corresponds to the *intersection* of two sets, $P \cap Q$, a fact that holds in more general universes than the one under consideration.

We leave the reader the task of continuing the analogy further by showing that, in the present instance, $P \cup Q = \{0, 1, 2, 4\}$ is the truth set of "p or q" $=$ "$p(x)$ or $q(x)$." Here the connective "or" has the significance of the legal term "and/or." In other words, to be in the solution set a number must be a perfect square or less than 3, but there is no objection to its having both properties as, for example, in the case of 1. In logic, the form "p or q" is symbolized as "$p \vee q$" and, even in more general universes, corresponds to the union of two sets, $P \cup Q$.

In our special universe I, the truth set of "x is an integer" is the universal set I. Hence the given sentence is a *law* for our universe. We can state that law as a *closed sentence* by *quantifying* (page 112) the open sentence as follows: *For all*

x in I, x is an integer. The reader can readily find other laws for our universe, for example: *For all x in I, x is not greater than 4.* At the other extreme from the universal truths there are propositional forms like $x < 0$, $x^2 = 2$, $x^3 = 5$, which have $\emptyset$ as truth set. What is the use of such universal falsehoods? Recalling that *negation* of forms corresponds to *complementation* of sets, we see that the negation of any one of the above forms will have I as truth set, that is, will be a universal truth. Thus *for all x in I, x is not less than 0, $x^2 \neq 2$, $x^3 \neq 5$.*

One might go further with our particular example to show how commutativity, associativity, etc. of union and intersection have analogues in the same properties of propositional forms, so that in an algebra of such forms in any universe, the Boolean laws for $'$, $\cup$, $\cap$ will transfer to identical laws for $\sim$, $\vee$, $\wedge$. But a single illustration does not constitute proof. Moreover, in a small, highly specialized universe, the propositional forms and the possible statements they yield are necessarily limited in nature. If symbolic logic is to be the universal language of which Lully and Leibniz dreamed, it must be possible to talk about things other than numbers in the set $\{0, 1, 2, 3, 4\}$. Of course, one can enlarge or vary the universe of discourse or consider forms like $p(x, y)$, $p(x, y, z)$, etc. where there may be different universes for x, y, z, etc. We shall do just that in our next chapter. But here we must ask whether increasing the number of variables and extending their domains would actually ensure the possibility of making all sorts of statements—about people, money, books, atoms, stars, love, life, etc. Even if the answer should be affirmative, the notation would be somewhat cumbersome if the number of variables is large, to say nothing of the need for numerous substitutions when universal sets are large.

Perhaps then we should free our p's and q's from their dependence on x, y, z's, etc. That is, in fact, what is done in the propositional calculus, where *logical propositional forms* like $p \wedge q$, $p \vee (q \wedge r)$, $\sim p \wedge (q \vee r)$, etc., contain p, q, and r as "independent" variables, *not* dependent on other variables—x, y, z, etc. The greater freedom makes it possible to replace p, q, r, etc., by *any statement whatsoever*, just so long as these statements express propositions. But then will the algebra of classes still hold? What will the "universal truths" be like and how will they be demonstrated? Let us see.

The universal truths of the propositional calculus are called *tautologies*, which are logical forms producing *true* statements no matter what propositions are substituted for p, q, r, etc., that is, for the variables contained in the forms. The calculus studies the conditions under which compound sentences are true solely as a result of their *pattern*, regardless of the nature of the component propositions. For example, the particular statement "3 is an odd integer *or* 3 is *not* an odd integer," is *true*, but so is every statement of the same *form*. In other words, any statement expressing a proposition can be used in place of "3 is an odd integer." Thus "oxygen is a metal *or* oxygen is *not* a metal," "George Washington is now President of the United States *or* he is *not* now President of the United States." All such statements are incorporated in the logical form, "$p \lor \sim p$," which subsequently will be proved to be a tautology, the "law of the excluded middle," as it is called in traditional logic: Either a proposition or its negation must be true. To say that "$p \lor \sim p$" is a universal truth (for all propositions p) is like asserting $P \cup P' = I$ in a Boolean algebra of classes. Once again, $\lor$, p, $\sim p$, and "universal truth" correspond to $\cup$, P, P', and I, respectively.

To start our discussion of the algebra of propositions more formally, we must remind the reader that a *statement* is a declarative sentence which expresses a *proposition*, an idea that can be pronounced either *true* or *false*. We cannot say that a proposition actually is a statement, because any proposition can be expressed in many different ways, for example, in English, French, Italian, etc. This is the same point made in Chapter 1, where it was emphasized that an idea like that of a "number" may have many different names. Having made the point, we shall not be pedantic but instead shall use "numeral" and "number," "statement" and "proposition," etc., interchangeably.

We have already indicated that symbolic logic makes use of the connectives "not," "and," "or," symbolized by $\sim$, $\land$, $\lor$, and that when propositions are compounded with the use of those symbols, the question of the "truth" or "falsity" of compounds is the all-important issue. The *postulates* or assumptions about the truth of various composites are usually incorporated into *truth tables*. Thus the assumptions that (1) if any proposition p is true (has *truth value* 1), then $\sim p$ is false (has *truth value* 0), and (2) if p is false, $\sim p$ is true, are tabulated as follows.

Truth Table for Negation

p	$\sim p$
1	0
0	1

Observe that this table of truth values is identical with the table for *complementation* in a binary Boolean algebra (page 169), a fact which is not surprising since we have already indicated (page 171) a correspondence between negation of propositional forms and complementation of sets. Again, a truth table symbolizes four postulates concerning "p and q," that is, "$p \wedge q$," the *conjunction* of any two propositions. Such a conjunction is assumed to be true if *both* p and q are true. In all other cases the conjunction is postulated to be false, as the following table indicates.

Truth Table for Conjunction

p	q	$p \wedge q$
1	1	1
1	0	0
0	1	0
0	0	0

To see that the truth table for the conjunction of propositions is identical with the multiplication table of a binary Boolean algebra, let us present the truth table in the following alternative form.

Truth Table for Conjunction

		Truth Value of q	
$\wedge$		0	1
Truth	0	0	0
Value of p	1	0	1

The truth table for the *disjunction* of any two propositions, that is, for "p or q," symbolized as "$p \vee q$," is given in the following two different forms, where the second form identical with the addition table for a binary Boolean algebra. Either form of the truth table indicates that the disjunction of two propositions is true unless both propositions are false, in which case it is false. Once again, we remind the reader that the symbol $\lor$ has the meaning of "and/or" as used in statements like the following: The residents of Smithtown and/or people who work in Smithtown must pay the income tax levied by that city.

Two Forms of Truth Table for Disjunction

p	q	$p \lor q$		$\lor$	Truth Value of q 0	1
1	1	1	Truth	0	0	1
1	0	1	Value of p	1	1	1
0	1	1				
0	0	0				

What our comparisons have shown is that if we interpret the elements of the binary Boolean algebra as *truth values* of propositions, and the operations $'$, $\otimes$, $\oplus$ as $\sim$, $\land$, $\lor$, then the truth-value algebra of propositions is a binary Boolean lattice. This signifies that all the laws of Boolean algebra hold for the truth values of propositions. Thus the commutative law $P \cup Q = Q \cup P$ for the Boolean algebra of classes has as its counterpart the law that $p \lor q$ and $q \lor p$ are "equivalent" logical forms, that is, must have the same truth tables. Again, one of De Morgan's laws in the algebra of classes states that $(P \cup Q)' = P' \cap Q'$. Therefore, in the algebra of propositions, $\sim (p \lor q)$ and $(\sim p) \land (\sim q)$ must be "equivalent" logical forms, that is, must have the same truth table. That this is the case is verified by the truth tables that follow. In the truth table for $\sim (p \lor q)$, the first three columns are exactly those of the truth table for $p \lor q$, and the last column is obtained by applying the truth table for negation to the third column. In the table for $(\sim p) \land (\sim q)$, application of the truth table for negation to the first two columns yields the third and fourth columns. Application of the truth table for conjunction to the third and fourth columns yields the last column, which is the *same* as in the preceding truth table, thus proving the "equivalence" of the logical forms in question. What *both* tables indicate is that either form yields a true statement if and only if *false* propositions are substituted for both p and q.

Truth Table for $\sim(p \vee q)$

p	q	$p \vee q$	$\sim(p \vee q)$
1	1	1	0
1	0	1	0
0	1	1	0
0	0	0	1

Truth Table for $(\sim p) \wedge (\sim q)$

p	q	$\sim p$	$\sim q$	$(\sim p) \wedge (\sim q)$
1	1	0	0	0
1	0	0	1	0
0	1	1	0	0
0	0	1	1	1

As stated in the very beginning of our discussion of the propositional calculus, a major issue is the search for universal truths or tautologies, that is, logical forms which result in true propositions when any propositions whatsoever are substituted for the variables (p, q, r, etc.) which the forms contain. We have already mentioned that the "law of the excluded middle," $p \vee \sim p$, is a tautology. Our "proof" consisted in saying that $P \cup P' = I$ in the Boolean algebra of classes. Then, since p, $\sim p$, $\vee$, 1 correspond to P, P', $\cup$, I, respectively, the truth value of $p \vee \sim p$ must always be equal to 1 and the tautology is established. Since this type of proof may seem a bit too informal, let us now provide a truth-table demonstration. In the table below, the first two columns are exactly those in the truth table for negation. The third column is then obtained by applying the truth table for disjunction to the first two columns. The truth values for $p \vee \sim p$, as listed in the third column, are obtained by using the first two columns and applying the truth table for disjunction.

Truth Table for $p \vee \sim p$ [*Law of Excluded Middle*]

p	$\sim p$	$p \vee \sim p$
1	0	1
0	1	1

Since all the entries in the third column are 1's, $p \vee \sim p$ is *always* true, regardless of the truth value of p, and therefore $p \vee \sim p$ is a *tautology*.

Let us now use the truth-table method to prove that one of the "laws of thought" which Aristotle and Leibniz considered the most important of all, namely, the *law of contradiction*, is a tautology. Its symbolic form is $\sim(p \wedge \sim p)$, and one way of expressing it verbally is: A proposition and its negation cannot both be true.

Truth Table for $\sim(p \wedge \sim p)$ *[Law of Contradiction]*

p	$\sim p$	$p \wedge \sim p$	$\sim(p \wedge \sim p)$
1	0	0	1
0	1	0	1

In the above truth table, the first two columns are the same as in the previous table. The truth values in the third column are obtained by using the first two columns and applying the truth table for conjunction. The truth values in the fourth column are obtained from those in the third column by applying the truth table for negation. Since the fourth column contains only 1's, $\sim(p \wedge \sim p)$ is *always* true, regardless of the truth value of p, and is therefore a tautology.

Thus far only the connectives "not," "and," "or" have been used in combining logical forms. Before we define further connectives, there are two points we wish to emphasize. The first is a reminder that in logical forms any propositions whatsoever may be substituted for the variables p, q, r, etc. Thus a particular substitution in $p \wedge q$ might lead to the statement: The earth is a planet *and* apple pie is nutritious. In ordinary conversation one would be unlikely to combine such unrelated propositions, but then symbolic logic is designed as a *universal* language, and we know that even stranger compounds than the one illustrated do occur in imaginative poetry or in the modern theater of the absurd. The second point is completely analogous to one in the algebra of classes where, by virtue of De Morgan's laws, it is possible to limit Boolean operation to $\cap$, $'$ or else to $\cup$, $'$. Thus instead of the logical sum $P \oplus Q$ one can use the equivalent $(P'Q')'$. The corresponding fact of the propositional calculus is that *disjunction* of propositions can be dropped, if one so desires, for instead of "p and/or q," that is, $p \lor q$, one may employ the equivalent "not-(not-p and not-q)," that is, $\sim[(\sim p) \land (\sim q)]$. One can see immediately, however, that this would make for lack of intelligibility in verbal expression. It is more lucid and more straightforward to assert that an insurance policy will pay benefits for illness and/or accident than to state that no benefit will be paid to any one who is not ill and has not met with an accident.

The two issues we have raised will have considerable bearing on the logical connective we shall next introduce. In the first place, we shall ultimately see that logic could manage without the new connective by using circumlocutions involving $\sim$, $\land$ or $\sim$, $\lor$. But we have just examined a small sample of the sort of verbal difficulties that may arise from such a procedure. Hence we shall now join two sentences by using "if ———, then," a connective used very frequently in everyday linguistic expression. "If p, then q," usually symbolized by $p \rightarrow q$, is described as a *conditional* form, and p is called the *antecedent*, q the *consequent*.

The following is an example of a conditional statement: If $1 + 1 = 5$, then Paris is a city in France. This sentence involves the second point considered above since, once again, two completely unrelated propositions are connected. But, as we have said, such composites are possible, and the only concern of the propositional calculus is whether to pronounce the results "true" or "false." We shall see (from the truth table below) that in modern logic the illustrative conditional is *true*. What is assumed in the truth table is that $p \rightarrow q$ is false only when the antecedent is true and the consequent false. Otherwise the conditional is postulated to be true.

Truth Table for $p \rightarrow q$

p	q	$p \rightarrow q$
1	1	1
1	0	0
0	1	1
0	0	1

To show that the truth table for $p \rightarrow q$ agrees with "common sense," let us analyze an example in which a father promises his son, "*If* your attendance record at school this term is good, *then* I'll give you a bicycle." At the end of the term, the son will pronounce judgment on the truth of his father's conditional statement according to which of the four following possibilities occurs.

(1) The boy actually does have a good attendance record, and his father does give him a bicycle. The boy will feel his father was telling the truth. Here we have the first row of the truth table, namely, truth values 1, 1, 1 for p, q, $p \to q$, respectively.

(2) The boy's attendance is good, but his father does *not* present him with a bicycle. "Dad, you were *not* telling the truth," the youngster says. Here we have the second row of the table, namely, truth values 1, 0, 0 for p, q, $p \to q$, respectively.

(3) The boy's attendance is *not* good, but nevertheless his father does give him a bicycle. Since the father made no threat, that is, did not cover the contingency just described, the boy would not question the truth of the original statement, and hence we have the third row of the table, that is, truth values 0, 1, 1 for p, q, $p \to q$, respectively. (Observe that these truth values also apply to the conditional "If $1 + 1 = 5$, then Paris is a city in France." Hence that conditional statement is pronounced to be *true*.)

(4) The boy's attendance is *not* good and his father does not give him a bicycle. The boy will feel that his father's behavior is just, and hence will not accuse his parent of making a false promise. Here we have 0, 0, 1 as truth values for p, q, $p \to q$, respectively (last row of the truth table).

For practice in the meaning of the conditional, the reader can convince himself that the statement "If $1 + 1 = 2$, then swords are plowshares" is *false* whereas the following assertion of Polonius (in which he refers to Hamlet and Ophelia) is *true*:

"If he love her not,
. . . .
I am no assistant for a state."

While we are on the subject of the conditional, let us prove that symbolic logic could do without that logical form since, as the following truth tables *prove*, the forms of $q \lor \sim p$ and $\sim(p \land \sim q)$ are both "equivalent" to $p \to q$, since the new forms have the same truth table as that for the conditional. But if we are never to use $p \rightarrow q$, we shall have to make use of circumlocutions like the following: The father gave his son a bicycle and/or the boy's attendance record was not good.

Truth Table for $q \vee \sim p$

p	q	$\sim p$	$q \vee \sim p$
1	1	0	1
1	0	0	0
0	1	1	1
0	0	1	1

The reader can obtain the third column in the above table by applying negation to the first column. He can then apply the truth table for disjunction to the second and third columns in order to obtain the fourth column.

Truth Table for $\sim(p \wedge \sim q)$

p	q	$\sim q$	$p \wedge \sim q$	$\sim(p \wedge \sim q)$
1	1	0	0	1
1	0	1	1	0
0	1	0	0	1
0	0	1	0	1

In the above table the third column is obtained by using negation on the second. The fourth column results from applying the truth table for conjunction to the first and third columns. The last column is obtained by negating the fourth column. This table, like the truth tables for $p \rightarrow q$ and $q \vee \sim p$, shows that a certain composite of p and q is *true* unless p is true and q false.

Although the conditional form $p \rightarrow q$ is *not* a tautology since the last column of its truth table does *not* consist entirely of 1's (and, of course, we have illustrated conditional statements that are false), nevertheless certain *specialized* types of conditional form are tautologies. For examples of such special cases, the reader can verify the truth tables we shall next present.

Truth Table for $(r \wedge s) \rightarrow (r \vee s)$

r	s	$r \wedge s$	$r \vee s$	$(r \wedge s) \rightarrow (r \vee s)$
1	1	1	1	1
1	0	0	1	1
0	1	0	1	1
0	0	0	0	1

In the above table the third and fourth columns are obtained from the truth tables for conjunction and disjunction. The last column is obtained by applying the truth table for $p \rightarrow q$ to the third and fourth columns. Since the last column is made up of 1's, the given logical form is a tautology. The law in question signifies that using the conjunction of two propositions as antecedent and the disjunction of the same propositions as consequent will *always* yield a *true* conditional statement. For example, it is not necessary to analyze the following statement for meanings since it must be true by virtue of its form: If Mars is a comet and the reader is a monkey's uncle, then Mars is a comet or the reader is a monkey's uncle.

The truth table below proves that one of the fundamental laws of logic, namely, the *law of the syllogism*, is a tautology: If p implies q and q implies r, then p implies r. The reader should examine the table, column by column, since there is the added difficulty of considering *eight* rows because there are eight triples of possible truth values for *three* propositions.

Truth Table for $[(p \rightarrow q) \wedge (q \rightarrow r)] \rightarrow (p \rightarrow r)$
[Law of the Syllogism]

p	q	r	$p \rightarrow q$	$q \rightarrow r$	$(p \rightarrow q)$ $\wedge$ $(q \rightarrow r)$	$p \rightarrow r$	$[(p \rightarrow q) \wedge (q \rightarrow r)]$ $\rightarrow (p \rightarrow r)$
1	1	1	1	1	1	1	1
1	1	0	1	0	0	0	1
1	0	1	0	1	0	1	1
1	0	0	0	1	0	0	1
0	1	1	1	1	1	1	1
0	1	0	1	0	0	1	1
0	0	1	1	1	1	1	1
0	0	0	1	1	1	1	1

If the reader has actually carried out the task of checking the eight rows of the previous truth table, he must have observed that the truth-table method may not always be an easy one for establishing laws of the propositional calculus. It is often easier to carry out the corresponding manipulations in the algebra of classes, since the procedures there are purely mechanical and are so much like those in common algebra. Thus one might prefer to establish the law of the syllogism by reasoning as follows. Since, as we have demonstrated, $p \rightarrow q$ is equivalent to $q \lor \sim p$, the Boolean class corresponding to the conditional can be symbolized as $Q \oplus P'$. Therefore the classes corresponding to the three conditionals in the law of the syllogism are $Q \oplus P'$, $R \oplus Q'$, $R \oplus P'$. Then the class corresponding to the larger conditional in which the three conditionals are embedded is

$$R \oplus P' \oplus [(Q \oplus P')(R \oplus Q')]'$$

If manipulation (by Boolean laws) can prove that this class is actually I, the *universal class*, then the corresponding logical form will be a *law*. To carry out the proof it will be easier to demonstrate that the complement of the above class is the null class, $\emptyset$, and hence that the class itself is I. In finding the complement of the above class, let us apply the De Morgan law which states that the complement of a sum is equal to the product of the complements of the addends. Then we must show that

$$R'P(Q \oplus P')(R \oplus Q') = \emptyset$$

If we multiply the first two factors and use the fact that $PP' = \emptyset$, the left member becomes

$$PQR'(R \oplus Q')$$

which is the same as

$$PQRR' \oplus PQQ'R'$$

Since $RR' = \emptyset$ and $QQ' = \emptyset$, each term in the above sum is $\emptyset$, and the total is $\emptyset$, which was the fact to be proved.

Our last considerations show that when the truth or falsity of statements is to be demonstrated logically, *both* the truth-table method and the technique of Boolean algebraic manipulation may become quite arduous. Therefore modern logic contains *rules of proof* which, in many situations, make it possible to avoid more cumbersome methodology. One such principle, called *modus ponens* in classical logic, is the *rule of detachment: If $p \rightarrow q$ is a true conditional, and if p is true, then q is true.* Thus when the premises of an argument contain both p and $p \rightarrow q$, then q can be *detached* and asserted to be true.

The rule of detachment can be derived from the truth table for the conditional. Since the rule assumes that p is *true*, only the first two rows of that truth table apply. But the rule also assumes that the conditional $p \rightarrow q$ is true. Hence the second row of the truth table is eliminated as a possibility. Thus only the first row remains and in that row q is true, which was the fact to be proved.

It is customary to symbolize the rule of detachment as follows:

$$p \rightarrow q$$
$$\underline{p}$$
$$\therefore \quad q$$

In this form it is applied to many arguments within mathematics itself, and in other areas as well. For example, one might reason as follows:

$p \rightarrow q$ If Smith was in Europe at the time a burglary was committed in New York City, then he did not commit that crime. (This is a *true* conditional.)

p (There is incontestable evidence that) Smith was in Europe at the time.

$\therefore q$ Smith did not commit the crime.

When the rule of detachment is applied to the law of the syllogism, one obtains another rule of proof, namely, the *rule of the syllogism: If $p \rightarrow q$ and $q \rightarrow r$ are both true conditionals, then $p \rightarrow r$ is a true conditional.* This rule can be proved by carrying out the three steps in the rule of detachment. Thus

(1) $[(p \rightarrow q) \land (q \rightarrow r)] \rightarrow (p \rightarrow r)$ is *true*. (Law of the syllogism)

(2) $[(p \rightarrow q) \land (q \rightarrow r)]$ is *true*. (The given rule of the syllogism *assumes* that each of the two conditionals is true. Hence their conjunction is true.)

(3) $\therefore p \rightarrow r$ is *true*. (Rule of detachment)

The *rule of the syllogism* is not to be confused with the law of the syllogism. The latter provides only the first step in the previous proof. In many cases where the law holds, steps (2) and (3) above may *not* be true. Thus, because the law of the syllogism is a tautology, we may assert, without further analysis, that the following somewhat bizarre statement is *true:*

$$\text{If } (2 > 1) \to (3 > 4) \text{ and } (3 > 4) \to (2 = 1),$$
$$\text{then } (2 > 1) \to (2 = 1)$$

It would *not* be permissible, however, to detach the final conditional and assert its truth. It is, in fact, *false* because it contains a true antecedent and a false consequent.

In deductive proofs one may make repeated use of the *rule* of the syllogism. Thus, in school geometry, one may prove that the opposite sides of a rectangle are equal by asserting: If a figure is a rectangle, then it is a parallelogram (by definition), and if a figure is a parallelogram, then its opposite sides are equal (theorem). Therefore, if a figure is a rectangle, then its opposite sides are equal (*rule of syllogism*).

In order to be able to verbalize complex conditionals like those we have been illustrating, mathematicians may read $p \to q$ in many different ways they consider synonymous with "If p, then q." Thus some logicians permit $p \to q$ to be read as "*p implies q*," but others object to this rendition because it suggests a causal relationship between antecedent and consequent. We have made a special point of indicating that no such logical connection need exist. Hence logicians may say that the truth table for $p \to q$ defines *material implication*, and may read $p \to q$ as "*p implies q in material meaning or as a matter of fact.*" This convention enables them to give *logical implication* a different meaning (but nevertheless one defined in terms of material implication).

The term "logical implication" carries with it the suggestion of logical inference or deduction, a process for which one would like to have *universal validity*. But then material implication, as expressed by $p \to q$, will not serve, since the conditional form is *not* a tautology. The trouble is that the variables p and q have too much freedom, since any propositions whatsoever may be substituted for them. But in relation to special subjects or problems, one is *not* interested in *all* propositions. The field of investigation places considerable restriction on the permissible substitutions for p and q, that is, it prescribes a special universe of discourse for those variables. Then, in relation to such a universe, $p \rightarrow q$ may become a *law* or universal truth (a sort of relative tautology).

Common algebra makes us familiar with the kind of situation we have described. Thus, given the open sentence $x^2 - 3x + 2 = 0$, its truth set in the domain of real numbers is $\{1, 2\}$. The given sentence is by no means a law for the specified domain. But if we *restrict* the domain of x to the set $\{1, 2\}$, then, relative to that small universe, we do have the *law* or universal truth: For all x, $x^2 - 3x + 2 = 0$.

To give an analogous illustration for the case of $p \rightarrow q$, the truth-table demonstration on page 181 indicates that if p is restricted to propositions of the form $r \wedge s$, and q to those of the form $r \vee s$, then $p \rightarrow q$ is a tautology relative to the universe thus prescribed.

Whenever the domains of p and q are restricted to special sets of propositions and *all* substitutions for p and q from the domains thus prescribed make $p \rightarrow q$ a true statement, then (according to the usage of some logicians) p implies q *logically* in the specified context. Logical implication is often symbolized as $p \Rightarrow q$.

When a theorem of a deductive science is expressed in conditional form, the statement is always a *logical implication*. For example, "If two sides of a triangle are equal, then the angles opposite are equal" can be symbolized by $p \Rightarrow q$, with interpretations as follows:

$$p = p(x): x \text{ has two equal sides}$$
$$q = q(x): x \text{ has two equal angles}$$

where the domain of x is the set of all triangles in the Euclidean plane. Here $p \rightarrow q$, that is, $p(x) \rightarrow q(x)$, refers to countless diagrams where x may be a small or a large triangle of any shape. There will be many pictures in which p is true and many in which it is false, and the same can be said about q, but there will *never* be a diagram where p is true and q is false. Hence the very numerous statements $p \rightarrow q$ will *all* be true, and thus $p \Rightarrow q$.

Again, let $I = \{1, 2, 3, 4\}$ be the domain of x and

$$p = p(x): x < 2$$
$$q = q(x): x \text{ is a perfect square}$$
$$p \rightarrow q: \text{If } x < 2, \text{ then } x \text{ is a perfect square}$$

It is easy to show that $p \Rightarrow q$ because $p \rightarrow q$ is a true statement in all (four) possible cases, namely:

If $1 < 2$, then 1 is a perfect square.
If $2 < 2$, then 2 is a perfect square.

If $3 < 2$, then 3 is a perfect square.
If $4 < 2$, then 4 is a perfect square.

In mathematics one often makes assertions of the form "$p \to q$ *and* $q \to p$." This logical form, called the *biconditional* of p and q, is usually symbolized as $p \leftrightarrow q$ (with superposition of an arrow pointing from p toward q on one pointing from q toward p). It can be expressed verbally as *p if and only if q*, abbreviated by mathematicians to *p iff q*. From what we have just stated,

$$p \leftrightarrow q = [(p \to q) \wedge (q \to p)]$$

We shall make use of this definition in deriving the following truth table for the biconditional.

Truth Table for $[(p \to q) \wedge (q \to p)]$ *[The Biconditional]*

p	q	$p \to q$	$q \to p$	$[(p \to q) \wedge (q \to p)]$
1	1	1	1	1
1	0	0	1	0
0	1	1	0	0
0	0	1	1	1

In the above truth table, the third and fourth columns were obtained from the first two by application of the truth table for the conditional, and the last column was obtained by applying the truth table for conjunction to the third and fourth columns. Since the symbol at the top of the last column is identical in meaning with the biconditional, $p \leftrightarrow q$, we can abbreviate the above table as follows.

Truth Table for the Biconditional

p	q	$p \leftrightarrow q$
1	1	1
1	0	0
0	1	0
0	0	1

Those logicians who read "$p \to q$" as "*p implies q materially*" read "$p \leftrightarrow q$" as "*p is materially equivalent to q.*" Thus the first and last rows of the truth table for *material equivalence* (the biconditional) show that two statements are *truly* equivalent in material meaning if they are both true or both false.

Again, there is the question of *logical equivalence*, $p \Leftrightarrow q$, which occurs in relation to special subjects or special problems that limit the domains of p and q in such a way that the logical form $p \leftrightarrow q$ *always* yields a true material equivalence when permissible substitutions (propositions in the prescribed domain) are substituted for p and q. Thus, we leave as exercises for the reader the task of proving

(1) (x is a perfect square) $\Leftrightarrow$ ($x < 2$)
    when the domain of x is $I = \{0, 1, 2\}$;
(2) (x is equilateral) $\Leftrightarrow$ (x is equiangular)
    when the domain of x is the set of all triangles in the Euclidean plane.

The reader will observe in both exercises that substitution of a value of x from the prescribed domain yields two true statements on both sides of the equivalence symbol or else two false statements so that, in every case, the material equivalence is true.

Earlier in this chapter we asserted that logical forms are "equivalent" if they have the same truth tables. Now we can reveal that *logical equivalence* was meant. The forms considered were composites of the same propositional variables. Given any two such forms, say, $f(p, q, r, \ldots)$ and $g(p, q, r, \ldots)$, substitution of certain truth values for $p, q, r, \ldots$ may cause f to have truth value 0. But in that case, g will also have truth value 0 because the truth tables for f and g are the same. Substitution of other truth values for $p, q, r, \ldots$ may give f truth value 1, and hence g truth value 1. But this means that f and g are both true or both false for every possible choice of truth values for p, q, r, etc. Then, in accordance with the truth table for the biconditional, f and g will be materially equivalent in every possible instance, and hence $f \Leftrightarrow g$, that is, f is *logically equivalent* to g.

The concept of logical equivalence is important because one of the logical rules of proof is the *rule of replacement for sentences*. That rule states that any logical form may be replaced by a logically equivalent form. It is often very helpful, in the course of a proof or logical argument, to be able to make such a replacement.

The form which one may wish to replace by a logical equivalent is very often a conditional sentence. Thus, in plane geometry, when it is required to prove that if alternate interior angles are equal, then lines are parallel, it is easier to demonstrate that if lines are not parallel, that is, if they intersect, then they form unequal alternate interior angles. The latter conditional statement is called the *contrapositive* of the original one and can be shown to be *logically equivalent* to it.

The *contrapositive* of $p \rightarrow q$ is defined to be $(\sim q) \rightarrow (\sim p)$. To prove the logical equivalence of the two forms, the reader can derive the following truth table for the contrapositive and verify that it is identical with that for the conditional.

Truth Table for $(\sim q) \rightarrow (\sim p)$

p	q	$\sim q$	$\sim p$	$(\sim q) \rightarrow (\sim p)$
1	1	0	0	1
1	0	1	0	0
0	1	0	1	1
0	0	1	1	1

Here once more the reader might prefer to use Boolean manipulations. The class corresponding to $p \rightarrow q$ can be symbolized by $Q \oplus P'$ and that corresponding to $(\sim q) \rightarrow (\sim p)$ would be $P' \oplus (Q')'$. But, since $(Q')' = Q$, the latter class is identical with the former. Hence the two logical forms are equivalent since they correspond to the same class.

The equivalence of the conditional and its contrapositive carries with it the fact that $p \Rightarrow q$ and $(\sim q) \Rightarrow (\sim p)$ are also equivalent.

If in his school days the reader did not make the acquaintance of the contrapositive form of a conditional proposition, $p \rightarrow q$, he surely encountered the *converse*, $q \rightarrow p$. He can now employ truth-table analysis to show that the conditional and its converse are *not* equivalent. Thus the truth or falsity of a conditional statement does not necessitate the respective truth or falsity of its converse. Hence, if a conditional sentence is a *logical implication*, this is not necessarily the case for its converse. For example, we have the logical implication: If a man lives in Chicago, then he lives in the United States. The converse would be: If a man lives in the United States, then he lives in Chicago. The truth of the latter conditional sentence is contingent on the man selected; its antecedent may be true (for example, when Mr. Jones actually lives in the United States) and its consequent false (Mr. Jones lives in Boston). Hence the converse sentence is *not* a logical implication.

On the other hand, consider: If the opposite sides of a quadrilateral are parallel, then it is a parallelogram—whose converse is: If a quadrilateral is a parallelogram, then its opposite sides are parallel. Here both conditional sentences are logical implications, that is, they are laws in the universe of plane quadrilaterals. In the particular illustration, the two implications provide the customary *definition* of a parallelogram. In fact, every definition involves a logical implication and its converse, which must also be a logical implication. In other cases, however, when it is given as the premise of an argument that some conditional sentence is a logical implication, it *cannot* be assumed that the converse is a logical implication, and reasoning is required to demonstrate whether or not this is so.

Suppose that the conditional $p \rightarrow q$ is transformed in a different way so as to form its *inverse* or *obverse*, $(\sim p) \rightarrow (\sim q)$. The contrapositive of this last conditional sentence must be logically equivalent to it, and this contrapositive is $q \rightarrow p$. But $q \rightarrow p$ is the *converse* of the original conditional sentence, and hence the inverse and the converse of any conditional are logically equivalent forms.

A common type of fallacy in everyday thought results from failure to realize that the converse or inverse of a logical implication and not the implication itself is being applied. This is the case when someone says, "There is no fracture because the X-ray was negative." Now if the X-ray reveals a break, then a fracture is present, but the inverse is false. It is not true that if the X-ray does not reveal a break, then no fracture is present. Or again, there is a comment like "He's so absolutely mad that he must be a genius." Now, granting (from a conventional point of view) the law that if a person is a genius, then he must be mad, the converse need not be a universal truth. It is not true that if a man is mad, he is necessarily a genius.

The rule of replacement for sentences makes it possible to substitute one logical form for another providing the two forms are *equivalent*. But the rules of proof of the propositional calculus permit a second type of substitution. The *rule of substitution for variables* states: In any tautology, it is permissible to substitute for all occurrences of a particular propositional variable any logical form whatsoever, and the result of such a substitution will be a tautology.

Thus, different substitutions for p in $p \lor \sim p$, the law of the excluded middle, would lead to the tautologies

$$(q \land r) \lor \sim(q \land r)$$
$$(q \to r) \lor \sim(q \to r)$$

Again, consider the tautology (page 181)

$$(r \land s) \Rightarrow (r \lor s)$$

(Since this is a tautology, it is a *logical implication* and hence we have used the symbol $\Rightarrow$). If we replace r by $p \lor q$ and s by $t \to v$, we arrive at the more complicated tautology,

$$[(p \lor q) \land (t \to v)] \Rightarrow [(p \lor q) \lor (t \to v)]$$

an implication true whatever the truth values of the *four* components, p, q, t, v.

In recent years there has been great interest in *logical machines*, that is, electronic calculators that will solve problems in formal logic. In the past, there were some purely mechanical machines like the "logical piano" designed by the logician William Stanley Jevons (1835–1882), but none of those machines was as versatile as the modern electronic "brains." It was Claude E. Shannon who, in a 1938 research paper, presented his discovery of the remarkable analogy between the truth values of propositions and the states of switches and relays in an electric circuit. Shannon showed, in fact, that "switching algebra" is a concrete interpretation of the abstract binary Boolean algebra and hence is isomorphic to the truth-table algebra of propositions. After Shannon's discovery, Boolean algebra became important in the design of switching circuits for all sorts of purposes— telephone networks, computers for general arithmetic calculation, computers to test the syllogisms of classical logic or the logical forms of modern symbolic logic, etc.

In Shannon's interpretation, a closed switch or a closed circuit (one in which current flows) can be considered to be in "state 1" and an open switch or an open circuit (one in which no current flows) can be described to be in "state 0." Then combinations of open or closed switches in a circuit will control the current, cutting it off or permitting it to flow, that is, yielding state 0 or state 1. We shall picture some circuits in which A, B, C, . . . will be used to represent switches. Switches in a circuit may operate so that two or more open and close simultaneously. In that case, our diagrams will label all such switches with the same letter, A, say. Again, A and A' will refer to different switches that operate simultaneously but are controlled so as to be in opposite states. In other words, when A is in state 1, A' is in state 0, and when A is in state 0, A' is in state 1.

In Figure 6.4 the switches A and B are connected in

Figure 6.4 $A \otimes B$ interpreted by switches in series

"series," a combination represented by $A \otimes B$, or by AB. Current will flow between the terminals if and only if both switches are closed, and this corresponds to the binary Boolean product $1 \otimes 1 = 1$. The possibilities where current does *not* flow (Figure 6.4) correspond to the other three entries

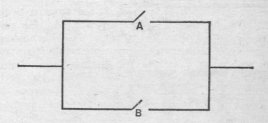

Figure 6.5 $A \oplus B$ interpreted by switches in parallel

in the multiplication table of the binary Boolean algebra, that is, to $0 \otimes 0$, $0 \otimes 1$, $1 \otimes 0$, products which are all equal to 0.

Again, in Figure 6.5 the switches A and B are connected in "parallel," a combination represented by $A \oplus B$. Current will flow between the terminals if A is closed, or if B is closed, or if both A and B are closed, states corresponding to the three entries $1 \oplus 0$, $0 \oplus 1$, $1 \oplus 1$ in the binary Boolean addition table. All three sums are equal to 1. If A and B are both open, one has $0 \oplus 0 = 0$, which signifies that no current flows.

No matter how circuits are constructed with switches in

series or in parallel, the total picture will be represented by an expression involving "sums" and "products" of A, B, C, . . . , A', B', C', . . . , that is, by a "Boolean polynomial." In turn, the *state* of the entire network will be determined by appropriate substitution of 1's and 0's and computation of the corresponding binary Boolean sums and products. The kind of mechanical manipulation one carries on when literal symbols stand for subsets of a universal set may be carried out when the symbols represent switches. In that way, simplification of a Boolean polynomial may make it possible to replace a complicated switching network by a simpler arrangement that is equivalent to it. For example, consider the circuit diagrammed in Figure 6.6. With Shan-

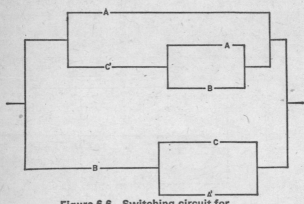

Figure 6.6   Switching circuit for
$$A \oplus C'(A \oplus B) \oplus B(C \oplus A')$$

non's interpretation, the circuit can be represented by the polynomial

$$A \oplus C'(A \oplus B) \oplus B(C \oplus A')$$

which, by application of the first distributive law (and the commutativity of $\otimes$), becomes

$$A \oplus AC' \oplus BC' \oplus BC \oplus A'B$$

The first two terms have sum A by virtue of the second law of absorption. The sum of the third and fourth terms can be expressed as $B(C' \oplus C) = B1 = B$. Hence the polynomial simplifies to

$$A \oplus B \oplus A'B$$

Applying the second law of absorption to the last two terms gives the sum B, and hence the original polynomial reduces to

$$A \oplus B$$

Thus the complicated network of Figure 6.6 is equivalent to the simple circuit of two switches in parallel pictured in Figure 6.5.

Our brief excursion into the algebra of switching circuits concludes our discussion of the elements of the first two divisions of symbolic logic (in Russell's partition). But there are several final points which require emphasis. The first of these is that we have actually treated some aspects of what logicians call quantification. When we found truth sets for open sentences (in the present chapter and also in Chapter 4), we observed that the sentences were true of *all*, *some*, or *no* values of the variables. To express such facts, we used quantifying phrases like "for all x," "for some x," thereby converting an open sentence into a proposition (page 112). When the sentence was true for *no* values, that is, when the truth set was $\emptyset$, we merely *negated* the sentence and found that the negation was true "for all x" (page 172). The only thing we failed to do was to introduce symbols for the quantifying phrases. Let us repair that omission by revealing that $\forall_x$ (read "for all x") is the symbol for the *universal quantifier* and that $\exists_x$ (read "for some x" or "there *exists* an x such that") is the symbol for the *existential quantifier*.

We remark that the symbolic treatment of quantification lends itself to mechanization of logical procedures involving quantifiers. However, the elementary logical material we have been discussing does not call for any elaborate manipulation of quantifier symbols. Only when quantification concerns two or more variables is it worthwhile to formalize the handling of the inverted A's and reversed E's. Such *multiple quantification* was involved implicitly when various algebraic postulates were stated, for example, "*For all x and for all y, $xy = yx$.*" This law can now be symbolized as follows:

$$\forall_x \forall_y \, (xy = yx)$$

Again, let us symbolize two quantified statements which were made (page 112) in connection with the solution of open sentences in the variables x and y, with domain $\{1, 2, 3, 4, 5\}$, namely,

$$\forall_x \forall_y \, (x + y > 1)$$
$$\exists_x \exists_y \, (x + y = 1)$$

The first statement is *true* and the second is *false*.

It would not have mattered if we had reversed the order of the quantifier symbols in the three instances just cited. But such symbols are *not* commutative in every case. Thus, if the domain of x and y is the set of integers $\{\ldots, -3, -2, -1, 0, 1, 2, 3, \ldots\}$, the first of the following statements is *true* and the second, formed by *reversing the order of the quantifiers*, is *false:*

$$\forall_x \exists_y \, (y < x)$$
$$\exists_y \forall_x \, (y < x)$$

The first statement can be read as "For each and every x, there exists a y such that $y < x$." The reader can convince himself of the truth of the statement by choosing $y = x - 1$, that is, the pairs $x = 3$, $y = 2$; $x = 2$, $y = 1$; $x = 0$, $y = -1$; etc. Or he can choose $y = x - 4$, with pairs like $x = 3$, $y = -1$ and $x = 2$, $y = -2$, etc.

The second statement above can be read as "There exists a y such that, for every x, $y < x$." In other words, "There exists an integer y smaller than every integer." This is false, since the scale of integers continues downward forever and ever. It never stops at some smallest integer. Even if we were to imagine such a smallest integer, it could not qualify as y in our statement, since such a y would be *equal* to one integer (the hypothetically smallest one) and hence would *not* be less than *every* integer. Thus we see that, in general,

$$\forall_x \exists_y \, p(x, y) \neq \exists_y \forall_x \, p(x, y)$$

where $p(x, y)$ is an open sentence or propositional form in two variables, x and y.

The algebra of multiple quantification is part of a general topic which will be treated more fully in our next chapter, namely, the logic of relations. In anticipation, however, we shall give a single example in which the concepts of "inverse" relation and multiple quantification make possible a certain kind of *non*syllogistic reasoning with which classical logic cannot cope. Thus if one accepts the premise that "someone loves everybody," Aristotelian logic does not permit a conclusion which seems obvious but can be rigorously validated by the modern algebra of relations, namely, that "everybody is loved by someone."

Finally, in accordance with our spiral scheme of organization, let us reveal that even after the treatment of relations in our next chapter, the story of modern symbolic logic will not be complete. The Boolean algebra of classes and the two-valued truth-table method were considered basic in logic until 1921, when two climactic research papers appeared, one by the Polish mathematician Jan Lukasiewicz on three-valued logic, and one by the American Emil L. Post (1897–1954) on general n-valued systems, where n is any integer greater than 1. One example of a three-valued truth table is given below.

Truth Table for $p \rightarrow q$ in Three-Valued Logic

p	q	$p \rightarrow q$
1	1	1
1	2	2
1	0	0
2	1	1
2	2	2
2	0	2
0	1	1
0	2	1
0	0	1

In the table, truth values 0, 1, and 2 have been assigned, but for the sake of clarity, the reader might replace 0 by $F =$ "false," 1 by $T =$ "true," and 2 by $M =$ "possible" (that is, not known to be either true or false). Examination of the above table shows that the first, third, seventh, and ninth rows represent the truth table for the conditional of two-valued logic. Also, the new table, even though more general, preserves the essential postulate for the truth value of conditional statements, namely, the assumption that such a statement is false if and only if its antecedent is true and its consequent false.

Chapter 7

Forefathers of Modern Mathematics and Their Legacy

In evaluating contributions to mathematics during any period of its history, the conceptions which must be judged most profound are those that unify what has gone before and, at the same time, open up wide avenues for future generalization. One such integrating, trail-blazing idea is to be found in the *method* of analytic geometry, as formulated by René Descartes (1596–1650) and Pierre de Fermat (1601–1665).

The two forefathers, as we have named them, arrived at their ideas independently and almost simultaneously. Fermat's thinking on the subject seems to have been carried on around 1629. In 1636 he communicated his thoughts through correspondence with other mathematicians, in particular in a special letter to the geometer and physicist, Gilles Persone de Roberval (1602–1675). Another of Fermat's letters (to Pascal) contributed to the beginnings of a different subject, probability theory (Chapter 13). But the full details of his conception of analytic geometry were published only posthumously in a paper entitled *Isogoge ad locus planos et solidos*.

Descartes arrived at his formulation after 1629, but he holds priority over Fermat in the matter of publication date. Descartes' scientific masterpiece, the *Discours de la Méthode pour bien conduire sa raison et chercher la vérité dans les sciences*, was published in 1637. The last of three appendices to this work was entitled *La Géométrie*. In Descartes' final afterthought, analytic geometry was first given to the world at large.

Descartes and Fermat, both French, both living in the

same era, both geniuses interested in some of the same mathematical questions, were both unaware that their geometric method was a major scientific bequest to posterity, something too important to be relegated to an appendix or to be confided casually in an epistle. In all other respects the two men were very different.

Descartes, forefather of modern mathematics, has also been called the father of modern philosophy. He was creative in other fields as well: physics, cosmology, chemistry, physiology, and psychology. The progenitor of so much science came of a noble family. His father was in comfortable circumstances and expected his son to lead the life of a French gentleman. René was a delicate child and did not start his formal schooling until the age of eight. At the Jesuit college at La Flèche the rector, Father Charlet, observed the boy's physical frailty and advised him to lie in bed as late as he pleased in the mornings. It was thus that Descartes formed the lifelong habit of spending his mornings in bed whenever he wished to think.

At an early age he entered the army, a strange thing for a man to do who expressed his personal philosophy in the words, "I desire only tranquillity and repose." As it happens, there was a brief interval of tranquillity and repose during the wars of William the Silent, and at that time Descartes began to think about analytic geometry. Then, at the age of twenty-five, he left the army for good. Later, in 1628, he retired to Holland for twenty years of research in philosophy and mathematics. He did not neglect other scientific studies, and much of his time was given to the preparation of an imposing treatise, *Le Monde*. This book presented a scientific rationalization of the Book of Genesis, and gave Descartes' physical doctrine of the universe. He determined to preserve all his work for posthumous publication as his legacy to science, but in 1637 his friends persuaded him to release his greatest work, the *Discours de la Méthode*.

In 1649 Descartes decided to vary his existence by accepting an invitation to the court of Queen Christina of Sweden. This headstrong, masculine girl, whose tyrannic behavior is historical, was Descartes' undoing. The poor scholar, who could not endure the harsh climate of Sweden or the difficult routine set by the twenty-three-year-old queen, fell ill and died of pneumonia within a few months of his arrival in Stockholm.

Words are an easy form of penance. The eccentric tyrant wrote to a friend: "The greatest of philosophers has just died. If I were superstitious, I should weep like a child over his death, and I should bitterly repent having drawn this bright star from its course. His death depresses me; it will always fill me with justified but useless regret."

The facts of Fermat's life are known, but there is not too much to tell. He was born in 1601 at Beaumont-de-Lomagne, near Toulouse, in southwestern France. His father was a leather merchant and his mother came from a family of parliamentary jurists. He received his early education at home and subsequently studied at Toulouse, where, in 1631, he became commissioner of requests. Seventeen years later he was promoted to the position of councillor in the parliament at Toulouse, and this job filled the next seventeen years, right up to the day of his death at Castres, where he was trying a case. In his official capacity he was noted for remarkable legal knowledge and strict integrity. His mathematical activities were carried on as a hobby.

A month after he had been appointed to his first position, he married Louise de Long, his second cousin. There were five children of this marriage, two daughters and three sons. Both girls became nuns, and Fermat's son Samuel carried on the family legal tradition by writing a number of books on law. He also edited his father's work and translated several Greek scientific and mathematical works.

Fermat was a "co-inventor" in relation to analytic geometry, probability theory, differential calculus. In a broad sense, he may also be said to have helped the launching of the "calculus of variations" and modern theories of "optimization." In the higher arithmetic or theory of numbers, however, he has few peers in mathematical history. We shall have more to say about his contributions to that subject later (Chapter 21), when we explain why "Fermat's last theorem" is still an enigma that challenges the best mathematical minds.

Nowadays historians of mathematics point out that Fermat and Descartes should not be given complete credit for the creation of analytic geometry, because some of its ideas were anticipated by others. The notion of coordinates is fundamental in Cartesian geometry, and that subject is in fact often called *coordinate geometry*. In this matter, however, ancient Egyptian surveyors were forerunners of Descartes and Fermat. Also, Hipparchus (*ca.* 140 B.C.), the

greatest astronomer of antiquity, used longitude and latitude
as the coordinates of a point on the earth's surface. Then,
too, analytic geometry associates algebra and geometry. But
Greek geometers, as we have already seen, stated fundamental algebraic laws in geometric terms, solved quadratic
equations by the geometric method of "completing a
square," and carried out a great quantity of painstaking geometric algebra. Again, the major content of traditional college textbooks in coordinate geometry involves properties
of curves described as *conic sections*. Emphasis on this material goes back to Menaechmus. Historians indicate that an
indubitable source of inspiration was the profound *Conic
Sections* of Apollonius of Perga (*ca.* 225 B.C.).

Actually none of these early contributions employed the
essential methodology of Descartes and Fermat, but in the
opinion of the author of the present book, thoughts that
came close to their ideas must be credited to Nicole Oresme
(1323–1382). A native of Normandy, he taught at the University of Paris, became headmaster of the College of
Navarre in 1356, and was ultimately named bishop of
Lisieux. One of his mathematical treatises, written about
1370, uses "Cartesian" coordinates (more than 260 years in
advance of our "forefathers"). He went beyond the ancients
by considering not only coordinates but *relations* between
them. Thus he derived the equation of a straight line, that
is, the *relation* between the coordinates of any point on the
line. He also considered the graphic representation of certain scientific formulas. He gave some thought to "solid" or
three-dimensional analytic geometry and even attempted to
formulate something analogous to a modern four-dimensional space. What prevented Oresme from getting beyond
first steps was the lack of a good algebraic symbolism. That
missing link was gradually made available, notably in the
work of François Viète (1540–1603) and in the contributions of Descartes himself.

Our brief historic résumé actually puts the cart before the
horse. For how can one render critical judgment about who
invented something without knowing just what the invention is? Hence the present chapter will consider the question: What constitutes analytic geometry and what makes it
important? We see the subject not as a geographic scheme
of location or an exercise in blending algebra and geometry
or a painless path to Euclidean and more advanced geometries, but as a means of expressing relationships (*relations*, in

mathematical terminology) of all kinds and making important deductions about them. This point of view makes analytic geometry the very core of mathematics, since many mathematical subjects—for example, trigonometry, calculus, "complex analysis," probability, mathematical statistics, and even one essential part of logic—are theories of general or special relations.

It is often said that Descartes and Fermat wedded algebra and geometry (after some preliminary matchmaking by predecessors). But today the key to that romance is found in other matings. A one-to-one correspondence can pair the real numbers with the points of a straight line and also match every geometric configuration (point set) on the line with some aggregate of real numbers (Chapter 2). The same sort of correspondence can mate the figures of plane geometry with sets whose members are *ordered pairs* of real numbers. The first of these "marriages" produces a "one-dimensional" analytic geometry. From the second, the plane analytic geometry of Descartes and Fermat can be derived.

For some purposes one might wish to develop analytic geometry on a straight line, and we shall do this to some extent in connection with relativity (Chapter 18) and other advanced geometries (Chapter 17). But a "one-dimensional" universe does not provide opportunities to indicate the full flavor and scope of analytic geometry. Descartes and Fermat developed their initial ideas with reference to a *plane* geometry, and we shall do likewise.

In coordinate geometry, as we have said, geometric configurations in the plane are matched or identified with sets containing *ordered pairs of real numbers.* For present purposes the concept of real number needs no elaboration beyond the material provided in our examination of the points of view of Eudoxus, Dedekind, and Cantor (Chapter 2). But we have not yet probed the general notion of *ordered pair,* and hence that idea must now be examined.

It is said that the novelist Charles Dickens kept a file of peculiar names so that he might combine them, as the need arose, to form appellations that would "sound" like the characters he created. Although we shall not list Micawbers or Pecksniffs, let us consider the following sets of names:

$$S = \{\text{Martin, Randolph, Spencer}\}$$
$$T = \{\text{Joyce, Leslie}\}$$

We can indicate the idea of an *ordered pair* by picking a name from S followed by one from T, and then reversing the process, for example, Randolph Joyce and Joyce Randolph. Here we have the same pair of names in each case but two *different* ordered pairs, since Randolph is the given name in the first pair and the surname in the second. Also, we might consider Randolph Joyce as the name of a man and Joyce Randolph as that of a woman.

If we form all possible ordered pairs resulting from the choice of a given name from S and a surname from T, we arrive at an aggregate that is called the *Cartesian product* of S by T, symbolized as $S \times T$ (read "S cross T"). Thus $S \times T$ will contain *six* full names like Martin Joyce, Randolph Joyce, etc.

Now $T \times S$ "T cross S") is a different set, containing the six ordered pairs formed by choosing given names from T and surnames from S. Although the six full names in $T \times S$ are not required to be listed in alphabetical or any other order, we shall present them in a pattern that can be associated with other concepts. Thus

$$T \times S = \begin{cases} \text{Joyce Spencer} & \text{Leslie Spencer} \\ \text{Joyce Randolph} & \text{Leslie Randolph} \\ \text{Joyce Martin} & \text{Leslie Martin} \end{cases}$$

Here we see that the ordered pairs or full names in $T \times S$ differ from those in $S \times T$. Hence the Cartesian product defines a *noncommutative* multiplication of sets.

In passing, we remark that the pattern of $T \times S$ matches Figure 2.3a, the Pythagorean figurate polygon for the numerical product, 2×3. In Chapter 2 we defined the multiplication of cardinal numbers as repeated addition. We stated that 2×3 was the result of adding 3 two times, that is, the cardinal number of the rectangular pattern formed by 2 columns each containing 3 elements. But, having defined the meaning of Cartesian product, we can now give a new definition of the multiplication of cardinals, one that matches a numerical product with a product of sets. Now 2×3 is defined as the cardinal number of the *Cartesian product* of a set containing 2 elements by a set containing 3 elements. Then either Figure 2.3a or our $T \times S$ would be such a product. The cardinal number of either set is 6, and hence $2 \times 3 = 6$. The new definition of multiplication is considered superior to the old not only because it matches two species of product but because it can be generalized to apply to *infinite* cardinal numbers.

If we give a slightly different interpretation to the sets S and T above, it will enable us to illustrate what is meant by a *binary relation*, a relation associating *two* elements, one in a set S and a second in a set T. Let us then think of the elements of S and T as the *given names* of five distinct individuals, three men and two women. Then Martin is the name of a man who may possibly be related to Joyce or Leslie. For example, he might be the father or the brother of either or both women. Then each of the statements, "Martin is the father of Joyce" and "Martin is the father of Leslie" associates *two* people, one in S and one in T. The other men might be cousins of the women, and one or more of the men might possibly be "related" to Joyce or Leslie in the mathematical sense of being taller than she is, or living within a mile of her home, or belonging to the same church as she does, etc. In mathematics, "is the father of," "is the brother of," "is taller than," "belongs to the same church as," etc. would all be described as *binary relations* on or from S to T. To assist us in formulating the meaning of such a relation more exactly, we now list the ordered pairs in $S \times T$ (once again in a pattern that can be linked with other ideas). Thus

$$S \times T = \left\{ \begin{array}{lll} \text{(Martin, Leslie)} & \text{(Randolph, Leslie)} & \text{(Spencer, Leslie)} \\ \text{(Martin, Joyce)} & \text{(Randolph, Joyce)} & \text{(Spencer, Joyce)} \end{array} \right\}$$

To avoid any ambiguity that may arise from verbal descriptions, we next introduce variables s and t with domains (replacement sets) S and T, respectively, so that we may provide exact formal definitions. Then the open sentence "s is the son of t" would be said to express a *binary relation* on or from S to T. Also, the truth or solution set of the open sentence is called the *graph* of the relation (because, so often, one provides a pictorial representation).

To obtain the graph of the above relation one can substitute in turn each ordered pair of $S \times T$ in the defining open sentence. Those pairs that lead to true statements form the graph. We must, of course, have such personal information about the five parties as will enable us to say what is true and what is false. At any rate, not all six statements resulting from the substitution of pairs can be true. Thus, if

it is true that Martin is the son of Joyce, then he is surely
not the son of Leslie. Suppose then that the facts are such
as to yield

$$\{(\text{Martin, Joyce}), (\text{Spencer, Joyce})\}$$

as the graph of the binary relation. We observe that this
graph is a *subset* of the Cartesian product, $S \times T$.

If the reader wishes to see the aptness of our terminology,
he can picture $S \times T$ in the Pythagorean figurate form as a
rectangular universe of 6 points, as in Figure 7.1. Then the
two enclosed points [representing (Martin, Joyce),
(Spencer, Joyce)] constitute a "geometric" graph of the relation on S to T, "is the son of."

Figure 7.1   Graph of the relation "is the son of"

We might find graphs for other binary relations on S to
T, and, in every case, the graph would be a subset of $S \times T$.
Thus the graph of "is the brother of" might be {(Randolph,
Joyce), (Randolph, Leslie)}, that is, the two points in the
second column of Figure 7.1.

Also, if we were to reverse the order of elements of the
pairs in the two relations whose graphs we have just considered, we would obtain the graphs of the respective *inverse* relations, "is the mother of" and "is the sister of,"
binary relations on T to S. Thus, in general, binary relations
on S to T will possess inverses whose graphs are subsets of
$T \times S$.

As additional examples of binary relations on S to T, let
us consider "is 300 years older than." Since we imagine S
and T to contain names of living people, no member of S
can possibly be 300 years older than a member of T, and the
graph of the relation in question is $\emptyset$, the null or empty set
(which is considered to be a subset not only of $S \times T$ but
of every set). The relation "is 300 years older than" can be
described as *nullary*.

Now suppose that all five persons named in S and T happen to live in the same town. Then the graph of the relation "lives in the same town as" would be our entire uni-

verse, $S \times T$, an improper subset of itself. Here we are dealing with a *universal* relation.

Because the graph of a binary relation on S to T, where S and T are *any* sets, is always a collection of ordered pairs forming a subset of $S \times T$, it is customary, even though an "abuse of language" is entailed, to identify relation and graph. Then a *binary relation* on S to T is *defined* as any subset of $S \times T$, that is, as *any set of ordered pairs* where each pair is a member of $S \times T$. We shall adhere to this definition from now on and reserve the term *graph* for a pictorial representation of a relation.

Then, in the illustration we have been considering, the reader can form different subsets of $S \times T$, thereby defining different relations on S to T. Thus he might form the subset

{(Randolph, Joyce), (Spencer, Joyce), (Spencer, Leslie)}

This subset of three ordered pairs is a binary relation by *definition*. One is not required to connect the members of each pair by an assertion like "s is taller than t" or "s presented a Christmas gift to t." The binary relation illustrated does not associate all members of S with elements of T. Hence, to indicate what elements are actually associated in a binary relation, that is, in an aggregate of ordered pairs, one calls the set of *first* elements of the pairs the *domain*, the set of *second* elements the *range* of the relation. In the relation above, the domain is {Randolph, Spencer} and the range is {Joyce, Leslie}. Thus the relation restricts the variable s to a smaller domain than its original replacement set.

If $\emptyset$ and the entire Cartesian product $S \times T$ are exceptional by being nullary and universal relations on S to T, some of the other binary relations are special in other ways. Thus, "husband of" (in a monogamous society) and "son of" are binary relations which a member of S can have to *at most one* member of T. On the other hand, a man in a set S could be "brother of," "cousin of," "taller than," more than one woman in T. The special nature of the former type of relation is indicated graphically in Figure 7.1. There the graph of "son of" exhibits *one point* in the first and third "vertical" columns and no points in the second column, that is, *at most one* point in any vertical column. When we defined the relation "brother of" as the aggregate {(Randolph, Joyce), (Randolph, Leslie)} with geometric graph the *two* points of the second vertical column of Figure 7.1, we were illustrating a less specialized type of relation.

A different choice of S and T would bring out more clearly the specialization we mean to indicate. If S is a list of items on sale in a supermarket and T is a list of prices, then an item in S can be paired with only one price in T. There might, of course, be a number of items with the same price. The relation might thus be considered a "many to one" correspondence, where each item s "determines" a unique price t. The same fact is often emphasized by calling s the *independent* variable and t the *dependent* variable. The inverse relation would be a "one to many" correspondence and would *not* be "determinate," because naming a price would not fix a unique article having that price.

The formula, $s^3 = t$, where s is the length of the edge of a cube and t is its volume, would define a relation on S to T, where S and T are certain sets of numbers. Here is a relation even more specialized than the price list, since a length "determines" a unique volume and inversely, for physical or geometric cubes. This binary relation is a *one-to-one correspondence* (Chapter 1).

Since, in many scientific situations, determinate or unique results are absolutely essential, the special type of binary relation we have illustrated is exceedingly important. It is called a *function* (a term due to Leibniz) or a *mapping*. To provide a formal definition, we now assert that a binary relation on S to T is called a *function* or a *mapping* if and only if it is a set of ordered pairs in $S \times T$ no two of which have the same first element. The set of *first* elements of the pairs is called the *domain* of the function, and the set of *second* elements is called the *range* of the function.

The use of the term "mapping" as a synonym for function derives from geography, where, for example, New York City, Boston, and Philadelphia may be represented by unique points, $n, b, p,$ on some map. If S is the set whose elements are the three cities named, T is the set of *all* points representing cities on the map, and $W = \{n, b, p\}$, a subset of T, the most recent usage in advanced mathematics would describe the situation as

$$f : S \longrightarrow T$$

which is read as "f is a mapping of S into T." Or, alternatively, there is

$$f : S \xrightarrow{\text{onto}} W$$

which is read as "*f* is a mapping of *S onto W*." In either case, *f* is defined by the set of ordered pairs, {(N.Y.C., *n*), (Boston, *b*), (Phila., *p*)}, and is a function or mapping because each city is paired with *only one* point of the map.

To provide illustrations of binary relations more like those of plane analytic geometry, we must choose $S = T$, where *S* is a set of *numbers*. Hence, let us consider $S = \{2, 5\}$ and form the Cartesian product $S \times S = S^2$. Then

$$S^2 = \{(2, 2), (2, 5), (5, 2), (5, 5)\}$$

We now study binary relations on *S* to *S*, or, in briefer terminology, binary relations on *S*, that is, subsets of S^2.

Thus the subset {(2, 2), (5, 5)} is a binary relation on *S*. Moreover, it is a *function* for which *S* is both domain and range. It is not necessary to express this function by sentence or formula. But if the reader wishes to do so, he can use (x, y) to symbolize an ordered pair in S^2 and then describe the above relation by $x = y$. The sentences $x^2 = y^2$, $x^3 = y^3$, etc. will all define this same relation (if we assume that substitutions like 2^2, 5^3, etc. are meaningful). Although the relation is a specific one, it may be characterized in these many varied ways. In fact, any set whatsoever has many different defining properties (Chapter 1).

As another example, {(2, 5), (5, 2), (5, 5)} is a binary relation on *S*, but not a function. Although a defining sentence is not required, the reader may wish to formulate the relation as "*x* and *y* are not both equal to 2" or as "$x = 5$ and/or $x \neq y$" (or in some other way).

With $S = \{2, 5\}$ there are 16 different subsets of S^2 (including $\emptyset$ and S^2) and hence 16 distinct binary relations on *S*. We leave to the reader the task of listing them. He can do this by starting with $\emptyset$ and S^2, continuing with all subsets containing one ordered pair, all subsets containing two ordered pairs, etc.

The concept of Cartesian product can be generalized to 3, 4, . . . , *n*, any finite number of given sets. If the sets are $S_1, S_2, S_3, \ldots, S_n$, the Cartesian product, $S_1 \times S_2 \times S_3 \times \ldots \times S_n$, is defined to be the set of all ordered *n*-tuples, $(s_1, s_2, s_3, \ldots, s_n)$, where $s_1, s_2, s_3, \ldots, s_n$ are variables whose domains are $S_1, S_2, S_3, \ldots, S_n$, respectively. Then, as a special case, $S_1 = S_2 = S_3 = \ldots = S_n = S$, and one has the Cartesian products $S^2, S^3, S^4, \ldots, S^n$.

If $S = \{2, 5\}$, we have already formed S^2, and now we

can consider the *eight* ordered triples in S^3. Thus the reader can complete the roster for

$$S^3 = \{(2, 2, 2), (2, 2, 5), (2, 5, 2), (2, 5, 5), \ldots\}$$

In this "three-dimensional" universe one can form subsets of S^3, that is, *ternary* relations on S. There are 256 distinct ternary relations (including $\emptyset$ and S^3).

The reader can complete the roster of 16 ordered quadruples in

$$S^4 = \{(2, 2, 2, 2), (2, 2, 2, 5), (2, 2, 5, 2), \ldots\}$$

He can also list some subsets of S^4, that is, some quaternary relations on S. By carrying out the exercise we have just suggested, the reader will be constructing a finite four-dimensional (sic) Cartesian "geometry."

Our illustrations have shown that the number and variety of binary, ternary, quaternary, etc. relations on S is dependent on the choice of S. Hence the essential difference between our finite "geometries" and the analytic geometry of Descartes and Fermat lies in the fundamental set on which relations are defined. In contrast to our petite $S = \{2, 5\}$, the basis of Cartesian geometry is R, the real number continuum (Chapter 2), the *infinite* aggregate of all real numbers arranged in order of size. This fact makes the geometry *analytic* because, crudely speaking, *analysis* is the part of mathematics which deals with variables which have *continuous* domains.

The founding "forefathers" were interested in binary relations on R, that is, subsets of R^2 and, to a lesser extent, with ternary relations on R (subsets of R^3). But, as our examples have indicated, modern analytic geometry would extend to subsets of R^4, R^5, $\ldots$, R^n. Now R and all its powers—R^2, R^3, etc.— are infinite sets (Chapter 24) and contain an infinite number of different subsets. This means that the number of distinct relations on R is infinite. Hence it would not be possible to provide a complete roster of binary, ternary, etc. relations on R in the manner we have employed for finite geometries. Thus one cannot examine *all* relations on R since their number is infinite, and therefore analytic geometry concentrates on certain types which are of special interest for practical or theoretical purposes.

In their formulation of plane analytic geometry, Descartes and Fermat arithmetized Euclidean plane geometry by matching or virtually identifying each point of the plane with an ordered pair of real numbers called the *coordinates* of the point. In this way every geometric figure in the plane was identified with a set of ordered pairs of real numbers, that is, with a binary relation. In other words, plane configurations like the vertices of a decagon, a straight line, or a continuous curve are merely binary relations. Definition by roster would be impossible for the infinite aggregate of points on a continuous curve. Hence Euclid, Descartes, Fermat, and all geometers made use of formulation by defining properties. Now, as we have pointed out, sets of ordered pairs, like sets in general, have many defining characteristics. But a major feature of analytic geometry is that defining properties are expressed *algebraically*, by equations and inequalities containing variables whose replacement set is R. Then such equations and inequalities are subjected to manipulations, and this makes *proof* a mere matter of *al-jabr w'almuqabalah*. The logic of the situation is inherent in the fundamental laws of algebra.

As we have stated, the essence of plane analytic geometry lies in the matching of ordered pairs of real numbers with points of a plane. Such a one-to-one correspondence can be established in many ways, but it seems appropriate to begin with an examination of Descartes' technique. The Cartesian coordinate system, which is a commonplace of school mathematics and everyday graphic representation, generalizes the coordinate system on a line (Chapter 2). In the plane, the Cartesian frame of reference consists of two perpendicular lines or coordinate axes with the same origin and the same unit of length (Figure 7.2). We can imagine the Cartesian scheme as resembling a network of streets and avenues, where streets run north and south, and avenues east and west. The X-axis is "Main Avenue" and the Y-axis is "Main Street." Streets east of Main Street are given positive numbers; those west receive negative numbers. Avenues north and south of Main Avenue are positive and negative, respectively. The *Cartesian coordinates* of any point in the plane are the street and the avenue (in that order) on which the point is located, for example, $(3, 5)$, $(-2, 3)$, $(-4, -1)$, $(0, -3)$. (See Figure 7.2.)

In the pure mathematical scheme, the "streets" and "avenues" are assumed to be capable of ever-so-fine subdivision, so that the plane is covered by a sort of gossamer network. This makes it possible to conceive of points like $(-4.00058,$

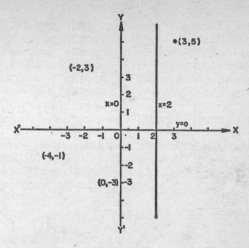

Figure 7.2

$\sqrt[3]{7}$) or $(6\sqrt[5]{3}, -2\pi)$; that is, in the pure conception, there is a "$6\sqrt[5]{3}$ Street" and a "-2π Avenue" which intersect at a point of the plane.

In summary, every point in the plane has a pair of coordinates, (x, y) where the x-coordinate or *abscissa* is the directed (signed) distance from the Y-axis and the y-coordinate or *ordinate* is the directed distance from the X-axis (distance being measured along a perpendicular). Conversely, every ordered pair of real numbers can be interpreted as Cartesian coordinates and applied to locating a point in the plane. Our summary establishes the oft-repeated claim of one-to-one correspondence between points of the plane and ordered pairs of real numbers.

But the one-to-one correspondence can be established in many ways. One can, for example, vary the position of the coordinate axes or use different units of length on the two axes or even use axes that meet obliquely instead of at right angles (Figure 7.3). Every point will have a pair of real coordinates, but the coordinates will vary with the frame of reference.

Let us develop some of the elements of plane analytic geometry by using a Cartesian *rectangular* coordinate system. Analytic geometry is a *method*, as Descartes implied, when he included the term, *la méthode*, in the title of his great

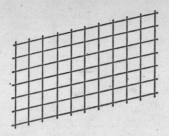

Figure 7.3   Oblique coordinate system

treatise. The technique is one of back-and-forth translation, from verbal statements to algebraic formulas and inversely. Descartes' appendix proceeded, in the main, from verbal definitions to algebraic equations, with just a few instances of the inverse routine. In this way, *La Géométrie* showed how to present Euclid in algebraic dress, but did not consider many new geometric figures. It was just the opposite in Fermat's posthumous *Isogoge*. There, many relations are first defined by algebraic equations, and then the equations are translated into geometric graphs. This inverse technique led to new curves never considered by Euclid or Apollonius.

Observation of the Cartesian network leads at once to elementary algebraic formulations. For example, in Figure 7.2, points of the Y-axis are seen to have coordinates like $(0, -3)$, $(0, -1)$, $(0, 1)$, $(0, 2.6)$, etc. The Y-axis, then, is identical with the set of all such ordered pairs in which the x-coordinate is equal to zero. Moreover, no point outside the Y-axis will be on "0 Street," that is, have abscissa equal to zero. Hence the equation $x = 0$ expresses a defining property for the set of ordered pairs, that is, for the binary relation with which the Y-axis is identified. In the language of analytic geometry, one says that $x = 0$ is the *equation* of the Y-axis.

The reader will see that "2 Street" contains points like $(2, -5)$, $(2, 0)$, $(2, 6)$, etc. and that points not located on this street cannot have abscissa equal to 2. Hence $x = 2$ is the equation of "2 Street," and, more generally, $x = a$ (where a represents any real number) is the formula for a "street," that is, for a line parallel to the Y-axis. Similarly, $y = b$ is the formula for an "avenue," that is, for a parallel to the X-axis. If $b = 0$, $y = 0$ is the equation of the X-axis itself.

In the equations for parallels to the coordinate axes, only one variable, either x or y, is named and there is no restriction on the missing variable. This thought will assist us if we ask, in the spirit of Fermat: Given the inequality $x < 2$, what is its geometric graph? To answer, we observe that the sentence $x < 2$ places no limitation on y. Then its geometric graph must contain all points whose abscissa is less than 2 and whose ordinate is any real number whatsoever. For example, *all* points of "1 Street," "1/2 Street," "0 Street," "—3 Street," etc. will belong to the graph. In short, the picture will contain all points of all streets to the left of "2 Street," that is, all points to the left of the line, $x = 2$. The graph of $x < 2$ is indicated by the shaded area in Figure 7.4a. In the

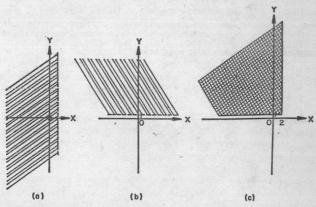

(a)   (b)   (c)

Graph of $x < 2$ Graph of $y > 1$ Graph of ($x \leq 2$ and $y \geq 1$)

Figure 7.4

diagram, $x = 2$ is dotted in order to indicate that it is not part of the graph. If that line were included, the graph would illustrate the relation $x \leq 2$ (x is equal to or less than 2). Figure 7.4b pictures the graph of $y > 1$, and Figure 7.4c indicates the graph of the compound sentence "$x \leq 2$ and $y \geq 1$." The reader will readily see that of all the graphs considered thus far, only the parallels to the X-axis, that is, the lines $y = b$, represent *functions*, since, in all other cases, there may be more than one value of y corresponding to a given value of x. The domain of the function, $y = b$, is the entire X-axis or real number continuum R, and the range is the single number b. One can therefore understand why $y = b$ is called a *constant* function.

A straight line need not be parallel to one of the coordinate axes, and we shall have to consider lines in more general positions in the plane. We now assert (leaving proof for the next chapter): The equation of *any* straight line is a first-degree equation in x and y, that is, an equation of the form

$$ax + by + c = 0$$

where a, b, and c are real numbers. Conversely (if we rule out the cases $a = b = 0$ and $a = b = c = 0$), the Cartesian graph of any such equation must be a straight line.

It is at once apparent that if $a = 0$ and $b \neq 0$ in the above formula, one obtains the parallels to the X-axis, and if $b = 0$, $a \neq 0$, one has the parallels to the Y-axis. Suppose now that $c = 0$, $a \neq 0$, $b \neq 0$. Then $ax + by = 0$ or, after some algebraic manipulation, $y = -(b/a)x$, which we shall write as $y = kx$. Let $k = 3$ and consider the straight line graph of $y = 3x$. Euclid tells us that there is one and only one straight line through two distinct points of the plane. Hence we need only plot two points of $y = 3x$. It is readily seen that $(0, 0)$ and $(1, 3)$ check in the given equation. Its picture is shown in Figure 7.5. In general, $y = kx$ is a straight line through the origin. The equation and the graph formulate a type of function that is said to represent a *direct variation*.

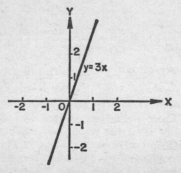

Figure 7.5

In physics, $y = kx$ becomes *Hooke's law* of mechanics if x is interpreted as the elongation of a spring when a force y is applied. Again, the same equation defines *Ohm's law* in electricity if y represents the electromotive force and x the current in a circuit with fixed resistance. Again, the type of variation represented by $y = kx$ is of frequent occurrence in geometry. For example, x might stand for the radius of a circle and y for its circumference.

In Figure 7.6 the lines whose equations are $y = 2x + 4$

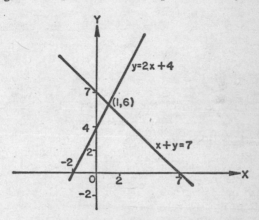

Figure 7.6

and $x + y = 7$ have been graphed. There, once more, only two points of each line were plotted, and then those points were joined by means of a straight-edge. One is free to graph any two points of the line, but very often one selects the points where it cuts the axes. In the case of $y = 2x + 4$, we can say that

for $x = 0, y = 2(0) + 4; y = 4$ (this is called the *Y-intercept*)
for $y = 0, 0 = 2x + 4;$ $x = -2$ (this is called the *X-intercept*)

The substitutions show that $(0, 4)$ and $(-2, 0)$ are points of the line. These points are plotted and joined in Figure 7.6. It is readily seen that for $x + y = 7$, both the X-intercept and the Y-intercept are equal to 7. The intercepts are graphed and connected by a line in Figure 7.6.

Now, if one is asked to solve the compound sentence "$y = 2x + 4$ *and* $x + y = 7$," he can do so graphically by consulting Figure 7.6. It is seen that the only point on both lines is (1, 6). Therefore {(1, 6)} is the solution set of the above compound sentence, that is, of the *system* of *simultaneous linear equations*,

$$y = 2x + 4$$
$$x + y = 7$$

We have just associated Cartesian graphs with the *solution* of *algebraic equations* and, in fact, some of the uses of analytic geometry are to clarify meanings in classical algebra and to provide *approximate* solutions when the technique of exact solution is difficult or impossible in finite terms.

If we refer to the equation $y = 2x + 4$, its form can assist us in the graphing of the inequality $y > 2x + 4$. In the equation, substitution of $x = 0$ yields $y = 4$. For the inequality, if $x = 0$, $y > 4$. Therefore (0, 4.1), (0, 5), (0, 6) are all points in the graph of the inequality. These points all lie on the Y-axis *above* the Y-intercept of the line, $y = 2x + 4$. We can reason similarly that $x = 1$, $y = 6$ is a point of the line, but that, for the inequality, when $x = 1$, $y > 6$. Then the graph of the inequality must contain all points above (1, 6) on the "vertical" line through (1, 6). By continuing with such reasoning, we can understand why the shaded region in Figure 7.7 represents the graph of $y > 2x + 4$,

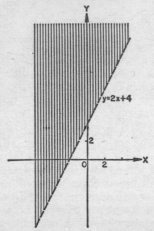

Figure 7.7 · Graph of $y > 2x + 4$

since that graph must contain *all* points above the line $y = 2x + 4$. The unshaded region below that line represents the graph of $y < 2x + 4$.

To provide algebraic definition for a straight-line *segment* (for example, the portion of the line $y = 2x + 4$ indicated in Figure 7.8) one may employ a compound sentence like "$y = 2x + 4$ *and* $-1 \leq x \leq 2$." The effect of the second clause is to restrict the domain of x (and hence the range of y). The effect is to cut the line down to the segment between the points $(-1, 2)$ and $(2, 8)$ in Figure 7.8.

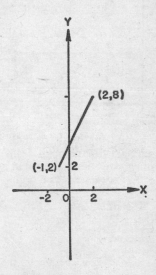

Figure 7.8   Graph of ($y = 2x + 4$ and $-1 \leq x \leq 2$)

The description of the Cartesian coordinate system applied various Euclidean concepts such as parallelism or perpendicularity of lines. Our discussion of graphs has also used Euclidean ideas, and we have translated some of them into algebraic equivalents. Now much of Euclidean geometry is *metric*, that is, concerned with *measurement*, and determination of a length or *distance* between two points is the basic procedure. Special theorems then make it possible to measure certain areas by determining two distances, and certain volumes by measuring three lengths. Hence, if analytic geometry is to be metric, one must express length or distance in algebraic form.

A distance formula for the Cartesian plane is obtained by translation of the Pythagorean theorem into an algebraic formula involving coordinates. In Figure 7.9 the distance

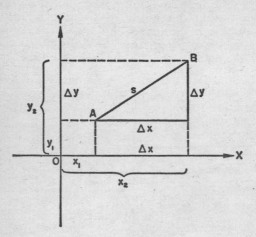

Figure 7.9

between A and B is the length AB, the hypotenuse of a right triangle. Figure 7.9 indicates that

$$s^2 = (x_2 - x_1)^2 + (y_2 - y_1)^2$$

In this equation, $x_2 - x_1$ is a change in the variable x or a difference between two of its values. A similar statement can be made about $y_2 - y_1$. It is customary to use the Greek letter Δ (delta) corresponding to the Roman D, the initial letter of Difference, to symbolize such changes. One writes Δx (read "delta x") for $x_2 - x_1$ and Δy for $y_2 - y_1$. Then the above equation becomes

$$s^2 = (\Delta x)^2 + (\Delta y)^2$$

and the formula for distance in the Euclidean plane is

$$s = \sqrt{(\Delta x)^2 + (\Delta y)^2}$$

We observe that if, in Figure 7.9, we reversed directions and proceeded from B to A, then Δx would symbolize

$x_1 - x_2$ and Δy would be equal to $y_1 - y_2$. It would not matter in the formula, because in it the differences are squared. Thus, if in one case $\Delta x = 3$ and in the other $\Delta x = -3$, then in both cases $(\Delta x)^2 = 9$.

Without drawing a diagram, we can apply our formula to find the distance between $(3, -2)$ and $(1, 5)$. Here, $\Delta x = 1 - 3 = -2$ and $\Delta y = 5 - (-2) = 7$. Hence

$$s = \sqrt{(-2)^2 + 7^2} = \sqrt{4 + 49} = \sqrt{53}$$

The line segment between the two points has an irrational length, that is, one incommensurable with our unit of length.

Let us now use our distance formula to translate the Euclidean definition of a circle into an algebraic equation. Euclid defines a circle as the set of all points at a given distance (called the radius) from a given point (called the center). If we choose $(2, -1)$ as the center of a circle of radius 4, and let (x, y) represent any point on the circle, then $\Delta x = x - 2$, $\Delta y = y + 1$, and $s = 4$ (the radius of the circle). Substitution in

$$(\Delta x)^2 + (\Delta y)^2 = s^2$$

yields for the equation of the circle

$$(x - 2)^2 + (y + 1)^2 = 16$$

To obtain a formula for the equation of *any* circle in the plane, we assume a pair of real numbers, (a, b), as the coordinates of its center and r, a positive real number, as its radius. Then

$$(x - a)^2 + (y - b)^2 = r^2$$

is the equation of the circle. If the center is at the origin, the equation takes the simple form $x^2 + y^2 = r^2$.

We observe that, for a rigorous proof, one ought to indicate that the solution set of the equation derived does *not* include any points not on the circle. If some ordered pair which we shall symbolize by (u, w) is part of the solution set, then it must check in the equation, that is

$$(u - a)^2 + (w - b)^2 = r^2$$

which means that the distance of (u, w) from the center (a, b) is equal to r. Therefore the point (u, w) must be on the given circle and nowhere else, in accordance with the Euclidean definition of a circle.

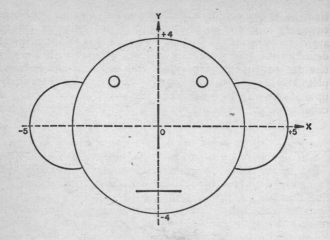

Figure 7.10   Cartesian Cherub

The reader can apply the analytic geometry developed up to this point by verifying that the lines, circles, or segments thereof, in the cartoon of the *Cartesian Cherub* (Figure 7.10) are geometric graphs of the following relations.

Face	$x^2 + y^2 = 16$
Right eye	$(x - 2)^2 + (y - 2)^2 = \dfrac{1}{4}$
Left eye	$(x + 2)^2 + (y - 2)^2 = \dfrac{1}{4}$
Mouth	$y = -3$ and $-1 \leq x \leq 1$
Nose	$x = 0$ and $-1 \leq y \leq 1$
Right ear	$(x - 4)^2 + y^2 = 1$ and $x > \dfrac{31}{8}$
Left ear	$(x + 4)^2 + y^2 = 1$ and $x < -\dfrac{31}{8}$

In spite of the apparent complexity of formulas for our Cartesian Cherub, he is nevertheless a kindergarten creature of analytic geometry, since he is composed of linear and circular segments, defined by first- and second-degree algebraic equations and inequalities. He does not even illustrate *all* types of curve that can correspond to *quadratic* equations in x and y. We now claim that all such curves are *conic sections*. The name is associated with the original definition of such curves in Hellenic geometry. If a right circular *cone* (hourglass figure like two ice cream cones placed end to end) whose curved surface extends indefinitely up and down is cut by a plane, the curve of intersection is called a conic section or merely a *conic*. In Figure 7.11 we

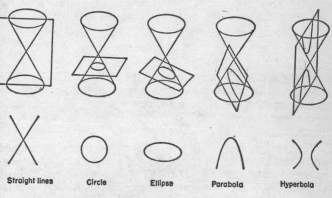

Straight lines   Circle   Ellipse   Parabola   Hyperbola

Figure 7.11   The conic sections

have illustrated the cone and the five typical conics: circle, ellipse, parabola, hyperbola (a curve of two branches), and two intersecting straight lines.

The geometric properties of the conics were worked out in thorough, beautiful, but not simple algebraic form by Apollonius. Without his work, the great astronomer Kepler (who lived *before* Descartes and Fermat) might never have been able to discover the laws of planetary motion (1609), and we might not as yet be living in an age of man-made satellites. One of Kepler's laws states that the path of each planet is an ellipse. Kepler had to create a sort of "integral calculus" to study planetary motion along the elliptic path (page 242). Newton went further with that idea but, in any event, without Kepler's laws he would probably have been unable to formulate his theory of universal gravitation, and Einstein would not have had the occasion to challenge that theory by inventing a new one. Hence some of the greatest moments in science go back to Apollonius' original inspiration.

Nature is very fond of the ellipse and almost equally partial to the other conic sections, as we shall illustrate. Now it is very much easier to derive important scientific properties of these curves by algebraic manipulation of their Cartesian equations than by using the methods of Apollonius. We shall not, however, carry out the translation from Apollonian properties to algebraic formulas, but shall merely give the results. For example, the equation of an ellipse in the standard position illustrated in Figure 7.12a is

$$\frac{x^2}{a^2} + \frac{y^2}{b^2} = 1$$

where a and b are the lengths of the semiaxes. We can give a rationale for this equation by observing that some ellipses, for example, the planetary paths, are almost circular. If, in

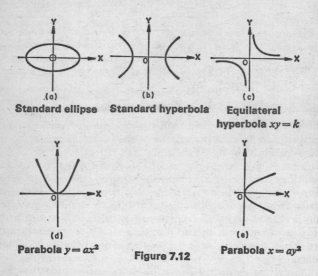

.(a)   (b)   (c)
Standard ellipse   Standard hyperbola   Equilateral hyperbola $xy = k$

(d)   (e)
Parabola $y = ax^2$ Figure 7.12   Parabola $x = ay^2$

fact, $b = a$ in the above equation, and one multiplies both sides by a^2, the result is $x^2 + y^2 = a^2$, the equation of a circle. Thus the ellipse might seem something like a distorted circle.

If one changes the sum in the above equation to a difference, the result is

$$\frac{x^2}{a^2} - \frac{y^2}{b^2} = 1$$

the equation of the standard hyperbola of Figure 7.12*b*. In this equation, if $b = a$, one arrives at a so-called *equilateral* hyperbola, not essentially different in appearance from the one in Figure 7.12*b*. But it is sometimes a convenience to rotate (Chapter 17) such a hyperbola to a position like that in Figure 7.12*c*. Then its equation becomes

$$xy = k$$

where k is any real number other than zero. The equation (or its graph) is said to express the *inverse variation* of the variables x and y. As an instance of such a relation, there is Boyle's law, $xy = k$, where $k > 0$, and x represents the volume of some gas when it is subjected to pressure y but kept at constant temperature. From a hyperbola like that of Figure 7.12*c* one can read volume, given pressure, and conversely.

Nature requires that the path of a bullet or baseball and the trajectory of a comet be (approximately) *parabolic*. The equations of the parabolas in the standard positions of Figures 7.12*d* and 7.12*e* have the form $y = ax^2$ and $x = ay^2$, respectively.

To derive the equations of the conics, one usually employs definitions that are more suited to algebraic handling than the descriptions as particular cross sections of a cone. Thus an ellipse is described as the set of all points (in a plane) for which the sum of distances from two fixed points is constant. (We note that this is a metric definition, which mentions distances.) Each fixed point is called a *focus* of the ellipse. Figure 7.13 shows how to draw an ellipse mechanically from this description. According to Kepler's laws, the sun is at one focus of each planetary orbit. Since the paths of the planets are almost circular, the foci of the ellipse are close together, and the position of the sun is almost central.

In analytic geometry it can be demonstrated algebraically that the ellipse has a property important for acoustical or optical applications. It is shown that if light or sound is emitted from one focus of an ellipse, it must be reflected to the other. This fact explains the phenomenon of whispering galleries with elliptical cross sections. A sound uttered

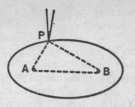

Figure 7.13   A loop of fixed length is allowed to slide around the foci while the tracing pencil holds it taut, tracing the curve. Because the length between the foci will always be the same, what remains of the cord (sum of distances) is also constant.

at one focus will be heard distinctly at the other even when foci are widely separated.

A similar property of the parabola is used in automobile headlights and reflecting telescopes. A parabola has a single focus which suggests that it is a sort of infinite ellipse, with a second focus "at infinity." If a light is placed at the focus F (Figure 7.14), all rays hitting the parabolic surface will

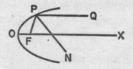

Figure 7.14

be sent out in a parallel beam, that is, reflected to the imagined second focus at infinity. In reverse, parallel rays from a star ("the focus at infinity") are all reflected to form a sharp image of the star at the focus of a parabolic reflecting telescope.

To avoid technicalities, we have, in many cases, given the results of the analytic method and have passed over details of the proofs. Let us then give some specific examples to indicate the clarity and effectiveness of Cartesian techniques. We shall explain just how Menaechmus and Omar Khayyám solved some interesting cubic equations by the use of conic sections. What they did was highly original and, from their viewpoint, *difficult* because all their reasoning was geometric, with the conics of the hourglass picture. For us everything will merely be a case of the most elementary sort of analytic geometry.

It is traditional to refer to certain questions as the "famous problems of antiquity." One of these is the "duplication of the cube" or the *Delian problem*. The story goes that Apollo, being angered, visited a plague on the people of Delos. They appealed to the oracle, who commanded them to double the size of the altar but to keep its shape the same. The form of the altar was cubic and, hence Apollo's command was to duplicate the cube, that is, to construct a cube with volume double that of the original.

Let us represent the side of the initial altar by 1 (linear unit). Then its volume was $1 \cdot 1 \cdot 1 = 1$ cubic unit. The new altar was to have a volume of 2 cubic units. Calling the length of its edge x, its volume would be x^3, and the condition of the problem would be expressed by the cubic equation

$$x^3 = 2$$

Today this cubic is no more difficult than $x^3 = 64$, for which we can give $x = 4$ as one root. The side of the new altar should be the irrational number or incommensurable length,

$$x = \sqrt[3]{2}$$

and if we desire a *rational* estimate, there are the Babylonian cube root tables, or our own. But we are considering Greek geometric algebra, and according to the rules that Plato had formulated, geometers were restricted to the use of straightedge and compasses, that is, straight lines and circles, in performing constructions. Therefore the problem of the Greeks was to construct, with straight-edge and compasses, a line segment of length $\sqrt[3]{2}$ units. Modern algebra has proved that this is an *impossible* task, and that the only irrationals the use of circles and straight lines will produce are square roots and combinations or iterations of such roots. Nevertheless, around 350 B.C. Menaechmus was able to "duplicate the cube," that is, to solve $x^3 = 2$ *geometrically*. But he had to defy Plato's stricture on tools. Instead of drawing circles and straight lines, Menaechmus drew a *parabola* and a *hyperbola*. The intersection of these curves provided the desired solution.

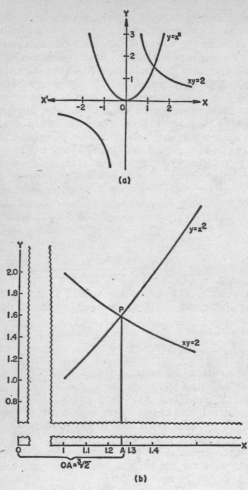

Figure 7.15

From the Cartesian point of view, Menaechmus' hyperbola can be considered to be the one in Figure 7.15a, that is, the hyperbola whose equation is $xy = 2$. Likewise, the equation of the parabola he used (Figure 7.15a) is $y = x^2$. These curves intersect (Figure 7.15b) at a point whose coordinates are approximately (1.26, 1.59). To do justice to Menaechmus, he actually stated that OA (enlarged to a suitable scale) would provide the *exact* length for the altar to appease Apollo. To prove that he was right, one can obtain the coordinates exactly by switching from graphic to algebraic considerations. The point (x, y) whose coordinates are sought lies on both curves or, algebraically, the values of x and y must meet the requirements of *both* the above formulas for the curves. Combining these formulas by substituting the second in the first,

$$x(x^2) = 2$$

or

$$x^3 = 2$$

and

$$x = \sqrt[3]{2}$$

Since $y = x^2$,

$$y = \sqrt[3]{4}$$

The equation $x^3 = 2$ is the cubic associated with the duplication of the cube, and $x = \sqrt[3]{2}$ represents the *irrational* number which answers this problem. In the graph, $x = \sqrt[3]{2}$ is pictured *geometrically* as OA, the x-coordinate of P, the point of intersection of the two curves. In other words, the *incommensurable* segment OA provides the answer to the problem of duplicating the cube.

Another way in which Menaechmus solved the same problem was to employ the two parabolas

$$y^2 = 2x$$

and

$$x^2 = y$$

Then OA in Figure 7.16 represents $\sqrt[3]{2}$. To demonstrate this algebraically, one can substitute the formula for the second parabola in the equation for the first, with the result

$$x^4 = 2x$$

or

$$x^4 - 2x = 0$$
$$x(x^3 - 2) = 0$$

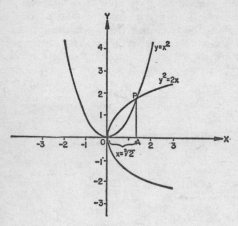

Figure 7.16

so that

$$x = 0 \quad \text{and} \quad x = \sqrt[3]{2}$$

These are the two real roots of the equation, and are the x-coordinates of the points of intersection of the two parabolas.

Now let us present an example of Omar Khayyám's methodology. As we explained in a previous chapter, he was seeking to solve cubic equations. Consider then the cubic

$$x^3 - 3x^2 + x + 1 = 0$$

The intersections of a circle and the upper branch of a hyperbola (Figure 7.17) were used by Omar to give the roots $x = 1$, $x = 2.4$ (approximately). The latter root is irrational, and Omar would have given the exact answer as the (incommensurable) length of segment OA in Figure 7.17.

Omar was, as has been emphasized, a geometric algebraist

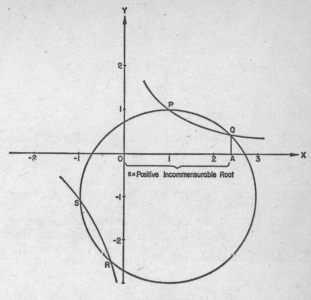

Figure 7.17

like his Greek predecessors. Therefore it might be difficult to follow the reasoning by which he proved his method to be correct. Modern algebraic symbolism will clarify it, however, and provide

$$xy = 1 \quad (\text{or} \quad y = \frac{1}{x}, \ \text{if } x \neq 0)$$

and

$$x^2 - 2x + y^2 + 2y - 2 = 0$$

as the Cartesian equations of hyperbola and circle, respectively.

To obtain the coordinates of the points of intersection of the graphs, one proceeds as in the previous examples, by substituting the first equation in the second. The result is

$$x^2 - 2x + \left(\frac{1}{x}\right)^2 + 2\left(\frac{1}{x}\right) - 2 = 0$$

or

$$x^4 - 2x^3 + 1 + 2x - 2x^2 = 0$$

or

$$x^4 - 2x^3 - 2x^2 + 2x + 1 = 0$$

This equation can be factored into

$$(x + 1)(x^3 - 3x^2 + x + 1) = 0$$

The first factor leads to the answer $x = -1$, which corresponds to point S in Figure 7.17. Since Omar did not consider negative answers, this factor did not appear in his reasoning. The second factor leads to the given cubic equation. Thus it has been proved that three points of intersection of the two graphs—namely, P, Q, and R—will provide the roots of this cubic. Again, R corresponds to a negative root, and therefore Omar used only one branch of the hyperbola to obtain the positive answers associated with points P and Q.

The examples of Menaechmus' duplication of the cube and Omar's solution of cubics were selected in order to suggest how and why analytic geometry is such a powerful tool. In our illustration we indicated certain conic sections by their equations and carried out algebraic processes with these equations, without any need for diagrams. When the algebra was complete, the final results were connected with a geometric picture. But in the interim it was not necessary to draw in points, lines, circles, or any other curves indicated by the algebraic work. Similarly, in all examples of analytic geometry, an advantage accrues because thought is not obstructed by complicated diagrams and proof is almost entirely a matter of mechanical algebraic manipulation.

Moreover, there is a further and greater advantage in the analytic method. Greek plane geometry defined and made deductions about geometric figures having counterparts in the physical world. But the abstract concepts of analytic geometry permit much greater freedom. Write any open sentence in x and y, that is, specify any subset of R^2. Then consider its geometric picture and possible applications. Will it provide approximate solutions for some problem? Will it be useful as a mechanical device? Will it describe the motion of some natural object? Since one is at liberty to consider *any* subset of R^2, infinitely more binary relations are available for study by the method of Descartes than by the geometry of the Greeks.

Straight lines and conic sections are amenable to algebraic representation in terms of Cartesian coordinates. But in order to give simple expression to other relations, different frames of reference may be preferable. In one of these, "avenues" meet "streets" obliquely—somewhat in the fashion that Broadway cuts Forty-Second Street in New York (see Figure 7.3). In another layout, avenues are concentric circles and streets are lines radiating from the center of the circles (Figure 7.18). Until surrealism hits the city

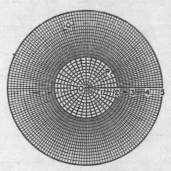

Figure 7.18   Polar coordinate system

planners, such a scheme will probably not be adopted. Still the Paris boulevards suggest the circular scheme, and the layout of Washington illustrates a radial arrangement of streets.

In the latter scheme, called a *polar coordinate system*, the coordinates of a point (boulevard and street) would be the *distance from the origin* and the *angle* formed with Main Street. In Figure 7.18 we have indicated origin and initial line, point P with coordinates $(2, 30°)$ and Q, with coordinates $(4, 120°)$. In this scheme, the equations of certain important curves are especially simple. A circle with center at the origin and radius k would have the equation $r = k$. For the *spiral of Archimedes* in Figure 7.19

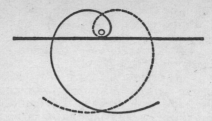

Figure 7.19   Spiral of Archimedes, $r = \theta$. (Dotted line corresponds to negative values of θ.)

there is $r = \theta$; for the *cardioid* of Figure 7.20 there is $r = 1 + \cos \theta$; for the *four-leaved rose* of Figure 7.21 there is $r = \sin 2\theta$. And mathematicians have other city layouts to which they can resort to simplify the algebraic representation of other important curves. To understand the last two equations above may seem to require a knowledge of elementary trigonometry, but the reader can appreciate the simplicity of their form if we state that the corresponding Cartesian equations would be

$$(x^2 + y^2 - x)^2 = x^2 + y^2 \quad \text{and} \quad (x^2 + y^2)^3 = 4x^2y^2$$

which are anything but simple, especially if the problem is to proceed from equation to geometric graph.

If one sort of generalization of the Cartesian coordinate system is to be found in the use of different frames of reference, another is furnished by the extension of Cartesian coordinates to space, as in Figure 4.3, where three mutually perpendicular number lines or coordinate axes are illustrated. Just as a 2-dimensional Cartesian coordinate system uses a network of squares, the 3-dimensional framework can be

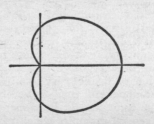

Figure 7.20   Cardioid

Figure 7.21   Four-leaved rose

pictured as an array of cubes. Then various surfaces become the geometric graphs of ternary relations expressed by equations in x, y, z, where (x, y, z) are the Cartesian coordinates of a point in space. As for 4-, 5-, or n-dimensional coordinate systems, we need not picture them—the algebraic work will take care of all the facts, and the geometric counterparts are superfluous. An algebraist does not balk at manipulating equations and inequalities involving many variables. On the other hand, a Greek geometer was decidedly limited by what he could see. An algebraist can create a fourth dimension merely by a stroke of his pen, and although he will not try to visualize the result, geometric language is a great convenience. To say that a relation like

$$x^2 + y^2 + z^2 + w^2 = 9$$

is a *hypersphere* with radius 3 is so much easier than to state that the relation is the set of all ordered quadruples of real numbers such that the sum of the squares of these four numbers is always 9.

We have featured analytic geometry as an important general method. We have also emphasized its service in representing binary and ternary relations graphically, and in providing terminology and techniques for the study of relations of higher order. Since a *function* is the most important type of binary relation, we shall close this chapter by discussing traditional and modern vocabulary associated with the function concept, and by presenting some additional and more general examples which will provide a link with the chapters to follow. The reader must become acquainted with the older modes of expression, because they are the ones he is likely to encounter in reading elementary mathematical literature which is not completely "new."

A function, as stated earlier, is a set of ordered pairs in which no two pairs contain the same first member. In other words, to each element of the domain there corresponds *only one* element in the range. Our illustrations have specified particular functions in various ways, namely, by tabulation, graph, defining sentence, or defining formula. The last method is associated with some special vocabulary, in which, traditionally, the value of a variable y is considered to be "dependent on" or "determined by" the value of the variable x.

Then if, for example, R, the real number continuum, is fixed as the replacement set for x and y, a particular function f might be specified as the set of all (x, y) for which $y = x^2 - x + 4$. In connection with the Cartesian graph of this function, we may wish to plot some ordered pairs, and hence to substitute $x = 1$, 2, 3, -1, -2, -3, etc. in the above defining formula in order to find the corresponding values of y. For this purpose, and also to show the "dependence" of y on x, one convenient notation is $y(x)$, which is read as "y of x." Another is $f(x)$, which is read as "f of x." In our example,

$$y(x) = x^2 - x + 4$$

or

$$f(x) = x^2 - x + 4$$

Then

$$f(1) = 1^2 - 1 + 4 = 4$$
$$f(2) = 2^2 - 2 + 4 = 6$$
$$f(-1) = 1^2 + 1 + 4 = 6$$

and therefore $(1, 4)$, $(2, 6)$, $(-1, 6)$ are ordered pairs belonging to the function, or coordinate pairs for points in its graph. All the symbols, $f(1)$, $f(2)$, $f(-1)$, are values in the range of the function, and hence $f(x)$ is the general formula for such a value.

For practice in the particular notation (and not for plotting the graph of the function) the reader should verify that

$$f(a) = a^2 - a + 4$$
$$f(a^3) = (a^3)^2 - a^3 + 4 = a^6 - a^3 + 4$$
$$f(x^2 + 1) = (x^2 + 1)^2 - (x^2 + 1) + 4$$
$$= x^4 + x^2 + 4$$

and that if

$$g(x) = x^2 + 1$$
$$f(g(x)) = f(x^2 + 1) = x^4 + x^2 + 4$$
$$g(f(x)) = g(x^2 - x + 4) = (x^2 - x + 4)^2 + 1$$
$$= x^4 - 2x^3 + 9x^2 - 8x + 17$$

where the last examples indicate that, in general, $f(g(x)) \neq g(f(x))$.

As far as the function originally defined is concerned, the new notation merely indicates that this function is the set of ordered pairs $(x, f(x))$ where $f(x) = x^2 - x + 4$, or it is the set (x, y), where $y = f(x)$. The meaning of $f(1)$ or "f of 1" is the value of y corresponding to $x = 1$, and the meaning of $f(x)$ or "f of x" is the value of the variable y corresponding to a given value of the variable x.

Now in some of the older usage there may be reference to "a function $f(x)$," which, taken literally, is confusing, since $f(x)$ is a value of the variable y, and not a set of ordered pairs. But if one accepts "a function $f(x)$" as an idiom, and reads it as "a function f of x," then the sentence $y = f(x)$ (which does define a function) will tend to be read as "y is a function f of x" or simply as "y is a function of x," which, again, is not literally true since y is a single variable, and not a pair of related variables defining a set of ordered pairs. The same idiom is applied when, in referring to the formulas $A = \pi r^2$ and $d = kt$, it is claimed that the area of a circle is a function of its radius, and that for a body moving uniformly (or, in fact, for any moving body), distance is a function of time.

Again, the reader will find $f(2)$ described as the value of the function at 2 (instead of the value of y corresponding to $x = 2$). The idiom makes $f(x)$ "the value of the function at x" (instead of the value of y corresponding to a given value of x). Also, such examples as $f(g(x))$ and $g(f(x))$ which we treated earlier may be called "composite functions."

The common usage which we have described may confuse because it appears to identify the function with the values in its range. Since such pains are taken to define a function exactly, the reader may wonder why the exact formulations are "more honored in the breach than in the observance." All we can say in explanation is that the function concept has a long history, rooted in antiquity (*vide* the many *tabulations* of the Babylonians), and that members of the modern mathematical world are like Shakespearean actors who have read and recited and studied Elizabethan English to such an extent that they slip into the outmoded idioms even in ordinary conversation, especially when they feel that the expressions have special aptness or beauty.

If then, we give in to tradition, we shall consider the symbol $f(x, y)$, read as "f of x and y" to *mean* a "function of x and y." But can it possibly be meaningful to say, for example, that $z = f(x, y)$ is a function defined by $f(x, y) = x^2 + y^2$? The equation $z = x^2 + y^2$ defines a *ternary relation*. Hence how can we speak of a *function*, which is a special *binary* relation?

Let us then justify the usage. If

$$f(x, y) = x^2 + y^2$$

we can find

$$f(1, 1) = 1^2 + 1^2 = 2$$
$$f(1, 2) = 1^2 + 2^2 = 5$$
$$f(1, 3) = 1^2 + 3^2 = 10$$

so that $(1, 1, 2)$, $(1, 2, 5)$, and $(1, 3, 10)$ are ordered triples belonging to the *ternary relation* defined. But let us interpret things somewhat differently by examining $z = f(x, y)$ once more, and also its Cartesian graph (Figure 7.22), which is

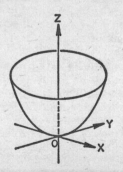

Figure 7.22   Surface $z = x^2 + y^2$

a surface in 3-dimensional space. If, now, we think of $(1, 1)$ or $(1, 2)$ or $(1, 3)$, etc. as a *point* or *vector* (Chapter 4) in the XY-plane, then each one of these ordered pairs can be conceived as a *single entity*. Then the above equation pairs each of these entities with a number. Thus $(1, 2)$ is paired with $f(1, 2)$ or 5, and $(1, 3)$ is paired with $f(1, 3)$ or 10, etc. Therefore, in the present instance a *binary relation* is formulated by the set of ordered pairs $((x, y), z)$ or $((x, y), f(x, y))$. Furthermore, the binary relation is a *function* because $f(x, y)$ has a *unique* value when $(1, 1)$ or $(1, 2)$ or any other real number pair is substituted for (x, y). This uniqueness can be seen from the diagram of Figure 7.22, where a "vertical" line through $(1, 1)$ or $(1, 2)$ or any point of the XY-plane meets the surface $z = x^2 + y^2$ in *only one* point.

In similar fashion, a quaternary relation, for example, the one we termed a hypersphere (page 231), can be converted into a *binary relation*, $((x, y, z), w)$. If we substitute $(1, 0, 2)$ for (x, y, z) in the equation of the hypersphere, the result is

$$1^2 + 0^2 + 2^2 + w^2 = 9$$
$$w^2 = 4$$

Therefore

$$w = +2 \quad \text{or} \quad w = -2$$

Here w is *not* determined uniquely, that is, the ordered pairs, $((1, 0, 2), 2)$ and $((1, 0, 2), -2)$, having the *same first member*, both belong to the binary relation, which is therefore *not a function*. But if $w = f(x, y, z)$ where

$$f(x, y, z) = x^2 + 2y - z$$

then $((x, y, z), f(x, y, z))$ is seen to be a function. In our examples, $f(x, y)$ and $f(x, y, z)$ symbolize values in the range of a function but, in common usage, may be referred to as *functions* (of x and y, of x, y, and z, respectively), and there are "functions" $f(x_1, x_2, x_3, \ldots, x_n)$.

By special interpretation, we have converted ternary and quaternary relations into binary relations, and we could do the same for n-ary relations, if $n > 4$. Here we have converted a relation into one of lower order. But we can reverse the procedure if it should suit our purposes. Perhaps we might prefer, in arithmetic or algebra, to base ideas on the concept of *relation* in preference to *operation*. Then, for example, addition, a binary operation defined by $z = x + y$, could be considered a *ternary relation*. A *unary* operation, say, "taking the square root of *one* number," can be defined by $y = \sqrt{x}$, which is a *binary relation*.

The concept of a relation, and its specialization, the notion of a function, form a central theme for classification and unification in mathematics. Many subdivisions of mathematics can be described as theories associated with special types of function or relation. The index to a general work on mathematics may well reveal as subheadings under "function" such qualifying terms as algebraic, analytic, Bessel, beta, complex, elliptic, entire, gamma, harmonic, Lagrange, Legendre, logarithmic, orthogonal, periodic, propositional, real, trigonometric, vector, etc. Some of these types have already appeared in our story, and others will arise as we continue. For example, open sentences or propositional forms were formerly called "propositional functions," that is, in common usage, functions of the variables contained in the sentences. *Periodic* functions are the mathematical tools for dealing with natural and man-made periodicity—the recurrent changes in tides, the orbiting of planets and satellites, business cycles, alternating current oscillations, mechanical vibrations, the waves and vibrations associated with physical theories of light and sound.

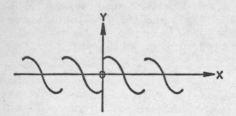

Figure 7.23   A periodic function

As usual, Cartesian graphic representation will clarify a concept. Figure 7.23 pictures a periodic function, so called because the same pattern is repeated again and again forever. If such a pattern is formulated by $y = f(x)$, then the fact that the height of the "wave" is periodically the same leads to the definition of a periodic function as one for which

$$f(x + p) = f(x)$$

If p is the least number for which the statement is true, it is called the *fundamental period* of the function.

Trigonometry, which some school students consider a glorified geometry with superimposed computational torture, has a more important aspect, which makes it the ABC of periodicity. Thus a thumbnail sketch would say that trigonometry is the study of the graph of the function $y = $ sine x (Figure 7.24). This graph shows that the fundamental period is 360° or 2π radians, since the pattern for x between 0° and 360° is repeated again and again, to left and right, forever. (Other periods are 720°, 1080°, etc.)

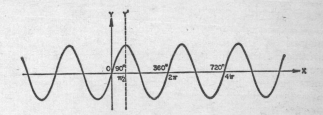

Figure 7.24   Graph of $y = \sin x$

The cosine curve, that is, the graph of the function $y = \cos x$ has the same shape as that for $y = \sin x$ and can be obtained either by shifting the sine curve through a distance $\frac{1}{2}\pi$ to the left or by sliding the coordinate axes through a distance of $\frac{1}{2}\pi$ to the right (the dotted position in the diagram) so that the reading for $\cos 0°$ will be the same as that for $\sin 90°$ and $\cos 30° = \sin 120°$, etc. The *tangent* function of trigonometry is defined by $y = \sin x/\cos x$, where the domain of the function is the set of all real numbers except those for which $\cos x = 0$. The cosine graph will tell which values of x are excluded from the domain.

Adjustment of the scales on the X and Y axes in Figure 7.24 will provide the graphs of $y = \sin 2x$, $y = \sin 3x$,

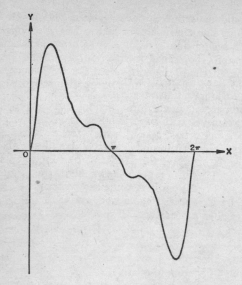

Figure 7.25   Pattern for $y = 5 \sin x + 3 \sin 2x + 2 \sin 3x$

$y = 5 \sin 7x$, etc. The sum of a number of such sine functions, for example,

$$y = 5 \sin x + 3 \sin 2x + 2 \sin 3x$$

will have an irregular wave pattern akin to Figure 7.25. The French mathematical physicist J. B. J. Fourier (1768–1830) showed that, conversely, any well-determined graph, subject to a few restrictions unimportant in science, can be resolved into a sum of sine curves. It is a remarkable fact that you might scribble a curve thus:

and it would nevertheless have a sine equation. Of course, three or four sine curves might be too few. You might need a dozen or even a hundred for a good approximation. Since such a graph represents a function, Fourier's discovery means that all the elementary relations of science are expressible in terms of sines. In a sense, then, trigonometry is at the base of all scientific formulation. The idea of periodicity dominates portions of pure mathematics as well as applied science. There is, for example, the theory of *elliptic functions*, a sort of higher trigonometry dealing with "doubly periodic" functions. Mathematicians and physicists alike hardly associate the importance of trigonometry with its initial elementary use in the fields of surveying and astronomy.

There are broader classifications of functions which include trigonometric and elliptic functions merely as subcategories. For example, one overall way of describing functions or relations is by means of their domains. Thus mathematics contains "a theory of functions of a real variable" and "a theory of functions of a complex variable." These descriptions employ the traditional idioms associated with functionality. Actually, general relations and not merely functions are studied in the subjects named. Also, modern pure mathematicians do not like the "function of" mode of expression, and therefore the older terms are now replaced by descriptions like "Real Analysis," "Complex Analysis," "Real Functions," etc. This nomenclature provides the transition to our next chapters, in which we shall be discussing the great names and the fundamental notions associated with the beginnings of "real analysis" or "functions of a real variable."

Chapter 8

A Calculus for Heaven and Earth

The place is Prague, where a young scientist in search of a job had brought his family. For a talented, genial, pious, imaginative, and romantic personality, who possessed a willingness to carry out the most laborious tasks at a salary of 500 florins less per year than the usual rate, employment was not hard to find. Thus, in 1601, our protagonist became court mathematician to Emperor Rudolph II. If he found the task of compiling the *Rudolphine* tables an arduous one, other duties must have been more pleasurable—casting the horoscope of the emperor, of Wallenstein, and of other political magnates, and writing mystical interpretations of the triple conjunction of Mars, Jupiter, Saturn. It is strange to recount that these were major activities of Johannes Kepler (1571–1630), the founder of modern astronomy. To quote Henri Poincaré, leading mathematician of the early twentieth century:

Even in its primitive, pseudoscientific phases, astronomy has been a boon to humanity, for it was astrology that enabled men like Tycho Brahe and Kepler to earn a living, by predicting the fate of naïve kings from the conjunctions of heavenly bodies. If these monarchs had not been so credulous, the great astronomers might have been too poor to engage in scientific research and we might still wallow in ignorance and believe that nature is governed by whims.*

During the years 1601–1609, Kepler's real scientific work was carried on as a sideline, but finally he completed his "great Martian labor" and, as he said, was able to "lead the

* Henri Poincaré *La Valeur de la Science*, Flammarion, Paris, 1913, p. 157. (Translation by the Author.)

captive planet to the foot of the imperial throne." It is our present purpose to examine the nature of his triumph over the planet Mars. Another decade was needed before he vanquished the solar system completely, and this second ten-year period followed the pattern of his earlier existence —financial difficulties, personal bereavement, laborious tabulations for all the states of upper Austria, and much astrology paralleling the development of the greatest satellite theory of all time. None of these hardships diminished his mysticism or crushed his romanticism.

In the *Harmonices Mundi* of 1619 he presented his final planetary law, but he actually devoted more space to the celestial harmonies to which the "spirit of the sun" was the sole auditor (except for Kepler himself). One need only examine the 1619 treatise to find exact musical notes for Earth's song of sorrow, the dull moan of Venus, the staccato rhythms of Mercury, and the contrapuntal role of the other planets. When the whole strange mélange of science and fantasy was complete, Kepler dedicated it to James I of England, in whom it must have struck a sympathetic chord, for the musical astronomer soon received an invitation to England's court.

Kepler demonstrated his extravagance in voluminous correspondence. In a typical letter addressed to Baron Peter Heinrich von Strahlendorf in 1613 he describes the courtship preceding his second marriage; he weighs the merits of eleven candidates for his hand; he writes:

I had been waiting impatiently for the visit of the wife of Herr Helmhard, wondering what she would have to say about the third candidate, and whether her words would sway me in favor of this third lady instead of her two predecessors. But when I had at last heard from Frau Helmhard, I made up my mind to accept the fourth candidate on my list. But I still felt bad that the fifth possible choice had in the interim withdrawn from the picture. Just then fate stepped in: The fourth lady became aware of some reluctance on my part and gave her word to someone else, a man who had wooed her persistently for a long time and had painted a glowing picture of their future together. Now I was as much annoyed about losing her as I had been at the withdrawal of the fifth. There must be something wrong with my emotions, which seem to be stimulated by any hesitation on my part, any weighing of pros and cons. From what I have learned subsequently, it was just as well that I had no success with the fourth. As far as the fifth is concerned, there is still the question of why, though she was destined for me, God permitted her to have six rivals in the course of one year. The name of my final choice is *Susanna*. If my bride lacks wealth and family background, she nevertheless has all the simpler virtues. Her father was a carpenter by profession. She received her education, which must take the place of a dowry, at the home of the Stahrembergs. She is not young, but she is modest and unpretentious. I feel that she will be highly efficient in running my household. The wedding will take place on the day of the eclipse of the moon, when the astronomical spirit is in hiding, as I want to rejoice in the festival day. . . .*

The celebration took place at Linz, and Kepler, with mathematical issues always in the back of his mind, became interested in finding the correct volume of the wine barrels associated with the festivities. He may have imbibed rather freely of the contents he was shortly to measure, for the problem was inspired by a heated argument with the wine merchant, whom Kepler accused of making errors of cubature in his own favor. The net result was the appearance in 1615 of the great astronomer's *Nova stereometria doliorum vinariorum* (New Solid Mensuration of Wine Casks). The mathematics of the wine barrels and that of the conquest of Mars can both be classified as a crude type of *integral calculus*.

When Kepler first came to Prague, remarkably accurate observations of the heavens were available. These were a legacy from his predecessor, the Danish astronomer whom he called the *phoenix*, Tycho Brahe. But years more of observation and computation were required before Kepler could state the first of his famous planetary laws: *The orbits of the planets are ellipses with the sun at one focus.* This discovery was the result of imaginative genius combined with prosaic *triangulation*, a type of mathematics that can be carried out by scale drawing or trigonometry. Kepler's second law states: *The focal radius joining a planet to the sun sweeps out equal areas in equal times.* We shall now examine the reasoning on which Kepler based his second law, in order to show that his technique helped to launch the subject we call integral calculus.

In the first place, Kepler chose the planet Mars for prolonged observation. This was a lucky choice, since Mars' orbit has greater "eccentricity," or differs more from a circle than all other planetary ellipses except that of Mer-

---

* This is a free translation by the author of pp. 25–27, Vol. 2, of M. Caspar and W. von Dyck, *Johannes Kepler in seinen Briefen,* Verlag Oldenbourg, Munich and Berlin, 1930.

cury. Therefore, even with the optical instruments available in his day, Kepler was able to observe the eccentricity of Mars' orbit. Having charted Mars' elliptic trajectory, Kepler made a more profound study of just how the planet moves in the course of its celestial journey. He concentrated on points like *A, B, C, D, E, F* in Figure 8.1*a*, which represent positions of Mars such that the time required for the planet's

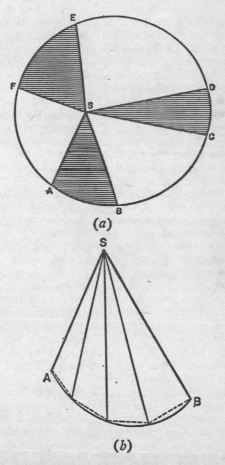

(a)

(b)

Figure 8.1   Kepler's second law.

progress from A to B is the same as that from C to D or from E to F. Drawing the focal radii SA, SB, SC, etc., Kepler computed the areas of sectors ASB, CSD, ESF and found them equal. He did this by a method of approximation that used elementary geometry. First, he subdivided sector ASB into very thin sectors, then sector CSD into very thin sectors, etc. In each of the small sectors there is little difference between the curved arc of the ellipse and its chord, so that for approximate purposes it suffices to measure the area of the triangle inscribed in the elliptic sector, and this is found by the elementary Euclidean formula $\frac{1}{2}bh$. Then the area of sector ASB can be found by considering it to be the sum of numerous small triangles (Figure 8.1b), and in the same way, areas can be computed for sectors CSD and ESF. Kepler found the three large sectors to be equal in area, and equal to other sectors formed by S (the sun) and focal radii to orbital points whose separation in time was the same as that from A to B or C to D, etc. These were the numerical results which he summarized in the second of his two laws, enunciated in 1609.

In the summation of numerous small triangles to estimate the area of an elliptic sector, Kepler may have felt that he was merely using common sense, but we would say that he had solved a problem in *integral calculus*, and that he had used approximate or *numerical integration*. His stereometry of wine casks comes under the same heading. In that instance, he visualized the volume of a barrel as made up of numerous shallow circular cylinders somewhat like those in Figure 8.2. The elementary formula, $\pi r^2 h$, for the volume of a circular cylinder, was then applicable to each thin layer

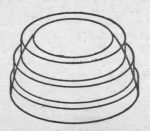

Figure 8.2   The sum of cylinders approximates the volume of the upper half of a barrel.

of the barrel. The indefatigable Kepler measured the circular periphery of the cask at each level, and substituting this length for C in $C = 2\pi r$, computed r for the circular bases of the shallow cylinders at each level. The value of h was the small distance between successive layers. With r and h determined, substitution in $\pi r^2 h$ gave the volume of the cylindric layer.

For more than two decades Kepler had struggled to find a formula that would connect planetary *distance* from the sun with the *time* required for the planet to describe its orbit. He finally succeeded in such a formulation. This was his third law, which appeared in the *Harmonices Mundi* of 1619, a decade after the publication of the first two laws. Some of the delay was caused by family troubles, which seem never to have been absent from the noted astronomer's life. A special source of anxiety appeared in 1615 when rumors of sorcery were circulated concerning Kepler's seventy-year-old mother. Catherine Kepler countered with a suit for libel; this dragged on and on until 1620, when she was arrested and charged with witchcraft. She was imprisoned for more than a year, subjected to the ordeal of interrogation under the imminent threat of torture, and only released after her son had exerted his utmost influence with the authorities. It is not surprising that her death followed shortly thereafter.

The "satellite" law that was released in the midst of all these troubles expresses a relation between the *time* for one complete satellite trip and the (average) *distance* of the satellite from the heavenly body about which it is revolving. Kepler found that, for every planet, the quotient T^2/r^3 has the same numerical value, where T is its *period*, that is, the time for a complete circuit, and r is its mean or average distance from the sun. In other words $T^2/r^3 = k$, where k is a numerical constant, or $T^2 = kr^3$. This last formulation is the one usually given: The square of the time which any planet takes to complete its orbit is proportional to the cube of its mean distance from the sun. Kepler considered this discovery his greatest. Is it any wonder, then, that his comments were even more extravagant than usual?

What I predicted twenty-two years ago . . . and believed in long before that . . . what I revealed to my friends . . . and sixteen years ago urged them to accept as valid . . . that for which I joined Tycho Brahe, for which I settled in Prague, the problem which inspired my lifelong devotion to astronomy . . . I have solved at last. . . . The book (containing it) may be read now or by posterity, it does not matter. If it must wait a century to be read, I care not, since God himself has had to wait six thousand years for a proper observer of His handiwork.*

It is true that Kepler's laws terminated millennia of geometrical astronomy based on the empirical study of the heavens. But his inductions were not the last mathematical word on the subject. Galileo's mechanics and Newton's universal gravitation were yet to come, and to provide the foundations for modern dynamical astronomy. By making certain assumptions about the gravitational attraction between two bodies, Newton was able to provide a *deductive* proof for Kepler's laws. Between Kepler's assertion of these rules to which all satellites must conform and the logical demonstration by Newton, about seventy years were to elapse. During this interval the mathematical tools required for Newton's proof were forged. The whole modern trend in mathematics was begun when analytic geometry was crystallized by Descartes and Fermat, and the calculus was given definitive form by Newton and Leibniz.

But did Newton or did Leibniz create the calculus? Such a question is pertinent only if one believes in the type of popular folklore which demands that all concepts be considered as originating during a specific period of history in the mind of a single mathematician. One result of this unfortunately typical attitude is that mathematical development has been accompanied by numerous priority disputes, often provoked by rival groups of scientists rather than by the mathematicians themselves. The calculus, with which this chapter is concerned, gave rise to the most prolonged and bitter of all controversies of this sort, the "two-hundred-year war" between British and Continental scientists concerning the question of whether Newton or Leibniz was the inventor of the subject. It is naïve to give complete credit to either of these renowned mathematicians, since the roll call of forerunners is lengthy and distinguished. The most serious consequence of the calculus dispute was its damaging effect on British mathematics. The late Norbert Wiener** described this sorry situation:

* M. Casper and W. von Dyck, *loc. cit.*
** Norbert Wiener, "Godfrey Harold Hardy," *Bulletin of the Amer. Math. Society*, Vol. 55, No. 1, Part 1 (January 1949), pp. 73–74.

We have not much doubt that Leibniz' work was somewhat later but independent (of Newton's), and that Leibniz' notation was far superior to Newton's. . . . It was not long before patriotic and misguidedly loyal colleagues of both discoverers instigated a quarrel, the effects of which have scarcely yet (1949) died out. In particular, it became an act of faith and of patriotic loyalty for the British mathematicians to use the less flexible Newtonian notation and to affect to look down on the new work done by the Leibnizian school on the Continent. . . . When the great continental school of the Bernoullis and Euler arose (not to mention Lagrange and Laplace who came later) there were no men of comparable calibre north of the Channel to compete with them on anything like a plane of equality. . . .

Not until the nineteenth century was well under way . . . was there awareness of what . . . Laplace and Lagrange had done in mathematics. Even then mathematical education at the English universities was devoted to (preparation for) the passing of severe examinations like the Cambridge Tripos, rather than to the development of original mathematical workers. . . . Mathematical talent in the British Isles went instead to the formation of a great school of mathematical physicists. . . . At about the turn of the century an awareness of the great work of the continental mathematicians smuggled itself into England by non-academic bypaths. . . . G. H. Hardy (1877–1947) and his associates . . . represent the first generation (of British mathematicians) to have had contact from the beginning of their training with modern continental analysis, and the first, except for William Henry Young (1863–1942) (Chapter 27) to have familiar personal contacts with all the leaders of their work on the Continent and to be regarded by the latter as friendly equals.

To avoid any continuation of the ugly controversy whose effects Wiener describes, Newton and Leibniz will *not* here be named as sole creators of the calculus, but rather as the mathematicians who made the major contributions to a subject that had existed since antiquity, first by establishing its "fundamental theorem," and second by providing a definite algebraic symbolism and a systematic set of rules for performing operations. These two elements are the essence of elementary calculus as it is studied by college students today, and if this is what any one means by "calculus," then he would be correct in attributing the source of such subject matter to Newton and Leibniz.

The true story of the creation of the calculus is the history of the gradual evolution of its various concepts. Where should one begin? If a logical, philosophical point of view is adopted in preference to the algebraic-manipulative stress of elementary calculus courses, then, as we have seen (Chapter 2), one might begin with the Pythagorean discovery of the $\sqrt{2}$ and Eudoxus' theory of the irrationals. These bring into focus the real number system, the need for "infinite" processes, the meaning of geometric continuity, all of which are essential to the *theoretical* foundations of calculus and the general (infinitesimal) analysis that includes it. If, on the other hand, one desires a mathematical tool related to the physical measurement of lengths, areas, volumes, weights, pressures, velocities, accelerations, etc., and this was indeed the viewpoint of Newton and Leibniz, one should start the story of the calculus with Archimedes.

Archimedes' ideas were imitated in Kepler's measurement of the areas of elliptic sectors and the volumes of wine casks. As an additional exercise in numerical integration in the spirit of Kepler, one might approximate the area within the curve of Figure 8.3. There are 161 *complete* small squares within the boundary, and if each square represents a square centimeter, say, then the desired area is somewhat in excess of 161 sq. cm. Counting each peripheral portion of a square as if it were entire, one obtained 214 sq. cm., an estimate exceeding the area sought. The area itself lies somewhere between the two estimates. "Common sense" suggests that the *mean* of the two approximations, namely, 187.5 sq. cm., would be a better estimate of the area than either previous figure. In similar fashion, one could ap-

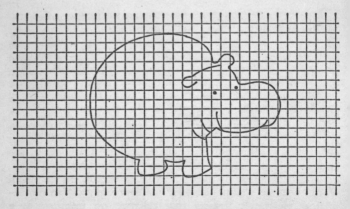

Figure 8.3

proximate the volume of a solid object by counting the number of very tiny cubes which could be packed within its surface.

A proper scientific attitude would call for some standardization in the techniques of approximate integration to replace the rough and ready methods mentioned, and also to decrease experimental errors and estimate their magnitude. In the sort of measurement used by Kepler, it is evident that finer cross-section paper, smaller cubes, "narrower" triangles, and thinner cylindrical layers would yield better estimates. If a first approximation of some area seems too crude, one can decrease the size of the squares or triangles, etc., and obtain a second approximation. If this again seems poor, one can use still smaller meshes in a third approximation and, in *theory*, if not in practice, such improvement in approximation could be continued *ad infinitum*.

This was the thought behind the Greek *method of exhaustion* initiated by Antiphon the Sophist (*ca.* 430 B.C.), perfected by Eudoxus, and put to such excellent use by Archimedes that, if popular demand for a unique originator must be satisfied, he, rather than Newton or Leibniz, should be credited with the invention of integral calculus. The method of exhaustion is still indicated, after a fashion, to school students of geometry in connection with deriving the area of a circle. First the pupils may inscribe a regular hexagon in a circle, then double the number of sides to obtain a regular dodecagon, double the number again to obtain a regular polygon of 24 sides, etc. As pupils study the sequence of inscribed regular polygons with 6, 12, 24, 48, 96, 192, 384, . . . sides, they are led to an intuitive justification of the claim that ultimately the polygonal area *exhausts* the area within the circumference. In more modern terminology, we would say that there is a *limiting* value to which all polygonal areas after the thousandth in the sequence, say, are very, very close. If such a *limit* exists, it is said to be the *exact* measure of the area sought.

In our discussion so far, we have assumed, just as Eudoxus, Archimedes, Newton, and all mathematicians prior to the nineteenth century did, that lengths, areas, and volumes are entities whose nature we comprehend intuitively. Thus, given a description or diagram of some object, our problem would become a computational one. But the modern mathematical viewpoint stresses that reliance on intuition is a dangerous logical procedure. Nowadays an "infinite process" of approximation is set up according to definite rules, and if a *limit* exists for the approximations in question, the limiting number is said to define a length or area or volume or pressure or quantity of work or any of the other entities that integral calculus serves to measure. Thus, if we are to advance beyond a naïve idea of area ·or volume, it is the concepts of *infinite process* and *limit* that we must master, and these are the basic notions of the calculus.

Archimedes, in his form of integral calculus, first considered various geometric figures as if they were material bodies to which those laws of mechanics which he had discovered were applicable. Having obtained formulas for certain lengths, areas, volumes by means of mechanical principles, he provided rigorous logical proofs that involved the method of exhaustion. In this way he was able to find areas of ellipses, parabolic segments, sectors of a spiral, certain volumes, and also the centers of gravity of segments of a parabola, cone, sphere.

After Archimedes' contribution, little was added to integral calculus until Kepler's day, when a number of mathematicians revived the Archimedean techniques and attempted to improve them. Among these, in addition to Kepler himself, were the Flemish mathematical physicist Simon Stevin (1548–1620) and Bonaventura Cavalieri (1598–1647), a pupil of Galileo and professor at Bologna. *Cavalieri's principle* makes an "integral calculus" of sorts possible in school mathematics today.

Cavalieri stated: Two solids (lying between parallel planes) have the same volume if cross-sections at equal heights have equal areas. Cavalieri conceived of a solid as if it were built of a stack of cards. Thus he pictured a box as if built of ordinary rectangular cards, all the same size, a square pyramid as if built of square cards of varying sizes, a triangular pyramid as if it were a stack of triangular cards diminishing in size toward the vertex, circular cylinders and cones as constructed of circular cards (Figure 8.4). Then, if the circular base of a cylinder and the rectangular base of a box are equal in area, and if the two solids have the same height (Figure 8.4) their volumes must be equal, in accordance with Cavalieri's principle. One might conceive of the box as a stack of 100 ordinary (rectangular) cards, say, and the cylinder as a stack of 100 circular cards, where a circular card face has the same area as the rectangular card face in the other stack. The cards are not

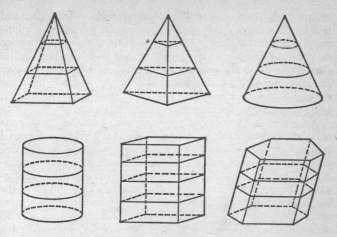

Figure 8.4   Cavalieri's principle

mere surfaces, however, but solids, since each has slight thickness. Then every card in either pack has the same small *volume*. If this volume is represented by x, the total volume of the box is $100x$, and likewise for the cylinder. But it is an easy matter to obtain the volume of a box if its dimensions are known. This volume is just the product of these dimensions, or the product of the base area by the height. The base area is just that of the rectangular cards (or the circular cards). Then the volume of the cylinder is the same as that of the box and hence is the product of the area of its (circular) base and its height. Thus the formula for the volume of a cylinder is $V = \pi r^2 h$. If a cylinder is not circular, that is, if it is built of elliptical cards or cards of some other shape, if in fact it is built of pentagonal or hexagonal or octagonal cards (in which case it is usually called a *prism*) (Figure 8.4), Cavalieri's principle is still applicable as long as the cards employed have face areas identical with those of the rectangular cards used for the box. In every case the volume formula will be $V = Bh$, where B is the area of the cylinder base = box base and h is the height of the cylinder (or box).

In addition to Kepler's approximative species and Cavalieri's intuitive type of integral calculus, there were many other pre-Newtonian contributions to the same subject.

Fermat, whose role in analytic geometry has already been discussed, created integral calculus methods to find areas like that in Figure 8.16, where the boundary consists of three straight-line segments (the X-axis and two ordinates) and an arc of a "general parabola," $y = x^3$. In fact, he developed a formula for such an area when $y = x^n$ (where n is *any* positive integer), also for the case $y = x^{m/n}$ (m and n are positive integers), and also where the curve is a "general hyperbola," $y = 1/x^n$ (where n is a positive integer greater than 1). He found still more general areas, determined the volume of a paraboloid of revolution, and located various centroids (centers of mass or gravity). In addition, he found the lengths of certain curves. This is called *rectification*,

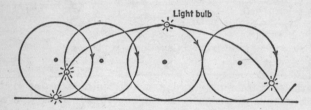

Light bulb

Figure 8.5   A light attached to one point of the rim of a wagon wheel in motion generates a cycloid.

and one might expect it to be easier than quadrature or cubature, because finding a length sounds so much simpler than determining an area or a volume. However, the opposite is true; rectification is, in general, a much more difficult procedure in integral calculus.

In 1658 Sir Christopher Wren, the great architect who designed St. Paul's Cathedral in London, achieved the rectification of the *cycloid* (Figure 8.5), a curve with so many beautiful properties that it is called the "Helen of Geometry"; he also determined the centroid of the area under a cycloidal arch. Blaise Pascal, whose correspondence with Fermat on probability problems provides one of the favorite anecdotes in mathematical history (Chapter 13), was also deeply interested in the cycloid, and in fact specialized in some of the more arduous issues of quadrature and cubature —for example, where the bounding curves or surfaces have trigonometric formulas.

Still another forerunner of Newton and Leibniz was

Christiaan Huygens (1629–1695). Surprisingly, his integral calculus techniques were, in the main, the classical methods of Archimedes. Perhaps his greatest service to the subject was the mathematical education which he gave to Gottfried Wilhelm Leibniz (1646–1716). Up to the age of twenty-six, the "co-inventor" of the calculus knew almost nothing about the more modern aspects of mathematics, even though he had formulated the basic notions of modern symbolic logic while he was still in his teens (Chapter 6). He had taken his bachelor's degree in philosophy at seventeen, and his doctorate in law at twenty. He then became a diplomatic assistant to the Elector of Mainz, and a particular diplomatic mission brought him to Paris in 1672. (Half a dozen years earlier, Newton had already formulated but not published his first thoughts on the calculus.) There Leibniz met Huygens and begged him for tutoring in mathematics. The Dutch mathematical physicist accepted the young diplomat as a pupil, since he recognized his genius almost immediately. Without any special instruction, Leibniz had already worked out details of his logic, and constructed his remarkable calculating machine, which was far superior to the first calculating machine in history, the one Pascal had invented at the age of nineteen. Whereas Pascal's machine could add and subtract, Leibniz' device could also multiply, divide and extract roots. But just now the point of emphasis is Huygen's influence on the integral calculus, directly, through his own discoveries, and indirectly, through his influence on Leibniz.

Another who can be mentioned for both his direct and his indirect influence is the Scotsman James Gregory (1638–1675). Like Pascal, he was short-lived, and like him, he solved some of the more difficult types of problem in integral calculus. His most important achievement was the theory of infinite series (Chapter 22), and here he and other British contemporaries influenced Leibniz. In fact, Leibniz is sometimes erroneously credited with discovering the "Gregory series."

But one must also mention the influences on Newton. The most immediate of these was John Wallis (1616–1703), British analyst and mathematics professor at Oxford for fifty-four years. It was a reading of his treatise, the *Arithmetica Infinitorum*, that precipitated Newton's considerations of a decade later. But the last and best pre-Newtonian ideas on integral calculus were provided by Pietro Mengoli (1626–

1686) of Bologna in his *Geometria Speciosa* (1659). In this work he represented certain areas as *limits* of sums of rectangles, and in doing so, provided a *theoretical* definition for an "integral." After Augustin-Louis Cauchy (1789–1857), the first of France's great modern analysts, had placed calculus on a sound logical foundation, the "limit of a sum" definition of areas, volumes, or other entities to be measured came to be known as the *Mengoli-Cauchy integral.* This completes the story of integral calculus prior to Newton and Leibniz. Since their major contribution was to the *differential* calculus, we shall pause here for further biographical facts about the two men prior to introducing that subject.

Isaac Newton (1642–1727), often cited as the greatest genius the race has ever produced, showed no signs of promise in his early years. Like many talented children, he found school a complete bore. In lieu of studying, he devoted himself to the construction of kites, water wheels, tops, mechanical toys, sundials, ingenious clocks, and all sorts of amazing gadgets. His academic record was so poor that his mother decided farming would be the ideal vocational choice for Isaac. His father, who had died shortly before the boy's birth, had been a Lincolnshire farmer, and it seemed natural to have the son continue in the same work. Newton's uncle had a better understanding of the boy's talents. One day he discovered Isaac reading under a hedge instead of performing his agrarian duties. That clinched matters, and he persuaded Newton's mother to send the boy to Trinity College, Cambridge.

In the years 1665–1666, when the Great Plague was raging in England, Newton went back to the farm and in spare moments started his work on gravitation, optics, and calculus. In connection with the third subject, he developed the *binomial theorem,* which was no mean stunt for a young man of twenty-three.

When Newton was twenty-six years of age, his teacher, Isaac Barrow, himself a mathematician of note, resigned from the Lucasian professorship at Trinity to devote himself to theology. He named his pupil as his successor. Newton's first work at Cambridge was in the field of optics. He built his own reflecting telescope, which won him a membership in the Royal Society. He advanced the corpuscular theory of light, which later scientists rejected in favor of the wave theory. Recent developments in atomic physics and quantum mechanics have caused scientists to reconsider Newton's notions about the nature of light, and the present opinion is best described by saying that for some phenomena it is convenient to accept Newton's view. Light in these cases is considered as particles of energy called quanta or *photons*. In other situations, theories are simplified by picturing light as one type of electromagnetic wave.

Newton presented the fruits of his most profound thought in the immortal *Principia* (1687). A brief summary can hardly convey a true impression of the monumental nature of this work. It contained, among other revolutionary scientific material, Newton's dynamics, his law of universal gravitation, and his "system of the world." The *Principia* seems to have ended the most important part of Newton's scientific career, and it was certainly a grand finale. After the publication of his work, Newton started life anew in a political capacity. A chance incident was the cause of it. In 1687 James II sought to impose his will on Cambridge University. Newton led the group that resisted and, as a reward for his courage, was elected to represent the University in Parliament the following year. This "opportunity" was fatal. He was later (1696) appointed Warden of the Mint and finally Master of the Mint (1699). He was one of the best Masters the Mint ever had.

Some mathematicians feel regret that a "high priest of science" should have wasted his genius in public office. Others cite Newton as a shining example of a scholar who deserted his ivory tower. Still others feel that Newton had spent himself early, that he realized his power for scientific thought was waning and hence sought other occupations. Some biographers assert that Newton's financial need was the cause of his action. We must remark that, whatever the evaluation of Newton's latter-day intellectual power, he was mathematically active to the day of his death at the age of eighty-five, although he did not produce any other work comparable to the *Principia*.

As for critical estimates of Newton's work, we first quote the generous tribute of his rival Leibniz, who said that, taking mathematics from the beginning of the world to the time when Newton lived, what Newton did was much the better half. Many still agree with Leibniz on this point. Lagrange, whom Frederick the Great named the "greatest mathematician in Europe," once remarked humorously that Newton was the greatest genius that ever lived and the most fortunate, since only once can the system of the universe be established.

Newton's modesty is revealed in his own appraisal of his work: "I do not know what I may appear to the world; but to myself I seem to have been only like a boy playing on the seashore, and diverting myself in now and then finding a smoother pebble or a prettier shell than ordinary, whilst the great ocean of truth lay all undiscovered before me."

Newton died in 1727 and was buried in Westminster Abbey. Voltaire attended the funeral, and it is said that, at a later date, his eye would grow bright and his cheek flush when he mentioned that a professor of mathematics, only because he was great in his vocation, had been buried like a king who had done good to his subjects.

Earlier in this book we discussed certain aspects of Leibniz' life in relation to his most important contribution to mathematics, the initiation of symbolic logic. Here we remark that if he was not, like Newton, the greates genius of all time, he was not very far from the highest rank. His talents were all-round, for in addition to mathematics and logic, he contributed ideas in such varied areas as law, religion, history, economics, and metaphysics. But his intellectual powers were not given the recognition they deserved during his lifetime. In fact, from the scientist's point of view, Leibniz' active life ceased at thirty, for he spent the last forty years of his life as historian of the Brunswick family. His last days were unhappy ones. In 1714 his patron, Elector George Louis of Brunswick, left for London to become George I of England. Leibniz would have liked to go with him for one last round with the English mathematicians and Newton, Master of the Mint. However, George left him at Hanover. Two years later Leibniz died and was buried in an obscure grave. Let us forget this unhappy ending and return to our theme—the branch of mathematics that he helped to develop for the proper handling of a world in flux.

We are now ready to talk about the evolution of the *differential calculus*. If we seek sources in antiquity, we find only one slight suggestion in the work of Archimedes. In fact, there was no real development of the subject before the seventeenth century. Like the *integral* calculus, the *differential* calculus is also concerned with infinite processes and associated limits. Its most beautiful and useful theorem provides, for many problems of area, volume, etc., a simple, truly easy alternative to the Mengoli-Cauchy "limit of the sum" procedure. For this reason, beginners in the calculus find it easier to master the concepts of the newer branch of calculus first, and then establish its connection with the older integral calculus. The names of those who paved the way for Newton and Leibniz in *differential* calculus will be revealed a little later on, since an appreciation of their contributions can be increased by a preliminary short journey along the "easier path" to the calculus.

"Wages have gone up 20 per cent this year." "And what about prices?" you ask before rejoicing at the approach of an era of prosperity. Johnny has gained fifteen pounds this year, but still wears that lean and hungry look, for he has also grown three inches. The ocean has made an inroad of five miles on this coastline. "What a disaster!" you feel, until you learn that it has taken a million years for this change to take place. *A comparison of two related changes* is called for in each case. We compare increases in wages with rise in prices before concluding that times are improving, increase in weight with growth in height before prescribing for Johnny, change in distance with change in time to realize that the speed of shoreline advance is slight.

Consider the comparison of change in *amount* with the corresponding change in *time* for a simple interest problem in which the principal is $100 and the rate 4 per cent. Initially the amount is $100; at the end of each year the amount is increased by the annual interest of $4, so that the amounts are

$$100 + 4 \cdot 1 \text{ at end of first year}$$
$$100 + 4 \cdot 2 \text{ at end of second year}$$
$$100 + 4 \cdot 3 \text{ at end of third year}$$
$$\text{etc.}$$

The formula connecting amount and time is obviously

$$A = 100 + 4t$$

where A is the amount and t the number of years. Newton referred to a variable like A, that is dependent on (is a function of) time, as a *fluent*.

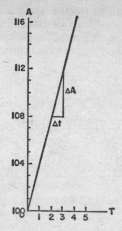

Figure 8.6

Note that this formula and its graph (Figure 8.6) are linear. The tabulation below indicates changes in time and the corresponding changes in amount.

Change in Time	Years t	$\$$ A	Change in Amount
1	0	100	4
1	1	104	4
1	2	108	4
1	3	112	4
	4	116	

The quotient,

$$\frac{\text{change in amount}}{\text{change in time}} = \frac{4}{1} = \frac{8}{2} = \frac{12}{3}$$

$$= \$4 \text{ per year}$$

The quotient derived from the table represents the change in amount for one year, or the *rate of change* of amount. In other words, the annual interest is the rate of change in amount with respect to time.

In the previous chapter, Δ (delta), the usual symbol for *change* or *difference*, was introduced. Applying this symbol, we assert that $\Delta A = 4$ and $\Delta t = 1$ between each pair of successive points in our table and graph. Then the

$$\textit{difference quotient} = \frac{\Delta A}{\Delta t} = \frac{4}{1} = 4 = \text{rate of change}$$

The fact that this difference quotient is the same between any pair of points is characteristic of a straight line graph; when a graph is not linear, the difference quotient varies, as will be indicated shortly. As another linear function, consider

$$y = \frac{2x}{3} + 5$$

If the values 0, 3, 6, 9, etc. are substituted for x and the corresponding values of y are found, the coordinates of points on the straight line graph are obtained (Figure 8.7). The changes Δy and Δx are tabulated below and lead to the

$$\text{difference quotient} = \frac{\Delta y}{\Delta x} = \frac{2}{3} \text{ for this line}$$

Δx	x	y	Δy
3	0	5	2
3	3	7	2
3	6	9	2
3	9	11	2
	12	13	

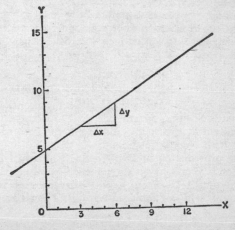

Figure 8.7

In other words, whatever the meaning of y and x, the rate of change in y is 2/3 of a unit for each unit change in x.

The rate of change $\Delta y / \Delta x$ is also termed the *slope of the line*. It is evident that this rate is actually connected with the ordinary "slope" of an incline. Here Δy represents the *vertical* rise from point to point, Δx the *horizontal* progress. The ratio of the two lengths tells what the rise in height is for one unit of horizontal advance. The greater the ratio, the steeper the slope. In our first illustration, the slope 4 gives a steeper line than the slope 2/3 in our second illustration.

By an examination of

$$y = 4x + 100$$

and

$$y = \frac{2x}{3} + 5$$

we see that the slopes 4 and 2/3 appear as the coefficient of x in the equation. We shall now prove that this is generally true. When a linear equation (for a nonvertical line) is put into the general form

$$y = ax + b$$

we can consider any two points satisfying this relation. Let the x-coordinates of these points be c and d, respectively. Then, by substitution in this equation, the corresponding y-coordinates are $ac + b$ and $ad + b$. Studying changes, we have

$$\Delta x = d - c \begin{cases} c \\ d \end{cases} \begin{array}{c|c} x & y \\ \hline c & ac + b \\ d & ad + b \end{array} \Big\} \Delta y = ad - ac = a(d - c)$$

and slope

$$\frac{\Delta y}{\Delta x} = a$$

since the factor $d - c$ divides out. Then the slope of

$$y = -\frac{3x}{2} + 5$$

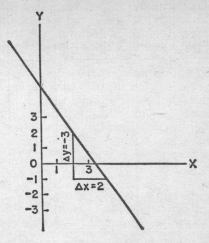

Figure 8.8

is $-3/2$. In other words,

$$\frac{\Delta y}{\Delta x} = -\frac{3}{2} = \frac{-3}{2} = \frac{3}{-2}$$

This means that when x increases 2, y decreases 3 (see Figure 8.8), or when x decreases 2, y increases 3.

Let us apply the notion of rate of change to some concrete situations. The following is a timetable showing the time of arrival and departure of a train at various stations. We have filled in the columns t (time), s (distance), Δs, Δt, and $\Delta s/\Delta t$ and plotted the data in Figure 8.9.

In the picture we have five different line segments representing the various portions of the trip. The five values of $\Delta s/\Delta t$ indicate the slopes of these segments, and also the velocity of the train from point to point. From A to B this velocity was 50 miles an hour; during the first stop the velocity was naturally zero; then the train proceeded at 40 miles an hour, etc.

To get the average rate for the entire trip, we seek the constant rate the train would have followed if it had proceeded uniformly from A to D without stopping. The picture of its motion would have been a straight-line segment from the first to the last points of the graph. The slope of

Δs (miles)	s (distance in miles)	Town	s (time in hours)	Δt (hours)	$\dfrac{\Delta s}{\Delta t}$ (miles per hour)
	0	dep. A	9:00		
25				½	50
	25	arr. B	9:30		
0				⅙	0
	25	dep. B	9:40		
20				½	40
	45	arr. C	10:10		
0				⅙	0
	45	dep. C	10:20		
15				¼	60
	60	arr. D	10:35		

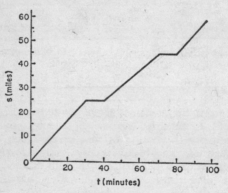

Figure 8.9

this line would have been the uniform velocity followed. In other words, this slope represents the average rate from A to D. Reading from either the graph or the table, we see that, from the first to the last points,

$$\Delta s = 60$$

$$\Delta t = 1\frac{7}{12}$$

$$\frac{\Delta s}{\Delta t} = \frac{60}{19/12} = 37.9 \text{ mi. per hr.}$$

This exercise illustrates how the quotient $\Delta y/\Delta x$ (above $\Delta s/\Delta t$) is useful even when the picture of a situation is not a single straight line. In our example the picture was a broken line, and in other cases it will be a curved line. We see that in such situations $\Delta y/\Delta x$ will give an average rate of change between two points.

As a further illustration let us now consider the famous apple whose fall is supposed to have initiated the theory of universal gravitation. It is shown in this theory that the formula

$$s = 16t^2 \qquad (t \text{ seconds, } s \text{ feet})$$

governs the motion of the apple.* Let us suppose that it took the apple exactly 1 second to fall. By the formula, we see that it fell 16 feet. Then

Δt	t	s	Δs
	0	0	
1			16
	1	16	

$\dfrac{\Delta s}{\Delta t} = \dfrac{16}{1} = 16$ ft. per sec. *(average velocity during the second)*

Was the apple moving 16 feet per second when it hit the ground? Evidently not for, as we know, the apple started with no velocity at all and increased its speed under gravitational attraction. Hence, since it averaged 16 feet per second, its velocity must have been greater than this at the end of the first second to balance its slow initial speed. Using the formula, we can find where the apple was at the end of half a second. Then

Δt	t	s	Δs
	1/2	4	
1/2			12
	1	16	

Thus $\dfrac{\Delta s}{\Delta t} = \dfrac{12}{1/2} = 24$ ft. per sec. *(average velocity during the half-second preceding impact)*

---

* Strictly correct only if the apple falls in a vacuum. The factor 16 is approximate also.

Similarly,

Δt	t	s	Δs
	3/4	9	
1/4			7
	1	16	

$\dfrac{\Delta s}{\Delta t} = \dfrac{7}{1/4} = 28$ ft. per sec. (*average velocity during the last quarter-second*)

Again,

Δt	t	s	Δs
	7/8	49/4	
1/8			15/4
	1	16	

$\dfrac{\Delta s}{\Delta t} = \dfrac{15/4}{1/8} = 30$ ft. per sec. (*average velocity during the last eighth-second*)

Finally,

Δt	t	s	Δs
	0.99	15.6816	
0.01			0.3184
	1	16	

$\dfrac{\Delta s}{\Delta t} = \dfrac{0.3184}{0.01} = 31.84$ ft. per sec. (*average velocity during the last hundredth of a second*)

It requires no Sherlock Holmes to sense that this last approximation is the best indication of the velocity of the apple when it hits the ground.

Now this simple fact is at the basis of the differential calculus. To get the *instantaneous rate*, in this case, we let Δt get smaller and smaller. Notice that Δs gets smaller too. The *limiting value* of $\Delta s/\Delta t$ is called the *instantaneous rate of change* or *derivative* of s with respect to t. In our particular problem, we have taken Δt as small as 0.01. We could take Δt as small as 0.001, 0.0001, etc. If we did so, we should find $\Delta s/\Delta t$ to have a value closer and closer to 32. We could get a value as close to 32 as we pleased by taking Δt small enough. This value, 32 feet per second, is the limiting value of $\Delta s/\Delta t$ as Δt approaches zero. Better and better average rates are obtained by taking smaller and smaller intervals, but there is no "best" average rate, since if the rate for any interval, however small, is figured, you can always furnish a still better rate by decreasing the interval further. The *limit* does the trick because it is a number to which all "good" rates are close.

Newton used the term *fluent* for the dependent variable in a function of time. Thus he would have called *s* a fluent in the function, $s = 16t^2$, which we have been discussing. He used the word *fluxion* for the derivative or instantaneous rate of change of a fluent, and referred to calculus as *fluxions*. But we shall not always be handling fluents and fluxions. Therefore let us define the instantaneous rate of change or derivative for *any* functional relation associating two variables, *y* and *x*, in such a way that the value of *y* is determined by the value of *x*. If there is a limiting value of $\Delta y/\Delta x$, as Δx approaches zero, we shall call it the instantaneous rate of change of *y* with respect to *x*. The process of finding the derivative is called *differentiation*, and hence the term *differential calculus*.

Let us illustrate differentiation, that is, the finding of an instantaneous rate. Suppose that a 2-inch metal cube is heated. Just how fast will it expand? The formula for the volume of a cube is

$$V = x^3$$

By substituting values of the edge close to 2 and using this formula to find *V*, we shall be able to obtain good *average rates of expansion*. Using the accompanying table, we see that, if the edge were to increase

x (inches)	2	2.01	2.1	2.5	3	4
V (cubic inches)	8	8.1204	9.3	15.6	27	64

from 2 to 2.5 inches, then

change in $x = \Delta x = 0.5$
change in $V = \Delta V = 7.6$

and

$$\frac{\Delta V}{\Delta x} = \frac{7.6}{0.5} = 15.2 \text{ cu. in. per in.}$$

If the edge increases from 2 to 2.1,

$$\frac{\Delta V}{\Delta x} = \frac{1.3}{0.1} = 13 \text{ cu. in. per in. (see table above)}$$

If the edge increases from 2 to 2.01,

$$\frac{\Delta V}{\Delta x} = \frac{0.1204}{0.01} = 12.04 \text{ cu. in. per in.}$$

The rates 15.2, 13, 12.04 are evidently getting closer and closer to 12 cu. in. per in. By taking $\Delta x = 0.001, 0.0001$, etc. the average rate would come still closer to 12, which is the *limit* of the series of numbers, and the instantaneous rate of expansion of the cube with respect to its edge is 12 cu. in. per in. when $x = 2$.

Naturally, serious workers in the calculus do not use the excessive computation we have employed for determining a limit. They have exact meanings and systematic methods. We shall shortly indicate the nature of such techniques.

Since graphs have proved themselves so revealing on previous occasions, let us see what they will do for our concept of the derivative. Let us graph the formula $V = x^3$, which we have just used, for those values of the edge selected in the table above. In Figure 8.10 we have plotted

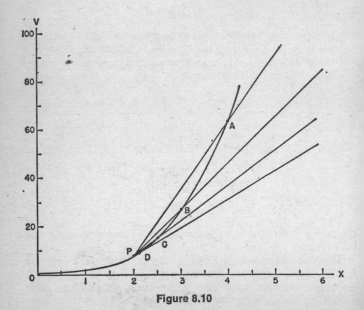

Figure 8.10

points and joined them by a smooth curve. Notice the relative positions of the lines PA, PB, PC, and PD with relation to the curve of the formula. They cut across it, and hence are called *secants*. But PC and PD cut off much less of the curve than PA and PB. The secant PC cuts off a very small segment, and PD barely grazes the curve. The line PC has the slope

$$\frac{\Delta V}{\Delta x} = \frac{7.6}{0.5} = 15.2$$

and PD has the slope 13. The *limiting* line, which all these secants approach, is called the *tangent* to the curve at P. It will touch the curve at P only. Thus the geometric meaning of a derivative, or instantaneous rate, is the *slope of a tangent to a curve*.

Let us now investigate more efficient ways of finding derivatives. Let us take the function $y = x^2$ and obtain a formula for the derivative for any value of x, that is, a formula for the slope of any tangent to the parabola $y = x^2$. In Figure 8.11 let P with coordinates (x, y) be any point on

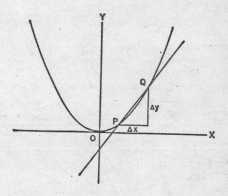

Figure 8.11

the curve. Then the coordinates of an adjacent point Q will be $(x + \Delta x, y + \Delta y)$.

The slope of the secant PQ is $\Delta y / \Delta x$. To find a formula for $\Delta y / \Delta x$, let us take cognizance of the fact that Q and P are points on the curve and hence their coordinates must satisfy the condition $y = x^2$, that is, for Q,

$$y + \Delta y = (x + \Delta x)^2$$

or

$$y + \Delta y = x^2 + 2x\Delta x + (\Delta x)^2$$

and for P,

$$y = x^2$$

Subtracting the second equation from the first,

$$\Delta y = 2x\Delta x + (\Delta x)^2$$

Dividing both sides by Δx,

$$\frac{\Delta y}{\Delta x} = 2x + \Delta x$$

This is the formula for the *slope of any secant* to the curve. If we desired the slope of the secant between the points whose x-coordinates are 3 and 5, respectively, we should have

$$x = 3 \quad \Delta x = 2$$

and

$$\frac{\Delta y}{\Delta x} = 2x + \Delta x = 6 + 2 = 8$$

To find the derivative or slope of the tangent, we want the limit of the slope of the secant as two points approach coincidence. If, in the formula just applied, namely,

$$\text{slope of secant} = 2x + \Delta x$$

we let Δx approach zero, that is, become smaller and smaller, the limit approached will obviously be $2x$, and this will be the formula for the derivative or slope of the tangent.

A symbol usually used for the derivative is dy/dx. Then, in this case,

$$\frac{dy}{dx} = 2x$$

Applying this formula, the slope of the tangent at the point where $x = 3$ is

$$\frac{dy}{dx} = 2x = 2 \cdot 3 = 6$$

and the slope of the tangent at any other point is readily found.

We might use this result a little differently. If we think of $y = x^2$ as the formula for the area of a square, $dy/dx = 2x$ is the formula for instantaneous rate of change of area relative to length of a side. Then if a square is expanding (as a result of temperature change, for example), its rate of expansion at the instant when its side is 3 inches is 6 square inches per inch.

The geometric interpretation of the derivative of a function as the slope of the tangent to the curve representing the function, is a good point of departure for discussing anticipators of Newton and Leibniz in the matter of the differential calculus. These forerunners were all interested in methods of constructing tangents to special curves, or to curves in general. This was, then, equivalent to finding derivatives for special functions, or for all functions. Fermat's consideration of tangents was, except for symbolism, virtually that explained above. He studied them in connection with maximum and minimum problems, handling these questions much as we shall later on. But then he went further and considered the more general idea that economy is not limited to specific problems but is an intrinsic characteristic of natural phenomena. He enunciated a "principle of least time" and from it deduced the laws of geometrical optics. Later such principles became the typical issues of the calculus of variations, an advanced calculus treating very general maxima and minima.

Archimedes had considered only one special case of tangent construction (or finding a derivative), namely, that connected with his favorite curve, the one we call the spiral of Archimedes. This is the faint inkling of differential calculus to which we have alluded. Nothing else was contributed until Fermat's time. He came closest to the ideas of the differential calculus, but there were others who contributed to the development by considering special cases or particular formulas. They were Descartes; Evangelista Torricelli (1608–1647), the mathematical physicist connected with the theory of the barometer; Isaac Barrow; Gilles Persone de Roberval (1602–1675); Johannes Hudde (1633–1704), mayor of Amsterdam. René François Walther (1622–1685), Baron de Sluse and Canon of Liège, studied Fermat's method and improved on it. There is no doubt that Newton's method of constructing tangents was identical with the De Sluse procedure, and in 1673, Newton actually gave priority to De Sluse, and at another time gave credit to Fermat and Barrow.

In the study of differential calculus, formulas for the derivatives of many types of function are established. In a fashion similar to that used for showing that the derivative of $y = x^2$ is $dy/dx = 2x$, it can be shown that the derivative for any power of x,

$$y = x^n$$

is

$$\frac{dy}{dx} = nx^{n-1}$$

Putting the symbols into words, the derivative is equal to the *exponent multiplied by the base with exponent reduced by 1*. In formal calculus this rule is proved to hold where n is *any* rational number. Hence n may be positive or negative or zero, integral or fractional.

Thus the derivative of

$$y = x^4$$

is

$$\frac{dy}{dx} = 4x^3$$

and the derivative of

$$y = x^7$$

is

$$\frac{dy}{dx} = 7x^6$$

and the derivative of

$$y = x \text{ (that is, } y = x^1)$$

is

$$\frac{dy}{dx} = 1x^0 = 1$$

If a coefficient is present, then the derivative of

$$y = ax^n$$

is

$$\frac{dy}{dx} = nax^{n-1}$$

The fact that the coefficient is carried along may be justified by a specific instance. Let us refer to page 268, where we derived the fact that if

$$y = x^2$$

then

$$\frac{dy}{dx} = 2x$$

If we go through a similar derivation for

$$y = 5x^2$$

then

$$y + \Delta y = 5(x + \Delta x)^2$$

or

$$y + \Delta y = 5x^2 + 10x\Delta x + 5(\Delta x)^2$$

But

$$y = 5x^2$$

Hence, by subtraction,

$$\Delta y = 10x\Delta x + 5(\Delta x)^2$$

and

$$\frac{\Delta y}{\Delta x} = 10x + 5\Delta x$$

Let Δx approach zero. Then, in the limit,

$$\frac{dy}{dx} = 10x$$

Now compare this procedure with that on page 267, and notice that the effect of the coefficient 5 is merely that all terms in the right member of each equation are multiplied by 5. Hence the net result is a derivative 5 times as great. Thus the derivative of

$$y = 3x^5$$

is

$$\frac{dy}{dx} = 15x^4$$

and the derivative of

$$y = 3x$$

is

$$\frac{dy}{dx} = 3x^0 = 3$$

and the derivative of

$$y = 4, \text{ (that is, } 4x^0)$$

is

$$\frac{dy}{dx} = 0 \cdot 4x^{-1} = 0$$

(if we assume that the fundamental law holds for $n = 0$).
    The derivative of any constant is zero, for if

$$y = a \text{ (that is, } ax^0)$$

then

$$\frac{dy}{dx} = 0 \cdot ax^{-1} = 0$$

The derivative of a sum is equal to the sum of the derivatives of the individual terms. The reason this law holds is that a derivative is a limit, and it is a fundamental fact that the limit of a sum is equal to the sum of the limits of terms. As an illustration of this statement, let x, y, z, and w represent four variables and S their sum, so that

$$S = x + y + z + w$$

Let us suppose that x, y, z, and w approach the limits 2, 4, 5, 10, respectively. We claim that S will approach the limit

$2 + 4 + 5 + 10 = 21$, for this reason: At some stage of their variation, x, y, z, and w will be within 0.001 of their goals. Suppose that at this stage each is 0.001 less than its limit. Then

$$S = 1.999 + 3.999 + 4.999 + 9.999 = 20.996$$

We see that S will be within 0.004 of 21. If the variables x, y, z, and w are within 0.000001 of their limits, then, at worst, S will be within 0.000004 of 21, so that S evidently approaches 21 as a limit. In fact, to repeat, it is generally true that the limit of a sum is equal to the sum of the limits of its terms.

Thus if

$$y = 2x^4 - 3x^3 + 7x^2 - 4x + 5$$
$$\frac{dy}{dx} = 8x^3 - 9x^2 + 14x - 4$$

and the derivative of

$$y = 3x^5 - 4x^3 + 2x - 7$$

is

$$\frac{dy}{dx} = 15x^4 - 12x^2 + 2$$

If the slope of the tangent to the curve

$$y = 3x^5 - 4x^3 + 2x - 7$$

at the point where $x = 1$ is desired, we merely substitute $x = 1$ in the formula for the derivative, thus obtaining

$$\text{slope} = \frac{dy}{dx} = 15 - 12 + 2 = 5$$

The fact that the derivative of

$$y = 3x$$

is

$$\frac{dy}{dx} = 3$$

that is, the derivative is a *constant*, can be readily interpreted graphically; $y = 3x$ can be pictured as a *line*. The tangent at any point is the line itself, and therefore its slope is always the same.

Since the slope of any line is a constant, the derivative of a linear expression should always be a constant. We see that this is actually the case. The derivative for any line

$$y = ax + b$$

is

$$\frac{dy}{dx} = a \quad \text{(a constant)}$$

The fact that the derivative of

$$y = 4$$

is

$$\frac{dy}{dx} = 0$$

can be interpreted by plotting the line $y = 4$ (see table and Figure 8.12). This is a line parallel to the X-axis. Its slope is actually zero.

x	y
0	4
1	4
2	4
3	4

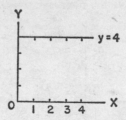

Figure 8.12

Let us apply our rules to a few practical problems. The distance s for stopping an automobile under normal conditions is given by the formula $s = 0.097V^2$, where s is measured in feet and V in miles per hour. Find how fast s increases with V when $V = 20$. First, differentiating in the formula, we have

$$\frac{ds}{dV} = 0.194V$$

Substituting $V = 20$,

$$\frac{ds}{dV} = 3.88 \text{ ft. per mi. per hr.}$$

that is, at the velocity under consideration (20 mi. per hr.), *the distance for stopping was increasing about 3.9 feet for each mile per hour increase in velocity.*

The arch of a certain bridge is parabolic, and the height (y ft.) above the water at any horizontal distance (x ft.) from the center is $y = 80 - 0.005x^2$. Find the slope of the bridge at any point (that is, the slope of the tangent) and, in particular, the slope 40 ft. from the center.

$$y = 80 - 0.005x^2$$
$$\frac{dy}{dx} = -0.01x$$
$$= (-0.01)(40) = -0.4 \quad \text{when} \quad x = 40$$

This means that for a horizontal advance of 10 ft., the tangent drops 4 ft. (see Figure 8.13).

To put the derivative to other uses, we remark that graphs of parabolas like those in Figure 8.13 and Figure 7.12d exhibit *maximum* or *minimum* points. Notice that at

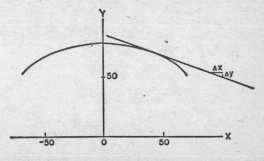

Figure 8.13

these highest and lowest points the tangent is horizontal, that is, its slope $dy/dx = 0$. Even if a graph is not a parabola, the derivative will be zero for *extrema*.

The fact that $dy/dx = 0$ at maximum and minimum points is useful in solving important practical problems. Suppose that a rectangular pasture, one side of which is bounded by a river, is to be fenced on the other three sides. What are the dimensions of the largest pasture that can be enclosed with 4000 ft. of fence? In Figure 8.14 we have represented

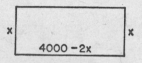

Figure 8.14

the unknown width of the pasture by x. Two sides of the fence are x ft. in length, and the third side must be 4000 − 2x. Let us call the area y. Then, since the area of a rectangle is equal to the product of the length by the width,

$$y = x(4000 - 2x)$$
$$y = 4000x - 2x^2$$

Now, it is just this quantity y, or $4000x - 2x^2$, which we desire to be a maximum. We could, of course, graph this equation for different values of x (different widths), and then, from the graph, estimate which value of x will produce the greatest area. Incidentally, this graph will be a quadratic parabola with a maximum point. If we recall, however, that the slope of the tangent is zero at a maximum point, we can avoid the work of graphing.

$$y = 4000x - 2x^2$$
$$\frac{dy}{dx} = 4000 - 4x$$
$$4000 - 4x = 0 \quad \text{at a maximum point}$$
$$\therefore 4x = 400$$
$$x = 1000$$
$$4000 - 2x = 2000$$

The dimensions of the rectangle should be 1000 ft. by 2000 ft.

Maximum and minimum problems can be solved approximately by the reading of a graph, but often this graph is difficult to construct with accuracy. Hence the technique of equating the derivative to zero is a most useful one.

To give another simple illustration of this fact: An agency agreed to conduct a tour for a group of 50 people at a rate of $400 each. In order to secure more tourists the agency agreed to deduct $5 from the cost of the trip for each additional person joining the group. What number of tourists would give the agency maximum gross receipts? (It was specified that 75 was the upper practical limit for the size of the group.)

If 6 people were to join the group, the reduction in the cost of the tour would be $30 per person. If 10 joined, it would be $50, etc. If we represent by x the unknown number of additional tourists, the reduction will be $5x$ dollars, and

$$\text{cost of tour} = 400 - 5x$$
$$\text{number of tourists} = 50 + x$$

If we multiply the number of tourists by the cost of the tour, we shall obtain the gross receipts of the company. Let y symbolize these gross receipts. Then

$$y = (400 - 5x)(50 + x)$$

or

$$y = 2000 + 150x - 5x^2$$

To find the maximum gross receipts, we use the technique of finding the derivative and equating the result to zero.

$$\frac{dy}{dx} = 150 - 10x$$
$$150 - 10x = 0$$
$$10x = 150$$
$$x = 15$$

If there are 15 additional tourists for maximum receipts, the number in the group will be 65.

To return momentarily to the process of differentiation, if

$$y = 2x^4 - 5x^3 + x^2 - 7x + 3$$

is a special formula or the equation of a curve or the expression of some physical law, then

$$\frac{dy}{dx} = 8x^3 - 15x^2 + 2x - 7$$

is its derivative, slope, or rate of change. Now one may find the derivative of a derivative, or the *second derivative*, symbolized by d^2y/dx^2. For the formula above,

$$\frac{d^2y}{dx^2} = 24x^2 - 30x + 2$$

Continuing, one may find the third, fourth, fifth, etc. derivatives. For the formula above,

$$\frac{d^3y}{dx^3} = 48x - 30$$

$$\frac{d^4y}{dx^4} = 48$$

$$\frac{d^5y}{dx^5} = 0$$

The most important derivatives in physical applications are the first and second, and these have various special meanings. For example, if x represents time and y distance, then dy/dx represents *velocity*. In this case d^2y/dx^2, the rate of change in velocity, is called the *acceleration*. The second derivative has other special interpretations, depending on the meaning of the related variables x and y. When the relation between x and y is graphed, then, in one interpretation, d^2y/dx^2 is associated with the *curvature* of the graph.

The meaning and use of higher derivatives are particular questions of the differential calculus. But in some applications of the calculus the situation is reversed—the derivative is known and the formula is to be determined. Suppose, for example, it is known that a ball is rolling down an incline, and that its velocity is changing at the constant rate of 10 ft. per sec. Rate of change of velocity is termed *acceleration*. Here we know that the acceleration

$$\frac{dV}{dt} = 10$$

It is not difficult to see that

$$V = 10t + c$$

for, if a derivative is constant, it must come from a linear function. In the equation, c is a numerical quantity or constant, to be determined by known physical conditions. For example, if we know that the ball was started down the incline with a velocity of 30 ft. per sec., that is, for

$$t = 0, \quad V = 30$$

we can substitute this information in

$$V = 10t + c$$

and get

$$30 = 10 \cdot 0 + c$$
$$c = 30$$

thus determining the constant in question. Then the formula for the velocity of the body at any time is

$$V = 10t + 30$$

We can use this formula to obtain another for the position of the ball at any time. *Velocity* is another name for *instantaneous rate of change of distance*, so that

$$V = 10t + 30$$

is equivalent to

$$\frac{ds}{dt} = 10t + 30$$

where s represents distance.

It is a little harder to guess this time, but not too difficult to see that

$$s = 5t^2 + 30t + k$$

where k is once again a constant to be determined by known physical conditions.

If we know that the ball started at a position 20 ft. from the top of the incline, that is, for

$$t = 0, \quad s = 20$$

we can substitute this information in the formula for s in order to obtain k.

$$20 = 5 \cdot 0 + 30 \cdot 0 + k$$
$$k = 20$$

and

$$s = 5t^2 + 30t + 20$$

In the problem just illustrated, ds/dt was given as a function of t, and then we found s as a function of t. This is the reverse of the first calculus process discussed, and hence it is called *antidifferentiation* or the finding of an *antiderivative*. Incidentally, the relation between ds/dt and t is described as a *differential equation*. If, then, we are given the differential equation

$$\frac{dy}{dx} = 3x^2 + 4x - 5$$

it is easy to guess that

$$y = x^3 + 2x^2 - 5x + c$$

and to sense the rule: *In each term raise the power by one and divide by the new exponent.*

It is not always easy to guess the formula for finding an antiderivative. Calculus has its set of rules and regulations for doing this. Whereas most of the functions that occur in elementary mathematics and science can be differentiated, even the most innocent-looking expressions may fail to be the derivatives of elementary functions. Then, too, it is evident that there will always be an unknown constant in the answer. Unless some additional information is given, it will not be possible to determine this constant.

In spite of these difficulties, antidifferentiation will handle many vital problems. Chief among the geometric types are the calculations of the *length* of a curve, or the *area* enclosed by a curve, or the *volume* bounded by a surface. Since Euclidean methods can handle only a limited number of curves and solids, the calculus is a far superior metric tool.

We shall give one illustration of how antidifferentiation will determine an area. Let us say that the shaded area, marked A in Figure 8.15, is a growing quantity, for our point of view demands that we consider all things in a state of flux. The small amount by which it grows when $P\ (x,\ y)$

moves to Q $(x + \Delta x, y + \Delta y)$ is marked ΔA. It is bounded by the curve, the X-axis, and the ordinates of P and Q. The area ΔA is made up of a rectangle, surmounted by a small triangular area, PQR, one side of which is the curve. We shall treat this little triangle as if it were a right triangle. If Δx, and hence Δy and ΔA, were very small, the error in this assumption would be negligible. Then

$$\Delta A = \text{rectangle} + \text{triangle}$$
$$\Delta A = y\Delta x + \tfrac{1}{2}\Delta x\Delta y$$

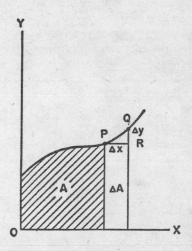

Figure 8.15

since the area of a triangle is one-half the product of base and height. Dividing both sides of this equation by Δx, we have

$$\frac{\Delta A}{\Delta x} = y + \tfrac{1}{2}\Delta y$$

Now if Δx approaches zero (see Figure 8.15), Δy and ΔA will do likewise. The limit of $\Delta A/\Delta x$ in this case is dA/dx and

$$\frac{dA}{dx} = y$$

that is, *the rate at which the area is changing at any point of a curve is equal to the height of the curve at that point.*

This proof lacks the mathematical rigor of twentieth-century standards, but even the great inventors of the calculus depended on intuition rather than logic at many points. Emulating them, we have given a demonstration sufficient for our present purpose.

To illustrate the use of the formula

$$\frac{dA}{dx} = y$$

let us find the area (Figure 8.16) under the curve $y = x^3$, and bounded by the curve, the X-axis, and the ordinates at $x = 1$ and $x = 4$.

$$\frac{dA}{dx} = y$$

or

$$\frac{dA}{dx} = x^3$$

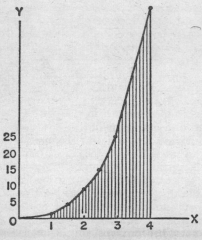

Figure 8.16

is the differential equation in this case. We readily guess that

$$A = \frac{1}{4}x^4 + c$$

is the *general solution* of the differential equation.

Now in the special case of a growing area that starts at $x = 1$ and ends at $x = 4$, we know that $A = 0$ when $x = 1$; that is, initially there was no area. Substituting this *initial condition* in the general solution

$$A = \frac{1}{4}x^4 + c$$

we have

$$0 = \frac{1}{4} \cdot 1 + c$$
$$-\frac{1}{4} = c$$

and

$$A = \frac{1}{4}x^4 - \frac{1}{4}$$

is a particular solution, the specific formula for the growing area.

We want the value of this area when it has grown to the position $x = 4$. Substituting this value, we have

$$A = \frac{1}{4} \cdot 4^4 - \frac{1}{4} = 63\frac{3}{4} \text{ square units}$$

This is an area Euclid could not measure—in fact, would not have considered—since the curve $y = x^3$ was unknown to him. Thus a little simple algebra will measure an infinite variety of areas unknown to Greek geometers.

An extension to three dimensions of the work involved in obtaining $dA/dx = y$ will give $dV/dx = A$. By increasing the dimension of each quantity by one, we can get this formula by analogy. Thus A (area) becomes V (volume); y (length) becomes A (area). In the first of these formulas y is the length of a line segment that varies its position, that is, moves so as to generate the required area. Then by analogy A is a generating area forming a volume as it moves. Therefore we can find the volume of those solids for which it is possible to express the area of a moving cross-section in terms of the distance from some fixed point, providing we can find an antiderivative for the expression thus obtained.

Suppose that we desire the volume of the cone of Figure 8.17, which is such that the radius of the circular cross-

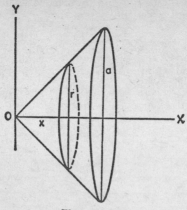

Figure 8.17

section is always equal to the distance from the origin, in other words, $r = x$. Then

$$\frac{dV}{dx} = A$$

leads to the differential equation

$$\frac{dV}{dx} = \pi x^2$$

whose general solution is

$$V = \tfrac{1}{3}\pi x^3 + c$$

But the growing volume was just starting when $x = 0$; that is, there is the initial condition, $V = 0$ when $x = 0$. Substituting this initial condition in the general solution,

$$0 = \tfrac{1}{3}\pi \cdot 0 + c$$
$$0 = c$$

and

$$V = \tfrac{1}{3}\pi x^3$$

is the particular solution, giving a formula for the growing volume. If the total height of the cone is a, and accordingly the radius of the base is also a, then the volume $V = \frac{1}{3}\pi x^3$ will grow until $x = a$ and

$$V = \frac{1}{3}\pi a^3$$

Again, suppose that the volume of the horn in Figure 8.18 is desired, and we are told that the radius of a cross-section is given by the formula

$$r = 0.04x^2$$

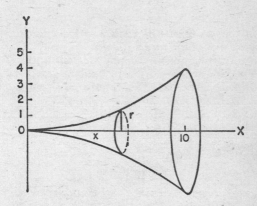

Figure 8.18

and the depth of the horn is 10. Then

$$\frac{dV}{dx} = A$$

leads to a differential equation

$$\frac{dV}{dx} = 0.0016\,\pi x^4$$
$$V = 0.00032\pi x^5 + c$$

Since

$$V = 0 \quad \text{when} \quad x = 0$$
$$0 = 0 + c$$
$$c = 0$$
$$V = 0.00032\,\pi x^5$$

Since the depth is 10,

$$V = 0.00032\,\pi(10)^5$$
$$V = 320\,\pi \text{ cubic units}$$

Numerous physical formulas can be found by antidifferentiation—for example, *the work done by a variable force.* Thus

$$\frac{dW}{dx} = F$$

or the *instantaneous rate of change of work with respect to distance is equal to the force.*

If the force required to stretch a certain spring x inches is $F = 20x$, how much work will be done in elongating the spring 5 inches? We have the differential equation

$$\frac{dW}{dx} = 20x$$

whose general solution is

$$W = 10x^2 + c$$

Since

$$W \;=\; 0 \quad \text{when } x = 0, c = 0$$

and

$$W \;=\; 10x^2 = 250, \quad \text{for } x = 5$$

We have seen how areas and volumes can be found by antidifferentiation. An analogous geometric problem is that of finding the *length* of a curve, *rectification,* as it is called. One might think that it would be easier to find a length by antidifferentiation than an area or a volume, but this is *not* the case, as we have already pointed out (page 252). Therefore, instead of going into the algebraic intricacies of rectification, it will be treated theoretically, and in the process, there will be a return to the questions which launched the present discussion of the calculus. From the original point of view, that of the early numerical integration, the approximate length of a curve PQ (Figure 8.19) can be found by measuring the length of the numerous small straight chords PA, AB, BC, etc. The closer together A, B, C, etc.

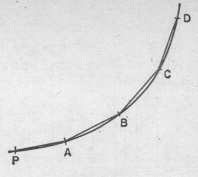

Figure 8.19

are, and the shorter the chords, the better they will approximate the arcs *PA, AB, BC,* etc. The sum

$$PA + AB + BC + \ldots$$

is the approximate length of the curve. The actual length of the curve is defined to be the *limit* of this sum as the chords become smaller and smaller but more and more numerous. Finding this limit, if it exists, is described as *integration*.

Again, the area under the curve in Figure 8.20 can be approximated by finding the sum of the numerous small rectangles. The more numerous and the narrower these rectangles, the better the approximation. The limit of the sum as the rectangles grow more and more numerous, and their widths tend toward zero, is defined to be the required area. Once again, finding this limit, if it exists, is called *integration,* and one would say that the area as well as the length above are *integrals* in the sense of Mengoli-Cauchy (page 283). But we have already found areas like that in Figure 8.20 by the process of *antidifferentiation.* The fact that, in most instances, antidifferentiation may be substituted for integration, or that integration is the process *inverse* to differentiation is known as the *fundamental theorem of the calculus.* A formal proof of this theorem will not be given. It has, however, been applied right along when the relatively simple reversal of differentiation was performed in preference to a consideration of limits of sets of approximating sums. The notation used by Leibniz for the *integral sign* is a me-

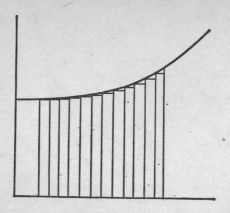

Figure 8.20

dieval S, standing for *summa*, and the area of Figure 8.16 can be represented by

$$A = \int_1^4 x^3 dx$$

Nevertheless the actual algebraic procedure for finding the numerical value of this area is the *same*, whether one uses the Leibnizian symbolism with its underlying notion of the limit of a variable, or employs the antidifferentiation process. That this is so in the vast majority of problems where a geometric or physical measurement is required was proved by Newton and Leibniz, a theorem which was their most vital theoretical contribution to that subject for whose complete creation their followers were much too eager to give them full credit.

Chapter 9

Determinism and Its Creators

To consider Newton merely an important figure in the development of the calculus is to give an inadequate picture of his position in the history of mathematics and science. Therefore we must now examine the *raison d'être* for his formulation of the "fluxion of a fluent," namely, the Newtonian *dynamics* which related forces to motions, terrestrial and celestial, and which culminated in his cosmological theory of universal gravitation. Our purpose is not only to consider Newton as a physicist, but also to establish a link with mathematical giants still to come—Euler, Lagrange, Laplace, Hamilton, and Jacobi—who developed Newton's mechanics to greater and greater heights in accordance with a principle that has come to be labeled "determinism."

The doctrine of scientific determinism, or the principle of causality, as it is sometimes called, originated in the fact that the motion of a particle in the mechanics of Newton, or of a system of particles in the analytic mechanics of Euler and Lagrange, or of a planet in the celestial mechanics of Laplace, is completely and unambiguously *determined* for all the future by the knowledge of the position and velocity of the particle or set of particles or celestial body at a single instant of time. This is the result of the fundamental postulates of each type of mechanics, in which laws are all formulated in a certain way. To quote Poincaré once more: "For Newton a physical law was a relation between the present state of the world and its condition immediately after, or, in other words, physical laws are differential equations."

Now in the previous chapter we solved some very elementary differential equations. In one case, a pair of such equations described a particular motion (page 279). In that example the given initial position and velocity enabled us to obtain definite algebraic formulas *determining* the position and the velocity of an object at all future times. Therefore this sort of physical determinism can come as no surprise to us. It seems a mere question of seeking *exact* formulation.

So much for determinism in the best sense of the word. But the virtue of the principle is destroyed if one extrapolates its application to nonscientific situations or converts it into a dogma for physics by insisting that a law of physics *must* be a rigorous rule that determines the evolution of a physical "system" uniquely through all of time when the state of the system at a single instant is known. Physicists did consider the doctrine a "must" up to the day of James Clerk Maxwell (1831–1879). Then his ideas and, later, modern quantum theory with its nondeterminate probabilistic laws showed the value of "may" instead of the "must" for determinism. Before that time, however, certain philosophers seized on the principle of causality with great avidity and proceeded to envision all of nature and human affairs in a mechanistic light, with no "free will" or the like.

We could give an account of the lives and works of the mathematicians who will be mentioned in this chapter without ever mentioning determinism, but we have discussed the idea in order to unify the mathematical activity of the eighteenth and early nineteenth centuries, and also so that we may be able to contrast the deterministic viewpoint with that of the probabilistic (statistical) mathematics and physics to be discussed in the next few chapters.

To start the story of determinism from the beginning, we must consider young Newton's thoughts at the time when the theory of universal gravitation was germinating in his fertile mind. Although the *Principia*, in which his classic laws of motion are stated, did not appear until 1687, he conceived the postulates of dynamics during the most creative period of his life, the years 1665–1667. Posterity clings to the legend of the falling apple as the inspiration for universal gravitation, but if Newton considered the motion of any terrestrial object at all, the thought was a momentary one, for he was more interested in cosmic motions and theories.

From antiquity up to the period just before Galileo (1564–1642) and Descartes, the explanation of celestial motion was almost as inadequate as having spirits, genii, or demons (figuratively, if not literally) shove the moon and the planets around their curved orbits in much the same way that humans or animals push or pull in order to support mundane motions. Even Kepler believed that planets held to their orbits or that, in general, objects remained in motion because they were sustained by some supporting force. With Galileo, the earlier theories of motion were completely altered. It is true that he had some precursors, for example, the Venetian, Giovanni Battista Benedetti, who, in his *Diversarum Speculationum Mathematicarum et Physicarum* (1585), set down ideas on accelerated motion that were akin to those which Galileo was soon to demonstrate experimentally at Pisa.

Galileo's concept, incorporated in the first two of Newton's laws of motion, was that *no force at all* is required to sustain motion, and that a body moving under no force enjoys constant speed in a constant direction. (If this speed is zero, the body is at rest.) If any force acts upon a body, Galileo, and then Newton, assumed that the speed or the direction or both must vary. They indicated that experimental data can merely *approximate* predictions made from their assumptions, since one cannot realize physical objects moving under no force at all. Galileo gave formulas for the distances, velocities, and accelerations of bodies falling near the earth's surface. We believe that young Newton, sent home from Cambridge to Woolsthorpe, Lincolnshire, during an epidemic of bubonic plague, stated to himself, if not to the world, the two laws that generalized Galileo's results:

Every body will continue in a state of rest or of uniform motion (constant velocity) in a straight line unless it is compelled by some external force to change that state.

If there is an impressed force, the time rate of change of momentum is proportional to this force and takes place in the direction in which the force acts.

In the second law of motion, *momentum* signifies the product of mass and velocity. Then the force is proportional to the *derivative* of *mv* with respect to *t* (time), or since mass was considered constant in classic mechanics, the second law states that

$$F = km \frac{dv}{dt}$$

where k is a proportionality factor and dv/dt, the exact rate of change of velocity, is the instantaneous *acceleration*. Symbolizing that by a, we have $F = kma$ as a concise formulation of Newton's second law. A still simpler form,

$$F = ma$$

is possible providing $k = 1$. This can be accomplished if suitable units of measurement are used, for example, if time is measured in *seconds*, distance in *feet*, force (hence weight) in *pounds*, and mass in *slugs*. For a reader not familiar with the *slug*, let it be stated that a *slug* is the mass of a body weighing about 32.2 pounds at the earth's surface.

In classical physics the mass of a body is assumed to be constant or unchanging, in accordance with the law of conservation of mass. The weight of a body, on the other hand, varies with its position, being more at the poles of the earth than at the equator, and much less on the moon than on the earth. But, as Newton wrote, "By experiments made with the greatest accuracy, I have always found the quantity of matter in bodies to be proportional to their weight." Thus, if m and w represent mass and weight, respectively, then, at sea level, $w = 32.2m$ or $m = w/32.2$ (approximately) if m is measured in slugs and w in pounds.

What was the thread of thought leading from the laws of motion to universal gravitation, where Newton first assumed that heavenly bodies exert forces on one another, and then went further in seeing such forces as a universal property of all the matter in the universe? The ultimate Newtonian postulate assigned a specific numerical measure to the gravitational attraction between any two particles of matter in the physical world. If the theory actually was initiated in the apple orchard of a Lincolnshire hamlet, the first question could have been: If the earth's gravitational force is responsible for the fall of the apple, how far does such gravitational influence extend—to the highest mountains, to the moon, or beyond?

In the orchard or in his study, somewhere, sometime in 1666, the Cambridge student might have continued: Since the moon is not at rest and does not move with constant speed in a straight line, there must be an external force pulling on it at every instant. Is this force due to the gravitational influence of the earth? If so, this influence is not merely a terrestrial phenomenon, confined to Woolsthorpe apples, or objects dropped from the leaning tower of Pisa, but it extends at least as far as the moon. Next—none of the planets fly off on tangents. What forces deflect them from straight-line paths and keep them in orbits around the sun? Perhaps the sun acts on them in the way the earth seems to draw the apple and moon toward its center. Then the sun must exert its own particular gravitational influence that attracts all the other objects in the solar system. Finally, the pulling of one heavenly body on another exists throughout the *universe* and is not a phenomenon limited to the force that makes nearby objects fall to the earth's surface.

Granting that this or any hypothesis is a good one, it must be given exact mathematical formulation so that it will lead to numerical results that can be compared with observations in order to provide a test of the theory in question. Thus what Newton required was a formula for the universal gravitational force that he imagined—that is, a function expressing the dependence of gravitational force on other variables. He assumed that the gravitational pull, influence, or attraction, exerted by a body would depend on its mass, and that a huge mass like the sun would be able to pull much harder than a relatively smaller planetary mass. But in spite of the tug of the earth on the moon, the latter does not fall to the earth, whereas the apple does. Again, the gravitational pull of the huge solar mass is just sufficient to divert the planets from linear to elliptic orbits, but not large enough to make them fall into the central fire. Therefore, Newton reasoned, gravitational force must diminish with distance. The simplest law he might have assumed would have been that the force varies inversely with the distance, that is, $F = k/d$, where F represents force, d distance, and k is a constant that contains other factors like the masses which are pulling on one another and the adjustments for particular units of measure. This would mean that when distance is doubled, gravitational force would be half as great, when it is trebled, the force would be one-third as great, etc. But Newton felt that gravitational attraction must fall off more rapidly than inverse variation permits. Hence he decided tentatively that this force might vary inversely as the *square* of the distance, that is, that

$$F = \frac{k}{d^2}$$

This implies that when distance is doubled, other factors remaining constant, the gravitational tug is one-fourth as great; when distance is trebled, the gravitational pull is one-ninth as great, etc. When, *ultimately*, Newton expressed k in terms of the masses, M and m, of the two bodies pulling on one another, his law became

$$F = \frac{GMm}{d^2}$$

where G is the "gravitational constant." By suitable choice of the units of mass and distance, one can obtain $G = 1$, and the force of attraction is just Mm/d^2. Also, in its initial form, the principle was applied only to bodies that were mass "particles." In its final form it became the *law of universal gravitation:* Any two particles of matter in the universe attract one another with a force directly proportional to the product of their masses and inversely proportional to the square of the distance between them.

But in 1666, all of this was *conjecture* on Newton's part, and he wished to provide a deductive *proof* that gravitational force actually obeys the inverse-square law, $F = k/d^2$. He was able to do so by assuming the validity of Kepler's third law. In later years Newton reversed the process by assuming the inverse-square law and deducing Kepler's formula from it. In a logical sense, one would say that the two laws are equivalent, or that, more generally, if the truth of proposition p implies the truth of proposition q and, conversely, q implies p, then p and q are equivalent propositions (Chapter 6).

Whether Kepler's third law is assumed and Newton's inverse-square law is deduced, or vice versa, would not matter in a pure (abstract) mathematical science. But in physical science, postulates are supposed to correspond approximately to reality. Therefore Newton devised a test in which he carried out certain calculations based on the actual motion of the moon. In his own words, "I compared the force requisite to keep the Moon in her Orb with the force of gravity at the surface of the Earth, and found the answer pretty nearly."

The "pretty nearly" may explain why he did not publicize the inverse-square law in 1666 when he first deduced it, but postponed the release for sixteen years. In his test, he had argued as follows: The distance of the moon from the earth's center is about 60 times the radius of the earth, and therefore, *if the inverse-square law is true* (in the physical universe), the gravitational effect of the earth on a unit of mass near its surface must be 3600 times its effect on such a mass located on the moon. But the "effect" for a body on the earth's surface is the weight of the body, given by the formula $w = 32.2m$. Therefore, if $m = 1$, $w = 32.2$ lb. Dividing this by 3600 gives 0.00895 lb. as the tug of the earth on a unit mass on the moon. But Newton's computation from the moon's motion (*without assuming the inverse-square law*) was 0.00775 lb., and this may have made him doubt the inverse-square law, for his "pretty nearly" signified a 15 percent difference between his test result and that predicted by the inverse-square law. But what had happened was that he had used 3440 miles as an estimate of the earth's radius, based on his assumption that a degree on a meridian measures 60 miles.

Although Newton is supposed to have been a typically "absent-minded professor," it is hard to reconcile the triviality of such a mistake with the magnitude of the idea being tested. Pemberton, a friend, said that "being absent from books" at Woolsthorpe, Newton confused English miles with nautical miles, or that he took the wrong value from an unreliable text he had with him at the farm. But it appears that although Picard made accurate measurements of the earth's radius in 1672, and gave 69.1 miles as the length of a meridional degree, Newton apparently did not become aware of this good approximation until 1682. The reader may wonder why Newton's tardiness matters at all except as an illustration of the remoteness of genius from all ordinary activity or the inability of great mathematicians to carry on everyday arithmetic. But the upshot of his failure to release the inverse-square law at the very beginning was an ugly priority dispute with the physicist Robert Hooke, with whom he had already begun to quarrel around 1672 concerning the nature of light. When this was combined with the controversy with Leibniz on the invention of the calculus, it cast a long shadow on Newton's personal life.

There are alternative explanations to the error-in-arithmetic supposition. Some feel that Newton was a perfectionist and would not accept the figure 32.2 pounds, which was based on Galileo's experiments, and that he wished to derive this result theoretically. This he was not prepared to do in 1666, for he had not advanced sufficiently far in the integral calculus. What he required was a theorem he finally established in 1685: The gravitational attraction between two homogeneous spheres acts as if their total masses are concentrated at their centers. The proof of this proposition and its importance in the theory of universal gravitation were revealed in the *System of the World*, the last and crowning portion of Newton's *Principia*. The theorem enabled him to treat heavenly bodies as if they were *particles* to which the universal law $F = GMm/d^2$ applies.

In 1684 Newton had released some of his ideas in a short treatise entitled *De Motu Corporum* (On the Motion of Bodies). This work, revised and enlarged, was to become Book I of the *Principia*. Neither the *De Motu* nor Newton's *chef-d'oeuvre* would ever have been issued if not for the persuasive powers of Edmond Halley (1656–1742), the great astronomer. He coaxed Newton into publication. The result was that the manuscript of *Philosophiae Naturalis Principia Mathematica* was presented to the British Royal Society on April 28, 1686. On May 19 the Society's council decided that "Mr. Newton's work should be printed forthwith." But the Society's treasury was completely depleted by the previous expenditure for the publication of a book on the habits of fish. Halley stepped into the breach, thereby rendering an immeasurable service to Newton, to the Royal Society, and to all of scientific posterity. The astronomer, who was in no sense a wealthy man, published the *Principia* at his own expense. Thus, in July 1687 there appeared the greatest work of science ever written, one small quarto volume of five-hundred pages, selling at nine shillings.

Some of the ideas in Book III of the *Principia* will eternally link Newton and Halley in men's minds. In this part of his work, Newton set down his notions on comets. Their paths had been considered *parabolic*. Hence a comet would travel on an open curve and never return to a previous position. Newton showed, however, that the parabolic path is just an approximation, that the orbits are actually elongated ellipses, and hence the motion of comets is periodic and they must return after a very long time. Halley applied Newton's comet theory to calculate the orbits of all comets for which he had any records of observations. He found that at intervals of approximately 75 years brilliant comets had been seen, specifically in the years 1531, 1607, and 1682, this last appearance having been observed by Halley himself. The Newtonian computations indicated *all three* comet orbits to be the same elongated celestial ellipse, that is, in reality there was *only one* comet, with a period of about 75 years!

The deterministic laws of universal gravitation predicted that *Halley's comet* would reappear at the end of 1758 or the beginning of 1759. Although neither Newton nor Halley was alive to witness the fact, the comet returned within a month of the time they had estimated. Moreover, it returned after another 76 years, in 1835, and then, after a 75-year interval, in 1910. Readers may question grandparents and great-grandparents about that last appearance. Even in 1910 some of the older superstitions about comets were still circulating. Halley's comet was substituted for the "bogeyman," and children were told that if they did not behave, the world would end when it passed through the tail of the comet.

To leave superstition and return to the *Principia*, we can quote Einstein's evaluation: "Nature was an open book to Newton." To give a brief description of the contents of the work which Laplace, the "Newton of France," termed the "most outstanding production of human genius in all of time," one should start with the introduction. There Newton discusses his space-time notions, acknowledges his debt to Galileo, and deduces from the latter's experimental results the three famous laws of motion. In Book I of the *Principia* there is the first *printed* statement by Newton concerning the discovery of the method of fluxions, also the deduction of Kepler's law from the inverse-square postulate, and the general "two-body problem." In that problem the orbits of earth and moon, sun and a single planet, etc. are deduced under the assumption that the gravitational tug of other celestial bodies is negligible. In the same portion of the *Principia* Newton deals with laws of force other than the inverse square. Such laws are applicable to the mechanics of rigid bodies. Newton shows that they lead to oscillatory motions, paths that are not closed, and so on. Book I concludes with material that seems irrelevant—Newton's thoughts on the "corpuscular" theory of light.

The second book of the *Principia* deals with motion in a resisting medium. Today these ideas would apply to the movement of ships, underwater missiles, bullets, rockets, and planes in the air. Newton assumed that for certain speeds, $F = kv$, or that the resistance of the medium is proportional to the velocity of the moving object, and that for higher speeds $F = kv^2$. The paths deduced from such axioms were suitable for ballistics and aerodynamics until modern times, when speeds far beyond any in Newton's experience became available.

Book II also contains the fundamentals of the science of hydrodynamics, the first printed mathematical discussion of wave motion, and a germ of the "calculus of variations" (Chapter 23). Newton discusses the optical "diffraction" phenomena which the Italian Grimaldi had first discovered. These are best explained by considering light to be made up of waves rather than corpuscles. Among the multitude of other physical concepts in Book II is Newton's notion of sound. He related how he had once determined the velocity of sound approximately by listening to the echoes in the cloisters of Neville's Court Walk at Trinity College. Therefore it has become traditional for Cambridge students to test the quadruple echo that Newton claimed to have heard. At another point of Book II Newton neatly demolishes Descartes' "vortex theory." The formulator of analytic geometry had explained planetary motion as the result of vortices or whirlpools sweeping the planets around the sun. Newton says, "The vortex theory is in complete conflict with astronomical observations, and instead of explaining celestial motions, merely confuses our ideas about them."

The *De Mundi Systemate*, the System of the World, which forms Book III of the *Principia*, contains the full development of the theory of universal gravitation. In it the orbits of the planets and their satellites are specified, comets are discussed, numerous difficulties with the moon's orbit are handled, a theory of tides is furnished, and the "precession of the equinoxes" is explained for the first time in scientific history. Astronomical observations, even in earlier eras, had revealed certain irregularities in the motion of the moon. Subsequently, similar orbit irregularities had been observed for the satellites of Jupiter and Saturn. Newton explains these phenomena as due to the "perturbative" effect of the sun. Here is the beginning of the famous "three-body problem." Kepler's ellipses are only valid when a planet moves around the sun, or a satellite orbits around a planet, *without* the presence of a third body nearby in the heavens. When such a body is present, its gravitational pull will draw a planet away from its elliptic course. In Book III of the *Principia* the numerical effect of "perturbations" is considered, and these correspond to the observed irregularities in satellite orbits. When, in the mid-nineteenth century, the orbit of

Uranus appeared to be "perturbed," the astronomers Adams and Leverrier independently came to the conclusion that the perturbation must be due to a planet as yet unknown to astronomers. They determined its position in the heavens on the basis of Newton's theory. Shortly thereafter the new planet was actually observed very near the point predicted, and it was named Neptune. Similar considerations led to the twentieth-century discovery of Pluto.

The source of these astronomic discoveries is, as we have emphasized, the Newtonian *System of the World.* Among the many consequences of universal gravitation treated in that part of the *Principia* is the fact that the earth must be flattened at the poles, that is, its shape is that of an oblate spheroid. In France, Giovanni Domenico Cassini (1625–1712), director of the Paris Observatory, and his son, Jacques (1677–1756), who succeeded him in the position, were misled by erroneous geodetic measurements and held to the theory of a prolate spheroid for the earth's shape, that is, to the idea of *elongation* rather than flattening at the poles. The French Academy of Sciences decided that a test must be made to decide between Newton and the Cassinis. Accordingly, expeditions were sent out to measure arcs on the earth's surface at widely separated points. In 1735 (eight years after Newton's death) an expedition under La Condamine was sent to Ecuador and another under Maupertuis was despatched to Lapland. Voltaire, who disliked Maupertuis, and also felt that Newton must have been correct, called the director of the Lapland expedition "Marquess of the Arctic Circle," "dear flattener of the world and of Cassini" and "Sir Isaac Maupertuis." He also addressed to La Condamine the rhyme

> *Vous avez confirmé dans les lieux pleins d'ennui*
> *Ce que Newton connut sans sortir de chez lui.*

(You have confirmed in dreary far-off lands
What Newton knew without e'er leaving home.)*

No other physical scientist has ever been able to create anything on a par with Newton's *Principia,* which is the source from which all subsequent (scientific) blessings flowed. Even when relativity and quantum theory made their appearance, Newtonian physics was the starting point —if only to challenge some of its postulates or to illustrate

* Translation by the author.

a deterministic pattern with which to disagree. But Newton had worthy successors who, in successive generations, modified and generalized his ideas. Nevertheless, on the whole, they followed the master by specializing in analysis, by applying that subject to the formulation of deterministic laws for physics, and by earning each in turn, the title of "foremost mathematician in Europe." Thus, the calculus became "analysis incarnate" in the hands of Léonard (Leonhard) Euler (1707–1783). Joseph-Louis Lagrange (1736–1813) produced the *Mécanique Analytique*, as profound an accomplishment in general mechanics as universal gravitation had been in celestial mechanics, and one of a sequence of events indicating that mechanics, perhaps even more than astronomy, is a source of inspiration for pure mathematical theory. This significant role of mechanics is evident in much of the work of Euler, Lagrange, and their mathematical disciples and contemporaries. But astronomy was to the fore in the research of Pierre-Simon Laplace (1749–1827). During the years 1799–1825 he released volume after volume (five in all) of his *Mécanique Céleste*. Many subjects were enriched by his mathematical fertility, but his devotion to celestial mechanics was almost an obsession; every concept he created was related directly or indirectly to the field in which he out-Newtoned Newton.

His production was small, however, compared to that of Euler, whose collected writings fill some eighty large volumes, an all-time record among mathematicians. There was quality as well as quantity in Euler's works, and among the many topics which claim space in the vast collection are number theory, artillery, northern lights, sound, the tides, navigation, ship-building, astronomy, hydrodynamics, magnetism, light, telescopic design, canal construction, annuities, lotteries. All such writing was outside his fields of major achievement. He completed and expounded all the formalisms of classic analysis in his *Introductio in Analysin Infinitorum*, which the mathematical historian Carl B. Boyer calls the "foremost textbook of modern times."* As if all this were not enough, Switzerland's greatest mathematician can be considered one of the founders of the *calculus of variations* and that exceedingly important research subject of today, *combinatorial topology* (Chapter 25).

* See his article bearing this title in the *American Mathematical Monthly*, April 1951, pp. 223–226.

Not only was Euler the most prolific mathematician in all of history, but he appears likewise to have given rise to the greatest number of legends. It is said that he could repeat the *Aeneid* from beginning to end. He was capable of remarkable concentration and would write his research papers with a child on each knee, while the rest of his youngsters raised uninhibited pandemonium all about him (he was the father of thirteen children in all). Euler, like most mathematicians, had a keen interest in music, but his book on *New Musical Theories* was said to contain "too much mathematics for musicians and too much music for mathematicians."

Frederick the Great was one of Euler's patrons. As a result, the mathematician found himself conducting a correspondence course in scientific subjects for Frederick's niece, Princess Philippine von Schwedt, to keep her busy while she (and the rest of the royal court) were interned at Magdeburg during the critical phases of the Seven Years' War. In a letter of August 1760 Euler was explaining to the princess the use of the level, a surveying instrument. As an exercise he asked, "Would a straight line drawn from your new home, Magdeburg, to your old home, Berlin, be a *horizontal* one?" Then he answered his own question in the negative, stating that Berlin is higher than Magdeburg, because the former city lies on the Spree, the latter on the Elbe, and the Spree empties into the Havel, which in turn flows into the Elbe. Euler's justification was wrong! The elevations of Berlin and Magdeburg are 33 and 41 meters, respectively. The fallacy in his argument lies in the fact that the junction of the Havel and Elbe does not take place at Magdeburg but at a point far below! "Even Homer was known to nod!"

The setting for Euler's more serious scientific activities was a world which had just witnessed the most bitter of all priority disputes, the Newton-Leibniz controversy concerning the invention of the calculus. Professor Rudolph Langer has described this situation and has given an account of Euler's career.[*]

The public condemnation of Leibniz by the British Royal Society took place in 1713, and three years later, before he had completed his defense, Leibniz died. The English stood to a man by Newton. Germany, on the other hand, was at this time in a state of utter political turmoil and exhaustion, and so it happened that

[*] R. E. Langer, "The Life of Léonard Euler," *Scripta Mathematica*, Vol. 3 (1935), pp. 61 ff.

no countryman of Leibniz was at hand to come to his defense or even to understand his work. It was fortunate for posterity, therefore, that there was, nevertheless, one man on the European continent who could champion his cause and who was equipped by ability and temperament to do so effectively. This man was Jean Bernoulli, of the famous Bernoulli family that was to produce eight mathematicians in three generations.

Jacques Bernoulli (1654–1705) was professor of mathematics at Basel, Switzerland, from 1687 until his death. Jean, his brother, thirteen years younger, was at first located in Holland, but succeeded upon the death of Jacques to the professorship at Basel. These two men were among the few to whom the publications of Leibniz were a revelation. They were fired by the importance of the invention of the calculus, and from its very birth took so decisive a hand in its development that Leibniz is known to have pronounced it as much theirs as his. The death of Jacques Bernoulli preceded that of Leibniz, and hence when Leibniz died Jean looked upon himself as the logical scientific successor and proceeded to champion the cause which had become his. A man of great genius, he was in his personal associations a game cock or a dragon, as the occasion required. It became his mission in life to defeat single-handed the whole tribe of the English. Unmerciful in his ridicule, of the greatest incisiveness as a critic and writer, pitiless of anyone who dared take issue with him, he turned out a veritable flood of publications which were filled alike with his own great works and discoveries and with invective for those (the English) who followed as disciples of a different system. Thus he helped to save the calculus of Leibniz from oblivion and, by applying the impetus of his own genius, he so accelerated its development as to insure for it subsequently an almost complete triumph over the fluxions of Newton. Bernoulli was active without interruption at Basel for forty-two years, and with ever growing fame, acknowledged as the greatest living mathematician, he drew to his circle, like an oracle, mathematicians from all the countries of continental Europe.

This was the environment Euler entered as a young man. He was born in 1707 not far from the city of Basel. His father, a country preacher, was fond of mathematics, had studied under Jacques Bernoulli, and was the young Euler's first teacher in this subject. An apt pupil in everything, Euler entered the university and obtained his baccalaureate at the age of fifteen. It was his father's wish that he turn to theology, but the boy's love for mathematics and the proximity of the compelling personality of Jean Bernoulli were not to be resisted. So Euler sought instruction from Bernoulli, and was given books and papers to read, with Bernoulli's promise to be available once each week to answer questions and clear up difficult points. It was during this period that Euler became a friend of Bernoulli's sons, Nicolas, Daniel, and Jean II, all mathematicians of high rank, the first two being twelve and seven years Euler's senior, respectively, and Jean II three years his junior.

Euler's first paper was published at the age of eighteen. In the succeeding year he wrote on the propagation of sound. When the Paris Academy offered a prize for an essay on the masting of ships, the young Euler, at the age of twenty and devoid of any practical experience with ships, wrote and won the prize. He remarked in the conclusion of his essay that he had not considered it necessary to check his results by experiment, for *since they were deduced from the surest foundations in mechanics, their truth or correctness could not be questioned.* This was characteristic of Euler's lifelong attitude. He never ceased to regard the deductive power of the mind as being of unquestionable supremacy.

Peter the Great of Russia had at the instigation of Leibniz conceived the plan of an academy at St. Petersburg, and his successor, the Empress Catherine the First, put this plan into effect. Thus it occurred that Nicolas and Daniel Bernoulli were called from Basel. At parting they promised Euler to seek an opening for him, and in the following year they wrote to him about a position in physiology, with the recommendation that he make haste to learn some medicine and anatomy and apply for it. This Euler proceeded to do, and in his twentieth year set out from his native city for St. Petersburg. Upon his arrival he was made an associate in mathematics—the matter of physiology apparently having been forgotten.

The academy consisted of twenty professors representing the various fields of learning and was an able, inspiring, and argumentative group of men. It had been stipulated in the contracts of appointment that each member was to bring with him two students, and when the academy was ready to function as a university the wisdom of this provison became evident. There was no other student body. In this circumstance the members found complete freedom for scientific work, and Euler immediately began voluminous publication in the academy's proceedings.

Soon, however, the academy fell upon evil days. On the very day Euler entered Russia, Empress Catherine died. The ensuing regency considered the academy a futile source of expense, and after three years Euler was driven to the verge of accepting a lieutenancy in the Russian navy. The sudden death of the boy Czar and the accession of the Empress Anna, however, brought a change for the better. Meanwhile Nicolas Bernoulli had died, and Euler had assumed the professorship of natural philosophy, a chair which he later resigned for the professorship in mathematics when the latter was vacated by Daniel Bernoulli's return to his native country. The betterment in Euler's financial circumstances was soon followed by his marriage to the daughter of a Swiss painter resident in St. Petersburg. He had formed many friendships. All along, his mathematical production proceeded at a fabulous pace.

The year following his marriage marked the first major misfortune in Euler's life. Because of illness, which legend ascribed to overexertion in a feat of astronomical calculation, he lost the sight of his right eye—in fact, the eye itself.

The great number and significance of Euler's works had meanwhile attracted serious attention throughout Europe. The extraordinary activity of Euler may be indicated by the fact that at the age of thirty-three he had produced a total of eighty papers and books in pure science alone, although he had all the while been engaged in an astounding number of other ways. Thus he is to be found as supervisor of the Russian government department of geography and as commissioner of weights and measures, giving much of his time to details and writing essays on the construction and testing of scales and other apparatus of measurement. He wrote the elementary mathematical textbooks for use in the Russian schools, was called upon to solve the problem of raising and hanging the great bell of Moscow, and so on. In 1741 Euler received a call to go to Berlin. The administrative state of the St. Petersburg Academy during the preceding years had not been an entirely happy one, and as the death of the Empress Anna was anticipated with foreboding, he welcomed and heeded the call. He had been active for fourteen years at St. Petersburg and had reached the age of thirty-four.

Frederick the Great became King of Prussia in 1740. The scientific society at Berlin which had been founded by Leibniz forty years earlier was in a state of decay, and the new king became bent upon invigorating it and reorganizing it into a great academy. To this end he brought to Berlin as an organizer the mathematician Maupertuis. Maupertuis was a scientist and an adventurer —a man of brilliant personality, a gifted conversationalist, an enthusiast for science, and a mathematician and philosopher of respectable accomplishment. He had studied under Jean Bernoulli on the Continent, but had also been in England, where he had developed a strong liking for the Newtonian methods. Mathematicians of acknowledged greatness were essential to add luster to Frederick's new academy, and strong efforts were immediately made to draw the Bernoullis—Jean, now seventy-three years old, and his sons, Daniel and Jean II from Switzerland, and Euler from St. Petersburg. The Bernoullis were not to be had, but Euler came to Berlin to join a brilliant association of scholars.

It was customary during this period for the Paris Academy to pose for each biennium a subject for a prize dissertation, and Euler often entered the competition. He won with such regularity that it has been said he must have almost come to regard the prize as a regular subsidy to his salary. It is interesting to note that this Parisian prize was carried off twice by Jean Bernoulli, four times by his son Jean II, ten times by Daniel Bernoulli, and twelve times by Euler. In all, the prize thus went twenty-eight times to these men who were all natives of the same city, Basel, Switzerland.

The epoch in which these events took place was marked by a number of intense scientific disputes which were widely participated in throughout Europe. The questions generally hinged on philosophical points, and Euler, who entered the discussions with vigor, soon showed himself to be a mediocre, or poorer, philosopher. It became evident to many through these controversies that the great mathematician was quite mortal in other fields, and Daniel Bernoulli is known to have advised Euler to stay out of print in matters nonmathematical. Euler, far from being daunted, continued, curiously, often on the wrong side of the argument. Such a turn of events was an occasion of much joy to Voltaire, who at the time was also at the court of Frederick and an aspirant for the royal favor; Euler was not spared the sting of his satire.

Voltaire ferreted out a paper written by Euler in his youth, in which he had treated the hypothetical example of a shaft through the center of the earth with a heavy particle moving in it under the earth's attraction. His formulas showed that, on reaching the earth's center, the particle would abruptly turn and retrace its course rather than continue through. This paradoxical result arose from an unpermissible interchange of the order of two infinite processes, a matter which at that time was not properly understood. Voltaire's attacks were enjoyed by Euler as much as by anyone. Incidentally, they never deterred him from engaging in philosophical disputes with gusto.

While Euler was at Berlin, the mathematician Jean le Rond d'Alembert (1717–1783) was active in Paris. He had attained acknowledged prominence and worked on many of the problems upon which Euler was also engaged. The correspondence between the two men was frequent and cordial until about 1757, when a difference of opinion concerning the solution of the problem of the vibrating string caused the association to lapse. D'Alembert was a man of fine culture. Besides his mathematical pursuits he was active as a philosopher and as a writer. It is a curious fact that his talent in letters never extended to mathematical exposition. In this of all subjects his writings were often so obscure and difficult to read that many of his results, in fact, became generally known only through Euler's presentations of them.

Despite his great scientific success, Euler was not spared frustration and discouragements in Berlin, mainly because he had never won real favor with the king. The management of the Berlin Academy had gradually fallen, in fact though not in name, into Euler's hands, and Euler was widely recommended to Frederick for the position of nominal as well as actual head of the organization. It was Frederick's wish, however, to have as the leader of his academy not just a scientist but also a man of the

world, a man of social grace and brilliance to dine at his board
and through his appearance to add luster to the institution. This
was a role for which Euler, the typical German burgher, was not
adapted. Accordingly, Euler found himself seeking in vain for
even the most trivial royal favors, such as suitable appointments
for his sons, and in Frederick's correspondence one may find
frequent sarcastic and disparaging references to Euler, his lack
of polish, his missing eye, the great cyclops of a geometer, etc.
This irritation of the king's no doubt had, in part, another cause.
Although mathematical accomplishments were regarded in highest
terms at the time, Euler's most serious efforts had never taken
him beyond the elementary stages of the subject, and this limitation had engendered a natural distaste and distrust. He had
repeatedly, and always unsuccessfully, tried to wring from men
of learning an admission that mathematics after all was of no
great account. Now Euler was a mathematician and a mathematician alone. Frederick would have none of the suggestion to
make him president of the academy. In this matter his choice fell
upon D'Alembert, much to Euler's consternation. Despite fabulous offers, however, D'Alembert refused to exchange his position
at Paris for a residence in Frederick's palace. He visited Berlin at
the insistence of the king, allayed Euler's fears by the great cordiality which he brought to the meeting—and by urging upon
the king the unsuitableness of placing any living person in a position of academic superiority over so great a man.

D'Alembert's refusal served only to heighten Euler's disfavor in
Frederick's eyes. After many irritating incidents, none of major
importance, matters came to a climax in 1766, and Euler, now
fifty-nine years old, felt compelled to resign his position and leave
the circle in which he had lived and worked for twenty-four
years. During all these years he had maintained the friendliest of
relations with the academy at St. Petersburg. He had published
regularly in its proceedings and had taken students coming from
there into his home. This cordiality was reciprocated to such a
degree that during a Russian invasion of Berlin two Russian
soldiers were especially assigned to guard Euler and his household,
and when his country home was inadvertently pillaged, he was
personally indemnified by the Russian Empress.

His resignation was finally accepted in Berlin, and Euler set out
for St. Petersburg with his entire household of eighteen persons.
The Empress Catherine (the Great) was elated at winning so
great a man for her academy, and Euler was entertained *en route*
by the Prince of Courland, by the City of Riga, and for many
days in Warsaw by the King of Poland. On his arrival in Russia,
the Empress presented him with a house completely furnished,
and with one of the royal cooks. His sons were given positions of
importance, and in every way Euler felt the greatest gratification.
Frederick meanwhile had made the best of his situation, and had
filled Euler's place with the one living man worthy to succeed

him, namely, Lagrange, then thirty years old. Euler's relations with Lagrange were of the warmest, the older being among the first and the most willing to admit and laud the greatness of the younger.

Euler's life had not been free from tragedy. At Berlin he had seen the death of eight of his children. Now, soon after his return to St. Petersburg, a calamity of another sort occurred—he lost the sight in his one remaining eye. The severity of such a blow to a man of Euler's profession and activity hardly requires description. Fortunately the calamity failed to have the anticipated effect. It served only to reveal completely the afflicted man's genius. With the stimulus of outer distractions removed, the play of Euler's imagination became greater than ever. His most phenomenal memory, which could instantly recall anything he had ever seen or heard, even to the minutiae of the uncountable formulas he had dealt with, allowed him to continue his work despite his blindness. Indeed, the rate of his publications increased, so that his papers written during his seventeen years of blindness number almost four hundred, not to mention a respectable number of complete books.

The mechanics by which this process of production was achieved seems roughly to have been somewhat as follows. A large table covered with a slate top to form a blackboard was placed in the middle of his large study. With younger men as his assistants, he dictated the text of his works and at the appropriate points he would write with chalk upon the table the formulas to be used. The increase in the rate of his papers was evidently due to the relief from the care for editorial details.

In the year 1771 there occurred a great fire in St. Petersburg which almost ended Euler's career. His house was engulfed by the flames and only through a servant's heroism was the blind man brought out to safety. His home and many manuscripts were destroyed, but the financial loss was made good to him by the Empress. Euler happened to be engaged at this time upon a theory of the motion of the moon, a work which involved computations of stupendous magnitude and complexity. It seems incredible that such a work should have been done in blindness and under such devastating distractions as that of the fire. Yet it was carried to so successful a conclusion that it won him two prizes at the Academy of Paris. The year of the fire also marked for Euler the birth of a great hope which was to end tragically. A surgical operation having been undertaken upon his eye, his sight was restored, to his unbounded joy—but not for long. Failure was somehow involved, and amidst agonies described as horrible, he was plunged again, and finally, into complete blindness.

Euler's blindness had raised his reputation to legendary proportions. His home became a scientific shrine visited by a steady stream of pilgrims, including even the heir to the Prussian throne. They would generally find Euler, to their surprise, as enthusiastic as in his youth for the discovery of new mathematical facts. The thrill had never worn off. And nonmathematicians were astounded at his fund of information on all conceivable subjects. He was conversant with the literature of the ancients, knew the histories of all nations in all periods, was versed in medicine and chemistry, and so on.

The final years of Euler's life were marked by the loss of his wife and his two daughters. His hearing became impaired, and as a result he took a less active part than formerly in the affairs of the academy. But his mathematical work did not diminish, nor did he lose the great imagination which had led him so well throughout his life. Thus in his papers on hydrostatics and hydrodynamics he considered the effects of varying density and temperature on the equilibrium of the air. From his results he read the general cause of winds and applied it to the trade winds and to the monsoons of the Indian Ocean. He determined the shape of the earth and its surrounding media, saw in his formulas the description not only of the tides but of the motions of fluids in vases, pumps, pipes, etc., derived from them the velocity of the propagation of sound, which in turn yields him the formulas for the notes of a flute, and so on.

According to legend, Euler's last mathematical activity was a prophetic one. On September 18, 1783, the greatest Swiss mathematician passed the afternoon in thoughts concerning the orbits of *satellites*. In his accustomed work habits since he had become completely blind fifteen years earlier, he outlined in large characters on a slate the calculation of the orbit of Uranus, the planet which Herschel had just discovered. After he had dined with friends, he resumed the calculations while he was drinking his tea. Next he asked for his grandson and played with the child for a few minutes. Suddenly he turned to the slate and inscribed "I die" beneath the satellite computations. The chalk dropped from his hand and, in the words of Condorcet *"il cessa de calculer et de vivre."*

Among Euler's young contemporaries were France's leading mathematicians of the era, Joseph-Louis Lagrange and Pierre-Simon Laplace. When one considers how many scientists, authors, and artists achieved fame only posthumously, these mathematicians were indeed extremely fortunate to receive in their lifetime the recognition and rewards they so richly merited. Napoleon, who was a greater admirer of men of science, honored Lagrange and Laplace by making them Senators, Counts of the Empire, and Grand Officers of the Legion of Honor. Through the influence of

Euler, who recognized the youthful genius of Lagrange, the latter was made an Associate of the Berlin Academy when he was only twenty-three, and somewhat later was made director of the mathematics division of the academy when the great Swiss analyst departed for St. Petersburg. And so in 1766, at the age of thirty, Lagrange went to Berlin, where for twenty years he served as court mathematician to Frederick the Great. In the words of that ruler, "the greatest monarch in Europe deserves the greatest mathematician." During the first few years in Berlin, he received several of the highest awards of the French Academy of Sciences, which also made him one of its associate members when he was only twenty-four. By 1785 he attained the lofty heights of full membership in this academy. In 1816 he was elected to membership in the academy of immortals, the French Academy, a distinction accorded only to the greatest French scholars.

Although Lagrange and Laplace worked in related fields of mathematics and might have been considered rivals, there is no evidence of disputes or harsh feelings between them. Temperamentally they were quite different. Lagrange was modest, retiring, shy, and the soul of tact. Most of his life he suffered from what was then called "bilious hypochondria," a malady whose symptoms were recurrent periods of mental depression. It is related that when Lagrange's masterpiece, the *Mécanique Analytique*, came from the printer, it remained unopened on his desk for two years. By contrast, Laplace was ambitious, outgoing, shrewd, and aggressive. Although he was on occasion severely criticized for failing to give proper credit to other mathematicians, it is remarkable that he appears to have made no enemies. In fact, he was considered a good politician because he was able to carry on his work through different regimes without any loss of position or prestige, and eventually he was made a marquis by Louis XVIII.

Lagrange and Laplace were far apart in their attitudes toward mathematics. The former revered complete abstraction, and his analytical mechanics is not physics but "pure" mathematics. Laplace, although capable of the highest type of abstract thinking, was more interested in putting theories to practical use, and hence is considered mainly a physicist, astronomer, and "applied" mathematician.

In their mathematical specialties both men carried forward the mechanics of Newton. Lagrange completed and gener-

alized the mechanics of rigid bodies. To emphasize the fact
that the *Mécanique Analytique* was "pure" mathematics, no
diagrams were included. This great treatise was called by
Hamilton (the successor of Lagrange in the field of mechanics) "a scientific poem by the Shakespeare of mathematics." Laplace continued the mathematics associated with
universal gravitation, that is, the *celestial* mechanics of Newton. The title of Laplace's greatest book is *Mécanique
Céleste*. Deterministic contributions of Lagrange and Laplace
to mechanics will be discussed in the present chapter. It
must be emphasized, however, that the two French leaders
made important contributions to other subjects as well.
Lagrange played an essential role in the advancement of almost every branch of pure mathematics, especially in the
calculus of variations, the theory of numbers, Diophantine
analysis, "invariants," and algebraic solvability (see Chapter
16). Laplace's researches, in addition to those in celestial
mechanics, concerned probability theory, potential theory,
partial differential equations, and various exceedingly useful
"operational" methods like the *Laplace transform* of modern
mathematical physics and engineering.

Joseph-Louis Lagrange was born in 1736 in Turin, which
was part of the Kingdom of Sardinia at the time. His grandfather, who was of French noble birth, had entered the
service of the King of Sardinia and had settled in Turin,
where he married into a prominent Italian family. Lagrange's father, an erstwhile wealthy man who ultimately
lost his entire fortune through unwise speculation, was war
treasurer of Sardinia. Young Joseph-Louis' extraordinary
mathematical talent displayed itself very early. Hence he
was able at the age of eighteen to become a professor of
mathematics at the Artillery School in Turin. When he was
nineteen he began a correspondence with Euler, who was
amazed at the young man's mathematical creativity. Some
four years later, Lagrange sent Euler a solution to a problem
that the latter had been working on without success for a
long time. It is to Euler's credit that he did not appropriate
the method as his own but instead allowed Lagrange to publish first and to obtain full credit as the discoverer of the
calculus of variations.

While he was at Frederick's court, Lagrange sent for one
of his female relatives in Turin and married her. This was
no romantic marriage. In fact, some of his correspondence
states that he had no taste for marriage but merely wished

to be cared for. Nevertheless he developed a genuine affection for his wife, and when she developed a fatal illness, he nursed her himself. Her death left him grief-stricken and precipitated one of his periods of depression.

In 1787 Lagrange was invited to Paris by Louis XVI, who offered him French nationality and made him a "veteran pensioner" of the French Academy of Sciences. When the French Revolution broke out two years later, friends of the mathematician urged him to return to Berlin, but he decided to remain in Paris, a decision he had occasion to regret when he witnessed the excesses of the Reign of Terror. It is recorded that he ran the great risk of expressing himself concerning the execution of Lavoisier, France's greatest chemist. He stated: "It took them only a moment to cause his head to fall, and a hundred years perhaps will not suffice to produce its like."

In 1792, at the age of fifty-six, Lagrange made a second marriage, this time to the sixteen-year-old daughter of Lemonnier, an astronomer who was his colleague in the Academy of Sciences. Despite the great difference in their ages, the marriage turned out to be a very successful one.

When the École Polytechnique was founded in 1797, Lagrange became its first professor of mathematics. It is interesting to note that Laplace, who was one of the chief organizers of the École, offered the position to Lagrange. It was also during this period that both mathematicians played leading roles on the committee that perfected the metric system of weights and measures.

During the last years of his life Lagrange devoted his energies to a revision and extension of his *Mécanique Analytique*. Unfortunately, in 1813, death intervened before the task was completed. Lagrange was aware that the end was approaching, and in the presence of friends he summarized his life thus: "Death is not to be dreaded and when it comes without pain, it is a last function which is not unpleasant. I have had my career; I have gained some celebrity in mathematics. I never hated anyone, I have done nothing bad, and it would be well to end."

When Lagrange was a schoolboy of thirteen in Turin, Laplace was an infant in a little Norman village a thousand miles away. He was born on March 23, 1749. Concerning his early years, the mathematical physicist Sir Edmund Whittaker (1873–1956) said that many statements by historians are erroneous. For example, Laplace's father was *not* a poor peasant, as usually claimed, but the owner of a small estate and a member of the bourgeoisie. One uncle was a surgeon and another was a priest who taught at the Benedictine priory at Beaumont. It is believed that the latter stimulated Laplace's interest in mathematics even before his admission to the University of Caen at the age of sixteen. While he was still a student at the university he wrote his first paper, which came to the attention of Lagrange just as, earlier, Lagrange's genius had been demonstrated to Euler.

At the age of eighteen Laplace decided to go to Paris to make a career for himself. Provided with a letter of recommendation, he sought an interview with D'Alembert to no avail. Later he tried a different approach by incorporating his ideas on mechanics in a letter. He got an immediate reply; D'Alembert wrote: "You needed no special introduction; you have recommended yourself, and my support is your due." Shortly thereafter Laplace was appointed a professor of mathematics at the École Militaire of Paris. This marked the beginning of the career which was to earn for him the title of the "Newton of France." He did, in fact, extend the implications of universal gravitation to the entire solar system. All his ideas in this area were included in his five-volume treatise, the *Mécanique Céleste* (1799–1825).

In 1784 Laplace received a lucrative position as "examiner to the royal artillery." In this capacity he had occasion to test the sixteen-year-old Napoleon when the latter applied for admission to the École Militaire. What might the course of world history have been if Napoleon had been failed by Laplace? Or, if he had been admitted over a protest by Laplace, what might Laplace's history have been? What it actually was like in some important respects is related by Whittaker.*

When Laplace began his active career as a mathematician, more than eighty years had elapsed since the publication of Newton's *Principia*. For long after its first appearance, that greatest of all works of science had met with considerable opposition. The most eminent mathematicians of the end of the seventeenth century— Huygens, Leibniz, John Bernoulli, Cassini—declared against the Newtonian theory of gravitation; this occurred even in Cambridge, Newton's own University. It was not until 1745 that the theory of the motions of the heavenly bodies began to be carried beyond the stage it had reached in the *Principia;* and for forty

* Sir Edmund Whittaker, "Laplace," *American Mathematical Monthly,* Vol. 56, No. 6 (June–July 1949), pp. 369 ff.

years after that, attention was focused almost exclusively on certain phenomena, which were well attested by astronomical observation, and which seemed to be irreconcilable with the Newtonian theory.

The most striking of these was what was called the great inequality of Jupiter and Saturn. From a comparison of ancient and current observations, it was found that for many centuries the mean motion, or average angular velocity round the sun, of Jupiter, had been continually increasing, while that of Saturn had been continually decreasing. Hence it could be inferred, by Kepler's third law, that the mean distance of Jupiter from the sun was always decreasing, and that of Saturn increasing; so the ultimate fate of Jupiter would be to fall into the sun, while Saturn would wander into space and be lost altogether to the solar system. This of course, assumed that the phenomenon was truly secular, that is to say, that it proceeded always in the same direction, with a cumulative effect. . . . Attempts to bring the great inequality of Jupiter and Saturn within the compass of the Newtonian theory of gravitation were made by Euler in 1748 and 1752 and by Lagrange in 1763, but without success. In 1773 Laplace, then aged twenty-four, took the matter up and . . . finally arrived at a complete explanation of the great inequality; it was not secular, but was periodic, of very long period; and it was due to the fact that the mean motions of the two planets were nearly commensurable. The comparison of his theory with observation left no doubt of its truth.

Laplace's explanation of the great inequality of Jupiter and Saturn was the first of a long series of triumphs, which are recorded in the two thousand pages of his *Mécanique Céleste*, and which achieved the complete justification of the Newtonian theory. He also made many important discoveries in theoretical physics, and indeed he was interested in everything that helped to interpret nature; pure mathematics for its own sake, however, did not greatly appeal to him, and his contributions to pure mathematics were mostly thrown off as mere by-products of his great works in natural philosophy. Yet there are several cases where Laplace's papers have become an important branch of pure mathematics. When in the course of his researches he comes to a situation where a heavy piece of pure mathematical working is needed, he often says, "*Il est facile de voir*," and gives the result without saying how he got it. His power of solving problems in pure mathematics has perhaps never been equaled, but he seems to have thought nothing of it, and to have assumed that it was possessed by all the readers of his works.

Lagrange's mechanics and Laplace's celestial mechanical discoveries involved the solution of differential equations, the essential feature of scientific determinism. Such equations involve not only variables like the x, y, z's of algebra but also derivatives, that is, rates of change, which, in physical applications, may be velocities, accelerations, or the like. To illustrate the most elementary sort of differential equation arising in mechanics, let us consider the case of a bullet that is fired straight upward from a point 5 feet above the ground with an initial speed of 1200 feet per second. Its future velocity and position are completely *determined* by the knowledge of its speed and position at the instant of firing. The effect of gravity will retard its motion and its speed will decrease until it comes to rest at the highest point reached. Then, reversing its direction, it will fall toward the ground with gradually increasing speed. This motion results from a negative acceleration and, according to Galileo and Newton, the acceleration does not vary as time goes on but is constant and approximately equal to -32 feet per second each second. (Since no account is taken of air resistance, this assumption is strictly true only for objects falling in a vacuum.) The expression of the physical law by a *differential equation* is

$$\frac{dv}{dt} = -32$$

By antidifferentiation, one obtains

$$v = -32t + c_1$$

Substituting the given fact,

$$v = 1200 \quad \text{when} \quad t = 0$$

(that is, the *initial* or *boundary* condition)* leads to

$$1200 = 0 + c_1$$

or

$$c_1 = 1200$$

and the formula that *determines* the future velocity of the bullet is

$$v = -32t + 1200$$

We can ascertain that after half a minute (30 seconds),

$$v = -32(30) + 1200 = 240$$

---

* Such particular requirements may be called *boundary conditions*, although conditions specified at $t = 0$ (or at any designated *time*) are usually called *initial conditions*.

so that the speed has slowed down to 240 ft. per sec. To find the time when the bullet begins to fall, $v = 0$ is substituted in the above formula:

$$0 = -32t + 1200$$

$$t = 37.5 \text{ sec.}$$

To find the height of the bullet at this instant or at any other time, we recall that $v = dx/dt$, and substituting this derivative in place of v leads to a second differential equation,

$$\frac{dx}{dt} = -32t + 1200$$

After antidifferentiation,

$$x = -16t^2 + 1200t + c_2$$

The knowledge that $x = 5$ when $t = 0$ indicates that $c_2 = 5$, and the deterministic formula for future position is

$$x = -16t^2 + 1200t + 5$$

The bullet reaches its maximum height when $t = 37.5$, and if we substitute this value, we find that the greatest height is $x = 22,505$ ft. We might wish to know when the bullet will return to its initial position, $x = 5$ ft. (the height at which it was fired). Substituting 5 for x yields

$$5 = -16t^2 + 1200t + 5$$

$$-16t^2 + 1200t = 0$$

$$16t(-t + 75) = 0$$

$$16t = 0 \quad \text{or} \quad -t + 75 = 0$$

$$t = 0 \qquad\qquad t = 75$$

The second answer indicates that the bullet returns to the position at which it was fired after 75 seconds, or that it rises for as many seconds as it falls.

The formulation of a physical law as a differential equation is rarely as simple as $dv/dt = -32$. For example, there is

$$\frac{d^4y}{dx^4} + 2k^2 \frac{d^2y}{dx^2} + k^4y = 0$$

a differential equation associated with the bending of an elastic plate. This equation involves an independent variable

x, a dependent variable y, as well as the *second* and *fourth* derivatives of y with respect to x. (The letter k is a constant whose numerical value is determined by physical facts associated with a particular problem.) The *order* of the equation is said to be equal to 4, because that is the order of d^4y/dx^4, the highest-order derivative appearing in the equation.

To *solve* the equation means to determine a relation between y and x satisfying the equation. If y should be expressible in terms of x, then substitution of the expression for y as well as its second and fourth derivatives with respect to x in the left member of the above differential equation should yield the result 0. Inspection of that equation indicates that no mere antidifferentiation will solve it, that is, will lead to a relation of the desired type. In the case of the above bullet problem which can be formulated either as

$$\frac{dv}{dt} = -32$$

or as

$$\frac{d^2x}{dt^2} = -32$$

and also in an equation like

$$\frac{d^5y}{dx^5} = 12x^2 - 6x + 3$$

a derivative of some order is expressed as a function of the independent variable. Solution merely requires finding a sequence of antiderivatives. Thus, in the last illustration, one obtains

$$\frac{d^4y}{dx^4} = 4x^3 - 3x^2 + 3x + c_1$$

$$\frac{d^3y}{dx^3} = x^4 - x^3 + \frac{3}{2}x^2 + c_1x + c_2$$

$$\cdots$$
$$\cdots$$

$$y = \frac{1}{210}x^7 - \frac{1}{120}x^6 + \frac{1}{40}x^5 + \frac{c_1}{24}x^4 + \frac{c_2}{6}x^3 + \frac{c_3}{2}x^2 + c_4x + c_5$$

This result, called the *general solution*, contains *five* arbitrary constants, corresponding to the fact that the differential equation is of *fifth* order. It is always true that the number of arbitrary constants in the general solution is equal to the order of the differential equation. If a sufficient number of initial or boundary conditions is given, the numerical values of the constants can be determined and a *particular solution* is obtained.

But it must be emphasized once again that the easy mode of solution just illustrated is not usually possible. The reader may inspect the following formulations of physical laws as differential equations to observe that in no case is the equation expressed so as to make a sequence of antidifferentiations possible.

$$\frac{dI}{dt} + 12I = 40 \sin 120\pi t$$

(*I* is the current at any time in a 20-volt AC circuit with a 6-ohm resistor and a 0.5-henry inductance)

$$\frac{d^2Q}{dt^2} + 12\frac{dQ}{dt} + 100Q = 40 \sin 120\pi t$$

(If a condenser with capacity 0.02 farad is placed in the above circuit, *Q* is the charge on this condenser at any time)

$$\frac{d^2y}{dx^2} = k\sqrt{1 + \left(\frac{dy}{dx}\right)^2}$$

(Curve of suspension of an inextensible flexible cable)

$$\frac{d^2v}{dx^2} - 2v\frac{dv}{dx} + 6v = 0$$

(Oscillator in quantum mechanics)

$$\frac{d^4y}{dx^4} = k^4y$$

(Curve of rotating shaft in rapid motion)

$$\frac{dy}{dt} = ky$$

(Law of growth if *k* is a positive physical constant. Law of decay of radium, uranium, etc. if *k* is negative)

If one returns once more to the elementary equation,

$$\frac{dv}{} = -32$$

then the general solution is

$$v = -32t + c_1$$

This solution would apply not only to the bullet in the original problem, but also to any object (*in vacuo*) subject to the effect of gravity. The arbitrary constant c_1 is the value of v when $t = 0$; that is, c_1 is the initial velocity with which the object is launched. Since c_1 can, in theory, be equal to any real number whatsoever, the general solution incorporates an infinite number of formulas, one for each value of c_1. This is shown in Figure 9.1, which pictures the

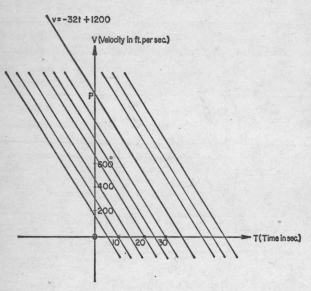

Figure 9.1   General solution of $dv/dt = -32$ and particular solution for a special initial condition

general solution as an infinite set of parallel lines with *slope* $dv/dt = -32$. The particular solution for the initial condition, $v = 1200$ when $t = 0$, is singled out from the set as the line through the point P (0, 1200).

But Figure 9.1 provides only the general solution for the

velocity v. To obtain that for the distance x, one can start anew with

$$\frac{d^2x}{dt^2} = -32$$

to obtain

$$\frac{dx}{dt} = -32t + c_1$$

and

$$x = -16t^2 + c_1t + c_2$$

This includes an infinite number of distance formulas for different initial velocities and different points of fire. Figure 9.2 reveals this general solution as an infinite set of parabo-

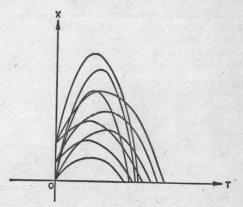

Figure 9.2   General solution of $d^2x/dt^2 = -32$

las. The curve corresponding to the initial conditions, $x = 5$ and $v = dx/dt = 1200$ when $t = 0$, is the parabola through Q $(0, 5)$ and tangent at this point to a line with slope 1200.

General solutions to ordinary differential equations can always be pictured as such infinite sets of curves, where given initial or boundary conditions select one curve as the particular solution for a specific problem. Figure 9.3 pro-

**Figure 9.3   General solution of a differential
equation of the first order**

vides an additional example. In addition to their aesthetic
appeal, such diagrams are helpful in clarifying a number of
issues. In the first place, they emphasize the advantage of
describing a type of phenomenon by a *single* differential
equation rather than by an infinite set of formulas or curves.
Secondly, sets of curves suggest certain procedures for solution.

Most differential equations, like most algebraic equations,
cannot be solved in "finite terms" (Chapters 5 and 16). But
for polynomial equations, there are approximative techniques like those of Horner or Newton, and similarly there
are graphic and numerical methods for obtaining approximate solutions to differential equations. The approximation
is a curve or a set of curves very close to the *exact* forms.
The analogy with algebraic equations will be continued in
order to provide further insight into the meaning of a differential equation and also to furnish a crude idea of graphic
or numerical approximative procedures. Given an algebraic
equation like

$$y = x^2 - 3x - 10$$

or

$$4x^2 + y^2 = 36$$

one can plot it graphically as a curve. A knowledge of the elements of analytic geometry would enable identification of the above equations as representing a parabola and an ellipse, respectively. But a student of school algebra will painstakingly assign a set of varied values to x and then compute the corresponding values of y so as to obtain the coordinates of points on the curve. The reader may place himself *in loco studentis* as far as differential equations go. Thus, if he is asked to obtain a graphic solution of

$$\frac{dy}{dx} = x - y$$

(an equation not solvable by antidifferentiation), he can substitute various pairs of values for the variables x and y in the right member, and then compute the corresponding values of dy/dx. What he will obtain if he substitutes $x = 2$, $y = 1$ is the slope $dy/dx = 2 - 1 = 1$, and hence the inclination $= 45°$ for the tangent to the curve through the point $(2, 1)$. If a large number of such substitutions are made and the corresponding tangent directions determined, these can be plotted as in Figure 9.4, where the *direction field* suggests

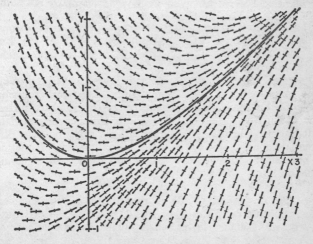

Figure 9.4   Direction field for $dy/dx = x - y$

the set of curves forming the general solution. The heavy line in the diagram is the curve through the point (0, 0), that is, the particular solution corresponding to the initial or boundary condition, $y = 0$ when $x = 0$.

Thus a crude graphic method for obtaining a particular solution of a *first-order* differential equation is as follows. One starts at the point corresponding to the boundary condition, say, $y = -1$ when $x = 4$. Then one substitutes these values in the differential equation to find the numerical value of dy/dx, the slope, and finally one plots the point $(4, -1)$ and a small arrow through this point in the direction specified by the value of the slope. Now one computes or else estimates from the graph the coordinates of the tip of the arrow. Suppose that they are $(4.2, -0.7)$. Next these values are substituted for x and y in the differential equation to find the numerical value of the slope dy/dx. A small arrow with this slope is drawn through the above point, the coordinates of the tip of this arrow are computed or read from the graph, and the whole process is repeated, and so on.

Sometimes one can obtain a solution or, at any rate, get some idea of its nature, by interpreting the differential equation geometrically (graphically) without carrrying out all the numerical work involved in plotting its direction field. Thus in the case of the first-order equation,

$$\frac{dy}{dx} = \frac{y}{x}$$

which is not solvable directly by antidifferentiation, the slope dy/dx at each point of the direction field is equal to the direction of the line joining that point to the origin (Figure 9.5). Then the lines through the origin (Figure 9.5) form the general solution, which must therefore have the form

$$y = cx$$

Note that the origin (0, 0) is an exceptional or "singular point," because substitution of $x = 0$, $y = 0$ in the differential equation yields $dy/dx = 0/0$, which is *indeterminate*. The graph of Figure 9.5 indicates why this is so, for instead of having a unique solution through the origin, there is an infinite number of solutions (straight lines).

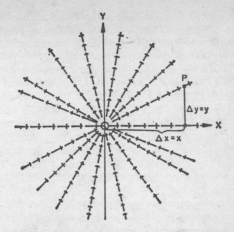

Figure 9.5   Direction field for $dy/dx = y/x$

Again, to solve

$$\frac{dy}{dx} = -\frac{x}{y}$$

through geometric considerations, one must use a fact of analytic geometry, namely that if m and m' are the slopes of two lines, then $mm' = -1$ is the necessary and sufficient condition for the lines to be perpendicular. Now if a line is drawn from the origin to the point (x, y), its slope is

$$\frac{\Delta y}{\Delta x} = \frac{y - 0}{x - 0} = \frac{y}{x}$$

which makes the line so drawn perpendicular to any line with slope $-x/y$. Hence, for the given differential equation, the direction field at every point is perpendicular to the line joining that point to the origin (Figure 9.6). The field is suggested in Figure 9.6, and indicates that the general solution is the set of circles

$$x^2 + y^2 = c^2$$

To obtain exact solutions of equations of first and higher orders when no fortuitous geometric property is present requires considerable theory and technique. Fortunately, the major theme of this chapter requires only special differential equations arising in mechanics, and there is no need to develop a detailed analysis of other types.

The study of the differential equations of *rational* or *analytic mechanics* was initiated by Euler and brought to fruition by Lagrange. Ultimately, Hamilton added a final generalization, one that is suitable even in today's quantum mechanics. Analytic mechanics provides a pure mathematical treatment of *dynamics*, the study of the *motion* of mate-

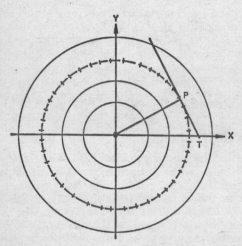

Figure 9.6   Direction field for $dy/dx = -x/y$

rial bodies subject to forces. Lagrange's abstract "systems" idealize the corresponding physical realities. The "state" of such systems at a particular time is described by two or more real numbers. (Above, two numbers furnished the *position* and *velocity* of the bullet.) As time goes on the two, three, . . . , n, real numbers describing the state of a dynamical system will in general vary, and if we name these real variables $x_1, x_2, \ldots, x_n$, a dynamical system is such that the rates of change, $dx_1/dt, dx_2/dt, \ldots, dx_n/dt$, depend merely on the values of the variables themselves. Hence the laws of motion can be expressed by n differential equations which give formulas for $dx_1/dt, dx_2/dt, \ldots, dx_n/dt$ in terms of constants and one or more of the variables $x_1, x_2, \ldots, x_n$.

In the example of the motion of the bullet, we may think of x, v as x_1, x_2 and then

$$\frac{dx_1}{dt} = x_2$$

$$\frac{dx_2}{dt} = -32$$

A pair of dynamical equations that cannot be solved directly by antidifferentiation in spite of simplicity of appearance is the following:

$$\frac{dx_1}{dt} = x_2$$

$$\frac{dx_2}{dt} = -kx_1$$

where k is a numerical constant. One of the first dynamical problems that gave rise to equations of this form arose in connection with clock-making. In 1656 Christiaan Huygens, Dutch mathematician and physicist, constructed the first pendulum clock. If the arc through which a pendulum swings is *small*, then the above are the differential equations for its motion, where x_1 and x_2 represent the position and the velocity, respectively, of the pendulum bob on this arc.

Equations of the same form express the motion of a stretched spring, according to a law discovered by Robert Hooke, that contentious contemporary of Newton. *Hooke's law* states that the distance by which a force will extend an elastic spring varies directly as this force. This means that if this force is doubled, trebled, quadrupled, etc., the same is true of the displacement of the spring. Algebraically, $F = Kx_1$, where K is a constant depending on the particular spring, F and x_1 are force and distance, respectively.

If the spring is released, there will be a reaction, a restoring force, in accordance with Newton's third law: *To every action there is an equal and opposite reaction.* Then the restoring force can be represented by $-Kx_1$. Newton's second law can be formulated as

Force $=$ Mass $\times$ Acceleration or, if x_2 represents velocity,

$$F = m \frac{dx_2}{dt}$$

(when suitable units of measure are used), and Hooke's law states that

$$F = -Kx_1$$

Equating the two different expressions for the force,

$$m \frac{dx_2}{dt} = -Kx_1$$

and

$$\frac{dx_2}{dt} = -\frac{K}{m}x_1$$

or

$$\frac{dx_2}{dt} = -kx_1$$

where we have replaced the constant K/m by the single constant k. In this way Hooke's law leads to a differential equation like the second one of the original pair. The first equation of the pair, $dx_1/dt = x_2$, merely states the familiar definition of velocity as rate of change of distance with respect to time.

Once more, a knowledge of the position and velocity at a single instant will determine the motion for all the future. For example, suppose that $K = 10$ for a certain spring on which a 5-pound weight is suspended. The weight is pulled 3 inches or ¼ foot below the equilibrium point, and then released. By Hooke's law, the restoring force is

$$F = -10x_1$$

Since a weight of 5 pounds has a mass of 5/32 slug (approximately), Newton's second law implies that

$$F = \frac{5}{32}\left(\frac{dx_2}{dt}\right)$$

Equating the two expressions for the force, one obtains

$$\frac{5}{32}\left(\frac{dx_2}{dt}\right) = -10x_1$$

or

$$\frac{dx_2}{dt} = -64x_1$$

as a differential equation to be satisfied by the motion of the spring. Mathematical theory supplies the general solution

$$x_1 = c_1 \sin 8t + c_2 \cos 8t$$

where c_1 and c_2 are to be determined from the initial conditions. At the beginning, or when $t = 0$, $x_1 = \frac{1}{4}$. Substituting,

$$\tfrac{1}{4} = c_1 \sin 0 + c_2 \cos 0$$

or

$$\tfrac{1}{4} = c_1 \cdot 0 + c_2 \cdot 1$$

and

$$c_2 = \tfrac{1}{4}$$

Therefore

$$x_1 = c_1 \sin 8t + \tfrac{1}{4} \cos 8t$$

In elementary calculus it is proved that the derivatives (with respect to t) of $\sin at$ and $\cos at$ (a, a constant) are $a \cos at$ and $-a \sin at$, respectively. Hence, differentiating with respect to t in the last equation above,

$$\frac{dx_1}{dt} = x_2 = 8c_1 \cos 8t - 2 \sin 8t$$

Initially the weight was *released*, that is, $x_2 = 0$ when $t = 0$. Substituting these values yields

$$0 = 8c_1 \cos 0 - 2 \sin 0$$

or

$$0 = 8c_1 \cdot 1 - 2 \cdot 0$$

and

$$0 = c_1$$

Therefore the motion is described by the pair of equations

$$x_1 = \tfrac{1}{4} \cos 8t$$
$$x_2 = -2 \sin 8t$$

The reader can check that these equations (as well as the general solution) satisfy the pair of differential equations

$$\frac{dx_1}{dt} = x_2$$

$$\frac{dx_2}{dt} = -64x_1$$

The deterministic formulas for x_1 and x_2 are the equations for a *simple harmonic motion*. The equation for x_1 indicates that, in theory, the weight will vibrate up and down forever between positions ¼ ft. or 3 in. above and the same distance below the equilibrium point. The period of the vibration is about 0.8 sec., that is, this will be the interval of time between an instant when the weight is at the lowest position and the instant when it is next at this position. Let us see what effect a change in initial conditions has on the motion. Suppose that when $t = 0$, $x_1 = 0$ and $x_2 = 3$, that is, the weight, initially in the equilibrium position, is struck so as to give it a downward velocity of 3 ft. per sec. Then substituting these conditions, one obtains $c_2 = 0$ and $c_1 = 3/8$ so that the equations for the simple harmonic motion in this instance are

$$x_1 = 3/8 \sin 8t$$

$$x_2 = 3 \cos 8t$$

The period is the same as in the previous case, but the oscillations take place between points 3/8 ft. or 4½ in. above and below the equilibrium point.

Since the small oscillations of a simple pendulum are described by a pair of differential equations of the same sort as those just considered, the pendulum will also have a simple harmonic motion. With our electric clocks and time-telling gadgets of today, we scarcely realize the epochal nature of Galileo's and Huygen's discoveries of the pendulum laws. Until these were known, it was not the common man, but the astronomer who suffered most, because it was not possible to measure small fractions of a day with any real precision. One day in 1583 the nineteen-year-old Galileo, while praying in the cathedral at Pisa, chanced to observe the swinging of the great lamp which had just been lighted. Using the beating of his own heart as a clock, he timed the oscillations and found the time to be about the same for every vibration, even after the amplitude of the swinging had greatly diminished.

Thus Galileo discovered that the motion of a pendulum is approximately *isochronous,* that is, the time of return to its initial position is about the same whether it makes a large movement at high velocity under a strong restoring force, or a small movement at low velocity with slight restoring force. Galileo used this fact to invent an instrument by which a doctor could take a patient's pulse, and then forgot about it until late in life, when suddenly he realized that the isochronism of the pendulum might make it possible to construct clocks that would constitute a great improvement over the crude timekeepers then in use. The pure mathematical pendulum of the differential equations above maintains its motion forever, but in clockmaking or other applications, some external source of power is required to prevent the pendulum from coming gradually to rest. Galileo never completed a mechanical design for supplying such power, and hence it was not he but Huygens who constructed the first pendulum clock. In such a clock the pendulum is kept in motion by a slight force applied as it passes its lowest point. Each time it swings it causes a spring or weight to move a wheel through a certain specified distance, and this motion is transmitted to the clock hands by means of gears.

Springs and clocks were some of the earliest practical applications of the Galileo-Newtonian mechanics, but in the strictest sense the classic laws of motion were not entirely suited to the physical problems involved. Newton's laws apply only to particles, that is, masses so tiny that they can be considered to be concentrated at points, and therefore have a position defined by one Cartesian coordinate x if located on a line, by two coordinates (x, y) or three coordinates (x, y, z) if located in a plane or in space, respectively. But if the motion under consideration is that of an entire physical body, and not merely that of a single particle, the mechanics of Newton must be generalized and the mathematics becomes tremendously more difficult. The generalized physical laws and the associated mathematical techniques were contributed by Euler, Lagrange, and Hamilton.

One far-reaching principle of mechanics was due to Euler's younger contemporary, D'Alembert, who is probably best known to general readers for his association with Diderot in the preparation of the *Encyclopedia*. In our discussion of the mechanics of rigid bodies, we have alluded to *external* or impressed, rather than internal, forces as the primary cause of motion. It is *D'Alembert's principle* that furnishes the reason for this fact. The internal forces of a rigid body are gravitational attractions, molecular reactions, various interactions among its numerous particles. External or impressed forces are those exerted by other bodies. The weight of a rigid body is an external force because it is exerted by another body, the earth. When men pull on a tow rope in removing a wrecked car from the road, the force exerted is external to the car.

Newton's second law, $F = ma$, applies only to a single particle. Here F represents the resultant or vectorial sum of all the forces, external and internal, acting on such a particle. It is this resultant force that is effective in producing the actual motion of the particle, and because this force is equal to the product ma, it is customary to call ma the *effective force* on the particle. In 1742 D'Alembert generalized Newton's $F = ma$ by the assertion that if ma, the effective force, is computed for each particle of a rigid body or general mechanical system and all these effective forces are totaled, this sum is equal to the total of *external* forces acting on the system. Such is *D'Alembert's principle*. An alternative statement of this law emphasized that the internal forces of a system have no effect on its motion and that it is only external forces that can cause any movement: *The internal actions and reactions of any system of bodies in motion are in equilibrium* (that is, they cancel one another and their total effect is nil).

After enunciating his principle, D'Alembert applied it to hydromechanics with fruitful results, and from that time on his researches in both pure and applied mathematics were of such outstanding quality as to win recognition not only from his native Academy of Sciences but also, as mentioned earlier, from the Berlin Academy of Frederick the Great. In his later years he acted as a sort of big brother to Lagrange, his successor in the field of mechanics. In the course of a lengthy correspondence he encouraged the young man's scientific efforts, counseled him to take better care of his health, and roused him from his periodic spells of despondency.

Lagrange, possibly the greatest figure in the history of

mechanics, considered very general dynamical systems. In 1834 Hamilton generalized Lagrange's methods still further. Hamilton expressed mechanical laws in the form of "canonical equations," which are the utmost in generality. Both these and the less general Lagrange equations resemble the differential equations expressing Newton's second law. If the acceleration of a body varies, then $F = ma$, or

$$F = m \frac{dv}{dt}$$

Since mass was considered to be constant in classic mechanics,

$$F = \frac{d(mv)}{dt}$$

Now mv, the product of mass and velocity, is called *momentum*, and if we examine the last equation above, we can see why Newton's second law is often stated as: *The rate of change of momentum* (of a particle) *is equal to the force.*

In the Hamilton differential equations the law expressed is: The rate of change of the *generalized* momentum is equal to the *generalized* force. The Hamiltonian equations are the most powerful generalizations of classical mechanics and are adequate to deal with the most complicated systems imaginable.

Although the basic postulates of quantum mechanics differ from those of the traditional subject in very fundamental aspects, it is a remarkable fact that the enormous generality of the Hamilton equations make them suitable, *mutatis mutandis*, even in the new, radically different mechanics. The same cannot be said of Lagrange's equations, even though in classical mechanics these imply the Hamiltonian equations and conversely. It is hard to explain this paradox without going into the details of quantum mechanics, but the essential point is that in Lagrange's mechanics the function defining the energy of the system is expressed in terms of generalized *velocities*, whereas the *Hamiltonian* is a function of generalized *momenta*. Now a momentum has meaning in quantum mechanics but a velocity has not. One might argue that, after all, momentum is equal to mv, the product of mass and velocity, so that a little algebraic manipulation can convert an expression involving velocities into one with momenta and vice versa. This is actually the classical procedure for deducing the Hamiltonian equations from the Lagrangian and conversely, but analogous reasoning would *not* hold in quantum mechanics, for there one starts with generalized momenta, the concept of momentum being autonomous. A momentum is a *matrix* (Chapter 10), an entity dealing with a whole set *en masse*, and is *not* the product of the mass and velocity of the subatomic particles that are the object of study in quantum mechanics. In fact, the nature of quantum theory does not permit a well-defined velocity concept, and it would be illogical to base other notions on an entity whose measurement is ambiguous. The indeterminism of velocity is part of the famous Heisenberg "principle of indeterminacy." In 1927 Heisenberg advanced the theory that it is impossible to fix both the position and the velocity of an electron with perfect precision, that if we increase the accuracy of one of these measurements, it automatically decreases the precision of the other. If our measuring tools were perfect, or nearly so, this would not be the case. Our instruments are part of the universe we are studying, and they share its characteristics, one of which, according to the quantum theory, is the *discreteness* or lack of continuity of matter and energy. This makes ever-so-fine subdivision of units of measure not only a practical but a theoretical impossibility. The smallest possible subdivision of mass is that of an electron, and the smallest unit of energy the "quantum." Such are the notions from which Heisenberg deduced the principle establishing the indeterminacy of velocity. This issue does *not* arise in classical mechanics because the phenomena considered are macrocosmic and it is not a question of motion in a subatomic world where the inevitable coarseness of our tools is important. The older mechanics is valid up to the boundaries of the atom, and in fact, for the outer confines of the atom the quantum equations become identical with the classical ones.

All our illustrations have exhibited "ordinary" differential equations, but the vast majority of physical laws are couched as "partial" differential equations. Therefore, to appreciate the significance of major physical laws, it is necessary to know what is meant by a partial differential equation. Thus we shall now introduce that concept.

In the discussion of calculus in the previous chapter, only functions of a single variable were considered, that is, there was an independent variable (x), and a dependent variable

(y). But the formulation of natural phenomena cannot be limited to relations containing only two variables, but may involve many variables. Even in elementary analytic geometry three variables are usually required for the equation of a surface in space. Thus $z = 2x + 3y + 1$ is the equation of a certain plane and $z = x^2 + 4y$ is the equation of a certain "quadric" surface.

In the equation for a plane, if one were to consider only those points for which $y = 1$, or those for which $y = 4$, or those for which $y = b$ (any constant value), the above equation would become $z = 2x + 3 + 1$ or $z = 2x + 12 + 1$ or $z = 2x + 3b + 1$, that is, a straight line in the given plane, and then the elementary calculus of the previous chapter would be applicable. The slope of each one of the straight lines would be $dz/dx = 2$. Reasoning similarly with the quadric surface, that is, considering only those points of the surface where $y = b$, the equation for such points becomes $z = x^2 + 4b$ (a *parabola* on the surface) and the derivative (slope of the tangent to the parabola) is $dz/dx = 2x$. In both examples treated, one is dealing merely with a *part* of the surface, a line or curve within it. This results from having y remain constant in value while only x and z change. To indicate this phenomenon, it is customary to refer to the derivatives just found as *partial* derivatives and to employ a special symbolism, namely $\partial z/\partial x$.

In analogous fashion one may consider only those parts of surfaces where x has a specified value, $x = a$. Then substitution in the equations above would yield $z = 2a + 3y + 1$ and $z = a^2 + 4y$, respectively, both straight lines, with $\partial z/\partial y = 3$ as the slope of the first line and $\partial z/\partial y = 4$ as the slope of the second.

It is thus possible to interpret partial derivatives, like ordinary derivatives, as slopes, rates of change, etc. As another example, consider $A = 2\pi rh + 2\pi r^2$, the formula for the total surface area of a circular cylinder, where r is the radius and h the altitude. Here $\partial A/\partial h = 2\pi r$ gives the rate of change of surface area when the radius is held constant while the height is permitted to increase or decrease so that the cylinder gets taller or shorter. If $r = 10$, then $\partial A/\partial h = 20\pi = 62.8$ (approximately) and the area is increasing or decreasing at the rate of roughly 63 sq. in. per in. (of height). If, on the other hand, the altitude is held constant and the radius varies, $\partial A/\partial r = 2\pi h + 4\pi r$. If $r = 10$ and $h = 5$ when the radius begins to increase (or decrease),

$\partial A/\partial r = 10\pi + 40\pi = 50\pi = 157$ (approximately), so that the area is changing at the rate of 157 sq. in. per in.

A simple example of the use of partial derivatives in physics is furnished by the thermodynamic law of Charles (1746–1823) and Gay-Lussac (1778–1850). That law, which expresses the relation of volume, pressure, and absolute temperature in an ideal gas, has the algebraic form $V = kTP^{-1}$. Therefore $\partial V/\partial T = kP^{-1}$ gives the rate of change in the volume of any gas when its pressure is held constant but its temperature is allowed to vary, and $\partial V/\partial P = -kTP^{-2}$ gives the rate of change in volume when temperature is held constant while pressure varies.

Partial derivatives, like ordinary derivatives, can also be extended to second or higher orders. Consider the surface

$$z = 2x^3 + 5xy^2 - y^3$$

If the reader will proceed as above, first taking $y = b$ (any constant), and then $x = a$ (any constant), he will find that $\partial z/\partial x = 6x^2 + 5y^2$ and $\partial z/\partial y = 10xy - 3y^2$. (Actually he will obtain $6x^2 + 5b^2$ and $10ay - 3y^2$. But this is understood in the formulas. In $\partial z/\partial x$ only x and z vary. Hence y must be a constant. Likewise x must be a constant in $\partial z/\partial y$. In a more general case, if u depends on x, y, z, t, w, etc., and $\partial u/\partial w$ is found, it is understood that only u and w are variables, and if other letters—x, y, z, t, etc.—appear in the formula for $\partial u/\partial w$, it is known that they are to be held constant.)

To obtain a *second* partial derivative, let $y = l$, a constant, in

$$\frac{\partial z}{\partial x} = 6x^2 + 5y^2$$

Then

$$\frac{\partial z}{\partial x} = 6x^2 + 5l^2$$

and

$$\frac{\partial^2 z}{\partial x^2} = 12x$$

For a different second derivative, let $x = k$, a constant, in $\partial z/\partial x$.

Then

$$\frac{\partial z}{\partial x} = 6k^2 + 5y^2$$

and

$$\frac{\partial^2 z}{\partial y \partial z} = 10y$$

Proceeding in similar fashion with the expression for $\partial z/\partial y$, one finds that

$$\frac{\partial^2 z}{\partial y^2} = 10x - 6y$$

and

$$\frac{\partial^2 z}{\partial x \partial y} = 10y$$

We observe that, in this case,

$$\frac{\partial^2 z}{\partial y \partial x} = \frac{\partial^2 z}{\partial x \partial y} = 10y$$

In many other cases (but not in all) it will be true that

$$\frac{\partial^2 z}{\partial y \partial x} = \frac{\partial^2 z}{\partial x \partial y}$$

that is, in such special instances, differentiation with respect to x and y is *commutative*, or if one differentiates first with respect to x and then with respect to y, the result will be the same as if one proceeds in the opposite way, varying y first while holding x constant, then varying x while y is constant. It can be proved that if the two partial derivatives above are continuous (for a pair of values of x and y), then these derivatives are equal (for the particular values of x and y) and there is "commutativity."

To reverse the procedure above, let us carry out some antidifferentiations with partial derivatives and, in the process, solve some *partial differential equations*. Consider first the ordinary differential equation

$$\frac{dy}{dx} = 2x$$

Then the general solution is

$$y = x^2 + c$$

Now if z is an unknown function of two variables, x and y, and if from the conditions of some problem it is known that

$$\frac{\partial z}{\partial x} = 2x$$

the solution of this partial differential equation can be found by anti-differentiation in a manner suggested above. The solution is

$$z = x^2 + g(y)$$

where $g(y)$ is an *arbitrary function* of y (instead of an arbitrary constant as in the case of the ordinary differential equation). To check, the reader may substitute any function of y for $g(y)$. Thus let

$$g(y) = y^5 - 17y^2 + 3$$

Then

$$z = x^2 + y^5 - 17y^2 + 3$$

and

$$\frac{\partial z}{\partial x} = 2x$$

so that the given condition is satisfied.

For practice the reader may solve

$$\frac{\partial z}{\partial x} = y^3$$

to obtain the answer

$$z = xy^3 + g(y)$$

Returning momentarily to ordinary differential equations, let us find the general solution of

$$\frac{d^2y}{dx^2} = 0$$

If we let

$$w = \frac{dy}{dx}$$

then the original equation is seen to be equivalent to

$$\frac{dw}{dx} = 0 \quad \text{and} \quad w = c_1$$

or

$$\frac{dy}{dx} = c_1 \quad \text{and} \quad y = c_1 x + c_2$$

Now if z is an unknown function of x and y, let us solve

$$\frac{\partial^2 z}{\partial x^2} = 0$$

Let

$$w = \frac{\partial z}{\partial x}$$

so that

$$\frac{\partial w}{\partial x} = 0 \quad \text{and} \quad w = g(y)$$

or

$$\frac{\partial z}{\partial x} = g(y) \quad \text{and} \quad z = xg(y) + h(y)$$

This general solution contains two arbitrary functions, just as the solution of the corresponding ordinary differential equation contained two arbitrary constants.

To connect the question of partial derivatives with that of physical laws, the partial differential equations of mathematical physics are generally of the "second order," which signifies that they contain no derivatives higher than the second. For example, there are generalizations of the differential equation $\partial^2 z/\partial x^2 = 0$, which was just solved. These are

$$\frac{\partial^2 z}{\partial x^2} + \frac{\partial^2 z}{\partial y^2} = 0 \quad \text{and} \quad \frac{\partial^2 u}{\partial x^2} + \frac{\partial^2 u}{\partial y^2} + \frac{\partial^2 u}{\partial z^2} = 0$$

They are called the *Laplace equations* in two and three dimensions, respectively, and are generally considered to express the *most important laws* of mathematical physics. It is easy to furnish particular examples of functions satisfying Laplace's equation, since the variety of such functions is infinite. Thus let us show that

$$\frac{\partial^2 z}{\partial x^2} + \frac{\partial^2 z}{\partial y^2} = 0$$

is satisfied by

$$z = x^3 - 3xy^2$$

For this function

$$\frac{\partial z}{\partial x} = 3x^2 \qquad \frac{\partial z}{\partial y} = -6xy$$

$$\frac{\partial^2 z}{\partial x^2} = 6x \qquad \frac{\partial^2 z}{\partial y^2} = -6x$$

and therefore

$$\frac{\partial^2 z}{\partial x^2} + \frac{\partial^2 z}{\partial y^2} = 6x - 6x = 0$$

In ordinary differential equations the problem is usually to find a general solution, that is, to find *all* functions meeting the requirements expressed by the equation. Then if a particular solution is desired, initial conditions are substituted and from these the arbitrary constants in the general solution are determined. In the case of partial differential equations, it is usually neither feasible nor desirable to seek general solutions, although we have done so for some special cases. Instead, one makes use, almost from the outset, of the special restrictions furnished by the conditions of the particular problem. Thus a vibrating string can be shown to satisfy

$$\frac{\partial^2 y}{\partial t^2} = c^2 \frac{\partial^2 y}{\partial x^2}$$

where (x, y) are the coordinates of a point on the string, and t represents time. The constant c is determined from the physical condition of the string. Thus, if the tension is constant throughout the string,

$$c^2 = \frac{\text{tension}}{\text{mass density}}$$

Suppose, for example, that the length of the string is 4 ft.,
its weight is 2 oz., and it is stretched so that the tension
throughout is 4 lb. Then mass (in slugs) is $1/8 \div 32 = 1/256$,
and mass density is $1/256 \div 4 = 1/1024$. Hence

$$c^2 = \frac{4}{\dfrac{1}{1024}} = 64^2$$

Therefore, under these conditions, the equation becomes

$$\frac{\partial^2 y}{\partial t^2} = (64)^2 \frac{\partial^2 y}{\partial x^2}$$

Suppose that a solution is required which will satisfy the
following conditions. First, there is the *boundary condition*
specifying that the ends of the string are attached to the
X-axis at the points (0, 0) and (4, 0). Next, there is the
initial condition stating that when $t = 0$, the string is
stretched slightly and drawn away from its straight-line
position so that its shape is given by $y = 1/4 \sin \pi x/4$
(Figure 9.7), and then it is released. The last fact signifies

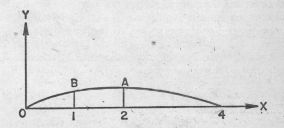

Figure 9.7   String stretched to shape $y = \frac{1}{4} \sin \pi x/4$

that initially the points of the string will have zero velocity
in a vertical direction, that is, when $t = 0$, $\partial y/\partial t = 0$. The
particular solution satisfying all these conditions can be
shown to be $y = 1/4 \sin \pi x/4 \cos 16\pi t$. This formula will
give the position of any point on the string at any time.
Thus, if one is interested in following the progress of the
midpoint of the string, this can be done by substituting
$x = 2$ (since the string is 4 ft. long) in the solution, to
obtain

$$y = \frac{1}{4} \sin\left(\frac{\pi}{4} \cdot 2\right) \cos 16\pi t$$

Now $\sin \pi/2$ (radians) $= \sin 90° = 1$, and the result is therefore

$$y = \frac{1}{4} \cos 16\pi t$$

Where is point A after 1/32 sec., or after 1/16 sec.? This calls for substituting $t = 1/32$ and $t = 1/16$ to obtain

$$y = \frac{1}{4} \cos\left(16\pi \cdot \frac{1}{32}\right) = \frac{1}{4} \cos \frac{\pi}{2}$$

and

$$y = \frac{1}{4} \cos\left(16\pi \cdot \frac{1}{16}\right) = \frac{1}{4} \cos \pi$$

Now π radians $= 180°$, $\pi/2 = 90°$, and $\cos 90° = 0$, $\cos 180° = -1$. The results are therefore $y = 0$ and $y = -1/4$, or point A is on the X-axis (at $x = 2$) after 1/32 sec., and is 1/4 ft. or 3 in. below it after 1/16 sec.

In the same way, it is possible to tell the position of any other point of the string at any time. For example, where is the point B in Figure 9.7 after 3 1/16 seconds? If we assume $x = 1$ for this point and substitute in the solution of the differential equation, then

$$y = \frac{1}{4} \sin\left(\frac{\pi}{4} \cdot 1\right) \cos\left(16\pi \cdot \frac{49}{16}\right)$$

$$= \frac{1}{4} \sin \frac{\pi}{4} \cos 49\pi$$

$$= \frac{1}{4}\left(\frac{\sqrt{2}}{2}\right)(-1) = -\frac{\sqrt{2}}{8} = -0.18 \text{ (approximately)}$$

Therefore, at the time specified, the point in question is 0.18 ft. or about 2.16 in. below the X-axis.

The question of whether any mathematical solution to a physical problem or to the corresponding partial differential equation (with arbitrary boundary conditions) can be found and the mathematical devices for obtaining such solutions

(Fourier series, for example) are all subjected to study in the modern theory of partial differential equations and their application to physical problems. In a certain sense, one might consider deterministic mathematical physics to be the theory of boundary value problems. Therefore, to discuss all the possible physical situations described by partial differential equations and associated boundary conditions would require a profound study of advanced mathematics and physics. Nevertheless it is possible to give a few elementary illustrations.

Suppose, for example, that the periphery of a thin metal plate, with insulated faces, is maintained at a constant temperature, or more generally that each point of the periphery is kept at a constant temperature which may, however, vary from point to point. Thus, in a circular plate half the circumference might be kept at one temperature, and the other half at a different temperature. Then after a while the distribution of temperatures in the plate will reach a "steady state," a permanent condition where the temperature at each particular point remains the same as time goes on. The specific temperatures at each point will then depend on the size and shape of the metal sheet and the temperatures maintained at the boundary points. It can be proved that the formula for the steady state distribution of temperatures must satisfy *Laplace's differential equation* in two dimensions, that is, if z represents the temperature at a point P of the plate with Cartesian coordinates (x, y),

$$\frac{\partial^2 z}{\partial x^2} + \frac{\partial^2 z}{\partial y^2} = 0$$

As to boundary conditions, it might be known, for example, that the boundary is a circle and the temperature at each point of the circumference might be specified. The solution would be different if the shape were rectangular rather than circular, and would also depend on just how the peripheral temperatures on the rectangle are assigned.

To give another example of a physical interpretation of Laplace's equation, one can assert that the possible distributions for the Newtonian "gravitational potential" in the region of space surrounding the sun, or any other material body, are governed by the differential equation in question. At a point (x, y, z) *outside* matter (or in empty space) the "potential" u (a term due to *Lagrange*) must satisfy

$$\frac{\partial^2 u}{\partial x^2} + \frac{\partial^2 u}{\partial y^2} + \frac{\partial^2 u}{\partial z^2} = 0$$

and at a point *inside* matter, the corresponding physical law is expressed by a slightly different partial differential equation, that of Poisson (1781–1840), namely,

$$\frac{\partial^2 u}{\partial x^2} + \frac{\partial^2 u}{\partial y^2} + \frac{\partial^2 u}{\partial z^2} = -4\pi\rho$$

where ρ is the density of mass at the point (x, y, z).

Without going too deeply into the meaning of the "potential," it can be described as a continuous numerical function $u(x, y, z)$ from which the gravitational or electrical or magnetic force acting at the point (x, y, z) can be derived. In classical physics the potential at this point can be interpreted as the *work* that must be done to bring a unit of mass or a unit of electric charge from a very great distance to the point in question. A "velocity potential" is one from which velocities can be derived. In an ideal, incompressible fluid where there are no vortices about which the fluid will tend to rotate, and where there is no change in the total amount of fluid (that is, no sources of increase or "sinks" causing decrease), the velocity potential must satisfy Laplace's equation. This fact is important in hydrodynamics and aerodynamics.

The partial differential equations mentioned thus far have not involved time as a variable, because the phenomena referred to have been permanent or static—the temperatures have been those for the "steady state," or the masses, charges, velocities have remained invariant as time goes on, although the physical entities involved have varied from point to point. If, however, one considers Poincaré's "present state of the world and condition immediately after," partial derivatives with respect to time must be involved. Most physical systems do, in fact, change with time, and t (time) will appear in equations and solutions. Also there will be *initial* ($t = 0$) as well as boundary conditions to exert restrictions on the possible answers to particular problems. Thus, in heat flow one may be concerned with the temperature distribution prior to the steady state, or such a condition may never be reached. For example, if z represents temperature, its distribution in a thin insulated rod at *any* time must satisfy

$$\frac{\partial^2 z}{\partial x^2} = k \frac{\partial z}{\partial t}$$

whereas the distribution prior to the steady state in an insulated plate must meet the requirement

$$\frac{\partial^2 z}{\partial x^2} + \frac{\partial^2 z}{\partial y^2} = k \frac{\partial z}{\partial t}$$

In these instances, the particular solutions will have to satisfy not only boundary conditions involving the shape and size of the object and its peripheral temperatures, but also initial conditions like the following: When $t = 0$ the temperature $z = 30°C$ throughout the rod or metallic plate.

The partial differential equation

$$\frac{\partial^2 y}{\partial t^2} = c^2 \frac{\partial^2 y}{\partial x^2}$$

has been related to the phenomenon of a vibrating string, but it is possible to give it a more general interpretation by which it is termed the one-dimensional *wave equation*, where c is equal to the velocity of propagation of the waves. A generalization is the three-dimensional wave equation

$$\frac{\partial^2 u}{\partial t^2} = c^2 \left(\frac{\partial^2 u}{\partial x^2} + \frac{\partial^2 u}{\partial y^2} + \frac{\partial^2 u}{\partial z^2} \right)$$

where c is the speed of propagation of the waves. This equation applies to all types of electromagnetic waves, or to waves in any homogeneous elastic medium. In mathematical physics, the electromagnetic condition in free space is said to be determined by two vectors, an electric force and a magnetic force. That the components of these forces satisfy the wave equation above is a consequence of *Maxwell's laws*, which have been the starting point of all electromagnetic and optical theories from Maxwell's day to the present time. These famous principles are expressed by a set of partial differential equations. Instead of recording the abstract mathematical form of Maxwell's equations, one might give their physical interpretation somewhat as follows:

(1) The electric flux across a closed surface is zero.
(2) The magnetic flux across a closed surface is zero.

(3) A variable magnetic field generates an electric field. (Faraday's law of induction).

(4) A variable electric field generates a magnetic field [Maxwell's hypothesis formulated on the grounds of symmetry with (3)].

In his general theory of relativity Einstein expressed by means of certain celebrated "field equations" the laws to which his four-dimensional space-time continuum was to conform. These were differential equations controlling the possible distributions and changes of the "gravitational field" and were the gravitational analogues of the Maxwell equations we have just discussed. When general relativity and the differential-geometric concepts fundamental to that subject are discussed later in this book, a reaffirmation of the theme of the present chapter will be found in the words of the famous Norwegian mathematician, Marius Sophus Lie (1842–1899), who stated as his belief, "The theory of differential equations is the most important branch of modern (nineteenth-century) mathematics."

But for a proper appreciation of *nondeterministic* physics —for example, quantum mechanics—it will be necessary to have some understanding of probability theory and statistics. These subjects will be discussed next, not only for the sake of application to quantum mechanics, but because they play an essential role in many other modern phases of mathematics.

Chapter 10

The Elements of Strategy in War and Peace

In tracing the development of arithmetic or geometry or other mathematical subjects, it is customary to point to motivations arising from the practical needs of advancing civilization. But the origins and the evolution of probability theory furnish a counterexample to the traditional evaluation of mathematics as a sort of virtuous handmaiden ever ready to serve worthwhile scientific purposes. The historic fact is that church and state have had to wage an age-long battle against the very games of chance which motivated a probability calculus, encouraged its development, and provided the simplest empirical counterparts for its theoretical results. To indicate that lowly gaming has continued to inspire lofty mathematics up to the present day, one need only reveal that the game of poker played a germinal role in the recent theory of games formulated by John von Neumann (1903–1957). The nature and significance of this theory are described in a statement made by Harold W. Kuhn and A. W. Tucker,* two of von Neumann's friends who are specialists in the field.

Of the many areas of mathematics shaped by his genius, none shows more clearly the influence of John von Neumann than the theory of games. This modern approach to problems of competition and cooperation was given a broad foundation in his superlative 1928 paper, *Zur Theorie der Gesellschaftsspiele* (Theory of Parlor Games). A decade later when the Austrian economist Oskar Morgenstern came to Princeton, von Neumann's interest

---

* H. W. Kuhn and A. W. Tucker, "John von Neumann's Work in the Theory of Games and Mathematical Economics," *Bulletin of the American Mathematical Society*, Vol. 64, No. 3, Part 2 (May 1958), pp. 100 ff.

in the theory was reawakened. The result of active and intensive collaboration was the von Neumann-Morgenstern treatise, *Theory of Games and Economic Behavior* (1944). Together, the paper and treatise contain a remarkably complete outline of the subject as we know it today.

Some of the basic concepts of the von Neumann theory will be discussed in the present work. The history of the subject shows that somewhat earlier (1921) than the 1928 von Neumann research paper, the great French analyst Émile Borel (1871–1956) had also attempted to mathematicize the concept of strategy. He considered only the simplest examples, however, and provided no proof of the basic theorem which is the crux of von Neumann's theory. A third leading mathematician of the recent period must also be brought into the story, namely, Abraham Wald (1902–1950), whose theory of *statistical decision functions* is intimately related to the theory of games but is somewhat broader in its scope and applicability. Professor J. Wolfowitz, a leading mathematical statistician of our day and a collaborator in some of Wald's important discoveries, has stated that Wald's decision theory includes almost all problems which are the *raison d'être* of mathematical statistics.

The overall purposes of Chapters 10–14 are, first, to survey the simplest features of the von Neumann and Wald theories; second, to present the most elementary aspects of the mathematical statistics which preceded Wald's decision theory and was embraced by it; and third, to discuss those probabilistic concepts required for the formulation or solution of problems of strategy, decision, or statistical inference. The treatment of probability will be integrated with the other subjects of discussion, and therefore in subsequent chapters will be related both to games of chance and to the Borel-von Neumann strategic games.

Before proceeding to the mathematics of strategy, however, it would seem fitting to say something about the mathematicians who contributed the content of recent theories. Because the creation of game theory was only a single phase of von Neumann's career, his name is bound to arise in connection with most of the important fields of modern mathematical research. It would be futile to list all the areas in which he made notable discoveries, partly because the list would be so lengthy, but chiefly because the mere names of the subjects do not usually convey meaning to nonspecialists. Perhaps, in addition to game theory, the only other mathematical activity of von Neumann to attract popular attention was that connected with his theory of automatic large-scale computers and machines that are self-repairing, self-correcting, and ultimately will be self-reproducing. His final efforts were made in this direction, and shortly before his death in 1957, he prepared (but was unable to deliver) a lecture comparing the human brain with a "mechanical brain" or computer.

Concerning von Neumann's individual "gray matter," Hans Bethe, a leading nuclear physicist, once said: "I wonder whether a brain like von Neumann's does not indicate a species superior to that of man." Those scientists who admired that brain went further—they worshiped it, and held the view that when the mathematical history of the present era is written, von Neumann's name will be placed first. Even without such forecasts, one must be interested in the biography of a contemporary hero.

John von Neumann's native city was Budapest, where his father was a wealthy banker. The boy's genius manifested itself early, and by the time he entered the *gymnasium* at the age of ten, his mathematical knowledge was so great that instead of attending regular classes he read advanced mathematics under the direction of leading Hungarian mathematicians. At the age of twenty-one he acquired two degrees, one in chemical engineering at Zurich, and the other a Ph.D. in mathematics from the University of Budapest. Three years later he became a *privat dozent* at the University of Berlin, and then, in 1930, accepted a visiting professorship at Princeton University. In 1933 he and Einstein were among the first full professors to be appointed to the newly organized Institute for Advanced Study. Von Neumann thus became the youngest member of its permanent faculty.

During World War II, he was consultant at Los Alamos, and his research speeded up the making of the A-bomb. Later he became chief adviser on nuclear weapons to the United States Air Force. He was also instrumental in the government decision to accelerate the intercontinental ballistic missile program. In October 1954, President Eisenhower appointed him to the Atomic Energy Commission; but after von Neumann had devoted his "giant brain" to this task for a brief six months, X-ray examinations revealed the source of the prolonged and cruel illness that was to terminate his career. Although he knew the diagnosis was cancer, he continued his heavy schedule on the AEC, and even when he became invalided, he maintained communication through a telephone connected directly with the AEC office.

There are, in addition to the facts of his accomplishment, many tales connected with his feats of memory and the rapidity of his thought. In the latter category is a story of how he obtained within a few minutes the answer to a problem that had required two years for solution by the research group known as Project Rand. As for memory feats, he could recite the smallest details in Gibbon's *Decline and Fall* or recount the minutest features of the battles in the American War between the States. It is said that during the last period of his fatal illness, his brother would read to him in German from Goethe's *Faust*, and that each time a page was turned, von Neumann would recite from memory the continuation of the passage on the following page. Dying at fifty-three, he was not able to finish his greatest mathematical "poems" in the leisurely way that the eighty-year-old Goethe had been able to complete *Faust*.

It is surprising to see in how many respects the life of Émile Borel was similar to that of von Neumann, with one strong exception. Borel lived to the ripe old age of eighty-five, dying peacefully just a year before the American game-theoretician succumbed to his tragic illness. Moreover, the age at which Borel *began* his consideration of games of strategy was approximately the same as that at which von Neumann gave his final thought to the subject. Probability theory and statistics are specialties to which Borel devoted his later years. He is more renowned for earlier discoveries which make him one of the founders of the twentieth-century phase of mathematical analysis. Although von Neumann's genius was far more universal, nevertheless as far as probability and analysis are concerned, both men were interested in the same problems. Both combined careers in mathematics with distinguished public service.

Émile Borel was born in 1871 in Saint-Affrique in south-central France. His father, a Protestant minister, was also the principal of the elementary school which Émile attended. The younger Borel's subsequent academic life was to be associated again and again with the great École Normale Supérieure of Paris, first as a student, later as an instructor, and in the decade from 1910 to 1920 as assistant director.

Thereafter Borel's scientific reputation was widespread. In 1921, he was elected to the French Academy of Sciences, and very soon scientific societies outside his native country recognized his merit. He received the Grand Cross of the Legion of Honor and was a member of the council of that order. In 1955, he was the first recipient of the Gold Medal of the French National Center for Scientific Research.

Although Borel was first and foremost a mathematician, he lent his ability to a variety of causes. For example, in 1926, when the Rockefeller Foundation offered to provide half the funds necessary for the creation of a French center of research in mathematics and mathematical physics, it was Borel who set up a suitable plan and who succeeded in getting M. de Rothschild to match the Rockefeller contribution. Within two years, the institute was inaugurated and named after Henri Poincaré, the renowned mathematical leader of the early twentieth century.

Émile Borel also displayed his versatility by participation in military and political activities. His services during World War I earned him the *Croix de Guerre*. In 1924, he started his political career as mayor of his home town. Then he was elected to the Chamber of Deputies and remained a deputy for twelve years. His abiding love for science is shown in his successful campaign for a law requiring industry to support pure research. In 1925 he became Minister of the Navy. Finally, he retired from politics in 1936, and returned to his first love, mathematics. During the German occupation in 1941, he was imprisoned in Fresnes because of his aid to the Resistance movement, for which he was later awarded the Medal of the Resistance. After World War II, his age did not deter him from writing a goodly number of semipopular mathematical monographs; he continued at this task right up to the time of his death in 1956.

More than thirty years earlier, he had written in a treatise on probability: "Probabilistic problems concerning military or economic or financial matters are not without analogy to questions about games. Their solution requires that mathematics be supplemented by *strategy*."

Borel's statement as well as the *date* of publication (1944) and *title* of the von Neumann-Morgenstern treatise on games of strategy indicate why, in the beginning, examples of such games were chosen from military or economic situations. Thus one was asked to picture the case of two planes in combat, or the arrival at a price in an economic exchange relation between buyer and seller. These are both approximated by the situation in a duel.

After World War II, game theorists offered less violent examples of strategic problems. Thus there is the "engagement game," where a girl believes that certain young men in her social circle are potential husbands. We shall imagine that the number of prospects is eleven. Since the girl is not too well acquainted with the young men, any one of them seems as appealing as another. She decides that she will pick one of them at random, attract his interest, and become engaged to him. As part of her plan, she expects to break her engagement if, after a while, she should feel that any one of the remaining ten men might be a more suitable husband. In that case, she will make a random selection from the ten, become engaged to this second man, etc. The question is: At what point should she marry? Should the second, third, fourth, etc. engagement be the final one? If she marries one of the earlier candidates, there may possibly be a more desirable man among those left. But if she delays, she will be getting older, may tire of the game, may have doubts that the few remaining men will be superior, and, in fact, may not find the same candidates left, since they may marry in the interim or depart from the locality. Therefore, she must decide on the best strategic choice for the number of engagements. Her decision will depend on a variety of special personal factors.

The "engagement problem" cannot be taken too seriously as far as *real* young men and women are concerned. If, however, the situation seems too frivolous or too extravagant, let us remind the reader that this very game was played more than three hundred years ago by the great Johannes Kepler who (as he himself recounts) considered in turn, each of eleven potential candidates for his hand (Chapter 8). It is evident that Kepler did not treat romantic situations in scientific fashion, and hence did not analyze facts in advance and then decide what the *optimum* number of engagements should be. Young ladies and gentlemen today will have greater faith in the von Neumann theory if we state that the "engagement problem" and the "duel problem" are both difficult to solve.

A duel would be called a *two-person game* because there are two players. Chess is described as a two-person game, even when the opponents are opposing teams. But the von Neumann theory also deals with three-person, four-person, . . . , *n*-person games, where $n > 2$, in which there are 3, 4, . . . , n players, respectively. Some of these games are *cooperative*, so called because the players form coalitions before the game starts in order to coordinate the strategies they will use. Solitaire, certain puzzles, Robinson Crusoe on a desert island, are all examples of *one-person games*, the simple random games of probability theory. Since no issues of strategy are involved, one-person games did not require the special scrutiny of Borel and von Neumann.

In most ordinary parlor games that are played for money, wealth is neither created nor destroyed. In technical language, these are described as *zero-sum games*, since at each move the sum of the gains of the players is zero. Matching pennies, for example, is a zero-sum game, because in each move one player wins what the other loses, and hence the sum of the gains is zero. But *non-zero-sum games* are also important in the general theory because they serve as models for economic processes in which the wealth of participants is increased or decreased. In the present work, however, discussion will be limited to zero-sum, two-person games because these are the model for Wald's decision theory and can therefore be applied to situations far more vital than parlor games or gamblers' activities.

The zero-sum, two-person games are called *rectangular* or *matrix* games because an overall picture of the possible outcomes of any particular move can be furnished by listing the potential gains of one player (and corresponding losses of the other) in the form of a rectangular array or *matrix*, to use the usual mathematical term. An example of such a game is one in which each of the two players writes a number on a slip of paper without permitting his opponent to see his choice. The first player is permitted to select 1 or 2 or 3, and the second player may choose 1 or 2 or 3 or 4. After the choices have been made, the two players match the slips of paper and the second player is required to pay the first an amount listed in the following *payoff matrix*. We shall name the players R and C as a mnemonic device for recalling that their choices involve, respectively, the *R*ows and *C*olumns of the matrix.

| | | \multicolumn{4}{c}{C chooses} |
		1	2	3	4
	1	2	1	4	2
R chooses	2	-3	2	5	0
	3	3	-1	-5	-1

From this point on, symbols like R_2 and C_3 will have a double meaning: R_2 will signify that R has written 2 on his slip of paper; C_3 means C has written 3; R_2 will also mean Row 2; C_3 will also mean Column 3. Then the entry in the second row, third column of the matrix, namely 5, indicates that C must pay five units of money to R. If the respective choices are R_3 and C_2, then the entry in the third row, second column, namely -1, indicates that C must pay -1 to R, that is, R must pay one unit of money to C. Thus R sustains a gain or loss according to whether the payoff is positive or negative. Thus the pair of choices (R_2, C_1) would result in a loss of 3 for R.

The rules of the game we have been considering are formulated by a "3 by 4" (symbolized as 3×4) payoff matrix, so called because there are three rows and four columns. In game theory it is customary merely to indicate the matrix without the marginal entries. This permits a variety of interpretations for the same payoff matrix. In the present instance, as a trivial variant, the players could point fingers (1 or 2 or 3 for R and 1 or 2 or 3 or 4 for C) in the fashion used in the Italian game of Morra. In a more subtle interpretation, R and C might be competing organizations where R must choose from three detailed courses of action (symbolized by 1, 2, 3), and C from four (1, 2, 3, 4). But the *matrix* itself is the game from the point of view of the von Neumann theory, where the word "game" means the set of rules, and where the word "play" is substituted for "game" in statements like "We engaged in two games of chess," which becomes "We engaged in two plays of chess."

Next, let us consider the game with the following 3×3 payoff matrix.

$$\begin{pmatrix} 3 & 1 & 2 \\ 6 & 0 & -3 \\ -5 & -1 & 4 \end{pmatrix}$$

The reader may, if he finds it helpful, visualize the game as consisting of two steps. First, there is the selection of one of the numbers 1, 2, 3 by both R and C; next, they match their choices, with the resulting payoff as indicated in the foregoing matrix. Let us suppose for the sake of simplicity that there is to be only a single "play." If the unit of money is worth \$1,000,000, a great deal is at stake in this one play, for an examination of the matrix indicates that the play (R_2, C_1) will require C to pay 6 units or \$6,000,000 to R, while if the play is (R_3, C_1), R will lose \$5,000,000 to C.

The problem then is as follows: Are there optimum "strategies" for R and C, that is, can a row and column be specified to assure least risk and maximum gain under the circumstances? The answer is in the affirmative, as will now be demonstrated. First, consider R's line of reasoning. The possibility of winning the \$6,000,000 indicated in position (R_2, C_1) of the matrix is tempting. If he is to aim for this, his selection must be R_2, the second row. But suppose C does *not* play C_1, but plays C_2 or C_3. Then the entries at (R_2, C_2) and (R_2, C_3) of the matrix, namely, 0 and -3, indicate that R's choice of R_2 may win nothing for him or else may cause him to lose \$3,000,000 to C. The entry -3 is the worst that can happen, the *minimum* payoff for the second row. R feels that if he selects that row, -3 is almost sure to be his lot. For, he reasons, C knows the rules, since the matrix is also available to him. Therefore he will *not* select C_1. Instead, he will surely choose C_3 so that R will have to pay him \$3,000,000.

Now R decides to examine the other rows. Perhaps I can win the \$4,000,000 in (R_3, C_3), he thinks. But, again, if I pick the third row, what's the worst that can happen? He sees that the entry -5 in (R_3, C_1) is the *minimum* for the third row, or that the worst that can happen from choosing this row is that he will have to pay \$5,000,000 to C. R_3 seems an even more risky choice than R_2. Finally, R examines the first row and sees that the worst that can happen is that he will win \$1,000,000. Hence he reasons that it is safest to select R_1 in anticipation of receiving the maximum of the minima, termed the *maximin* of the row payoffs. His rationale is that in playing a competitive game a person always considers his opponent's potential behavior and that C will therefore put himself in R's place, duplicating the complete argument outlined above. As a result, he will realize that R dare not select R_2 or R_3 and must choose R_1. That being the case, C

will feel that he himself should select C_2 in order to cut R's winnings to a *minimum*. Then from R's point of view, the solution of the game must be the pair of "strategies," R_1 and C_2, with a *value* of $1,000,000 to him.

But is this the best solution for C, who stands to lose $1,000,000 by it? Let us see how the matrix appears to him. He would like to aim at the -5 in (R_3, C_1). But, he thinks, if I pick the first column, R could defeat me either by an accidental selection of the second row or by a choice of this row because he suspects my purpose. Then instead of winning $5,000,000 I would have to pay him $6,000,000, the *maximum* payoff for the first column. No, I cannot risk playing C_1 *if* a better course is open to me. Perhaps I should aim for the -3 (gain of $3,000,000 for C) in position (R_2, C_3) of the matrix. But if I play C_3, R may play R_3. I would then stand to lose the $4,000,000 corresponding to (R_3, C_3). Finally, what would happen if I were to play C_2? I would be hoping for (R_3, C_2) where I would win $1,000,000, but the worst that could happen is indicated by the *maximum* payoff in this column, namely, $1,000,000 at (R_1, C_2). This is the *minimax* of the column payoffs, that is, the minimum of the three column maxima, which are 6, 1, 4 for C_1, C_2, C_3, respectively. Hence, I shall select the strategy C_2, knowing that R will be able to duplicate my line of reasoning, and accordingly will pick R_1. It appears to me that the solution of the game must be the pair of strategies (R_1, C_2) where I lose $1,000,000 to R. Therefore, I consider the proposed game unfair!

Since the reasoning of both R and C leads to the same pair of strategies and to the same entry in the game matrix, the Borel-von Neumann theory would say that the game in question is *determined* or solvable. In general, a matrix game is said to have a solution in the form of a pair of *pure* (row-column) strategies if

$$maximum\ (minimum\ of\ a\ row) =$$
$$minimum\ (maximum\ of\ a\ column)$$

For this reason, von Neumann used the term *"minimax* solution." The matrix entry corresponding to C's minimax and R's maximin is called the *value* of the game (to R). The reasoning of both players forces the value to be the lowest payoff in its row and the highest in its column. Hence its position in the matrix is often called a *saddle*

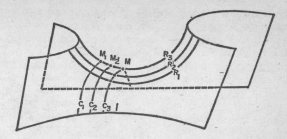

Figure 10.1 The surface in the diagram is shaped like a *saddle*. On it the curves R_1, R_2, R_3 are analogous to matrix rows, and C_1, C_2, C_3 are analogous to matrix columns. The points that are "row" minima and "column" maxima are indicated. Point M, which is both the greatest of the minima and the least of the maxima, is called a *saddle point*.

point by geometric analogy (see Figure 10.1), even though positions in a matrix lack the continuity of those on a surface.

Let us apply the minimax criterion to the game with the following payoff matrix.

$$\begin{pmatrix} 2 & -2 & -3 \\ 1 & 0 & 2 \\ -1 & -1 & 3 \end{pmatrix}$$

Here R must examine the row minima, which are -3, 0, -1, and find

$$\max \ (\min \text{ of row}) = 0$$

C must consider the column maxima, which are 2, 0, 3, and find

$$\min \ (\max \text{ of column}) = 0$$

Since R's *maximin* = C's *minimax*, the game has a solution, namely, (R_2, C_2). The value of the game is *zero*, and hence it is *fair* because neither player will gain at the other's expense if the game is played in minimax fashion.

The reader can verify that the game with payoff matrix

$$\begin{pmatrix} -4 & 3 & 0 & 15 \\ 5 & 6 & 4 & 5 \\ 8 & 0 & 2 & 6 \end{pmatrix}$$

has value 4 (to R) with optimal strategies R_2 and C_3, and that the game whose payoff matrix is

$$\begin{pmatrix} 3 & 1 \\ 4 & 1 \end{pmatrix}$$

has two solutions, both with value 1, namely, (R_1, C_2) and (R_2, C_2). Evidently there would be something inconsistent about several optimal solutions if they led to different values; and it can be proved, in fact, that where more than one solution exists, the value is the same for all solutions.

In some of the matrix games, a preliminary consideration of the matrix may eliminate certain choices immediately and thus simplify the process of locating a saddle point. In the 3×4 rectangular matrix above, for example, the fourth column can be eliminated as a choice for C. By comparing its entries with those in the third column, C would observe that each number in the fourth column is greater than the corresponding one in the third. Hence, no matter what row R chooses, C would be worse off by playing C_4 than C_3. Therefore his optimum strategy should be obtainable by removing the fourth column and considering only the first three. Also, since R can readily figure out what his opponent's line of reasoning must be, *both* players will consider the first three columns only, that is, the 3×3 matrix

$$\begin{pmatrix} -4 & 3 & 0 \\ 5 & 6 & 4 \\ 8 & 0 & 2 \end{pmatrix}$$

Now from R's point of view, the first row of this matrix should never be selected as a strategy, since the payoffs in the second row would always be greater, no matter what column C chooses. Hence R's strategies should be chosen from

$$\begin{pmatrix} 5 & 6 & 4 \\ 8 & 0 & 2 \end{pmatrix}$$

and C will figure out that R must limit himself to the above 2×3 matrix. In that matrix the first column would be eliminated as a strategy when C compares it with the third, and only

$$\begin{pmatrix} 6 & 4 \\ 0 & 2 \end{pmatrix}$$

would remain. Here

$$\max (\min \text{ of row}) = \min (\max \text{ of column}) = 4$$

which is the value of the original game to R. To find the optimum strategies one must locate the entry 4 in the original matrix, and so arrive at the solution (R_2, C_3). (Observe that one could carry the process of elimination still further by eliminating the second row of the 2×2 matrix.)

The reader can apply the procedure followed above and thus remove strategies that would be inadmissible for R or C in the following 4×3 matrix game:

$$\begin{pmatrix} 0 & 3 & 12 \\ 2 & 3 & -7 \\ 8 & 2 & 5 \\ 6 & 3 & 8 \end{pmatrix}$$

The solution arrived at should be (R_4, C_2) with value 3 to R.

Let us next see whether the minimax criterion will provide a solution for the familiar game of matching pennies. In this game, each player places a penny in his hand with heads or tails up, without letting his opponent see his choice. Next, the players match the coins. If both are heads, or both are tails, C gives his penny to R. If the coins are different, R gives his penny to C. Hence the payoff matrix is

$$\begin{pmatrix} 1 & -1 \\ -1 & 1 \end{pmatrix}$$

If R examines this for row minima, he obtains $-1, -1$, and hence

$$\max (\min \text{ of row}) = -1$$

If C examines this for column maxima, he obtains 1, 1, and

$$\min (\max \text{ of column}) = 1$$

Since the maximin and minimax are not equal, there are no optimal pure strategies for a single play. In other words, the game has no solution of the type we have considered thus far.

But almost every one has engaged in matching pennies and tried to choose heads and tails in about equal numbers in *repeated plays*, being careful not to follow any regular pattern which can be observed by his opponent. The very symmetry of the payoff matrix would suggest that this is a good strategy. The strategies for R and C are the same, and can be achieved practically by having each player toss his penny at every play with the result that, in the long run, the relative frequency for each player's choice of heads (or tails) will be ½.

The solution in the game of matching pennies is typical, for in those rectangular games where a saddle point is lacking, the von Neumann solution always consists of varying choices in random fashion from play to play in a way that will produce the optimal long-run results. The player is then said to employ a *randomized* or *mixed* strategy in contrast with the *pure* strategy where the same row or column must be selected no matter how many times the play is repeated. In general, the problem of solving a matrix game consists in determining the optimal relative frequencies for the selection of different rows and columns. In the case of matching pennies, the choice is (½, ½) for R and likewise for C. Pure strategies can, in fact, be classified as special cases of mixed strategies. Thus, instead of saying that the matrix game originally considered has as solution the pure strategies R_1 and C_2, one can say that its solution is the pair of *randomized* or *mixed* strategies, (1, 0, 0) for R and (0, 1, 0, 0) for C.

Will intuition provide a solution to the game with the following payoff matrix?

$$\begin{pmatrix} 2 & 1 \\ 0 & 3 \end{pmatrix}$$

since

$$\max \, (\min \text{ of row}) = 1$$

and

$$\min \, (\max \text{ of col}) = 2$$

there is no saddle point and one cannot pick an optimal pair of pure strategies. Hence, if there is a best policy, it must involve randomized strategies. From R's point of view it might seem desirable to select the first row, because he would be sure to win something no matter what strategy C chooses. But there are good arguments for selecting the second row in some plays, because there is always the chance of winning 3. Moreover, R should not risk the pure strategy of always playing the first row, for then C would become aware of what is happening, and after a few plays would always select the second column, and in successive plays R's winnings would always be limited to 1. Therefore it would be sensible for R to vary his choices in different plays but in accordance with a relative frequency favoring the selection of the first row. Now C's reasoning would lead him, like R, to use a mixed strategy which varies the choice of C_1 or C_2 in random fashion from play to play.

In the next chapter it will be *proved* that the *optimum* mixed strategies for R and C are ($\frac{3}{4}$, $\frac{1}{4}$) and ($\frac{1}{2}$, $\frac{1}{2}$), respectively, which means that the random mixing of choices should be such that R chooses the first row three times as often as the second in the long run, and C selects both columns equally frequently. To achieve randomness in successive plays, C might toss a coin and R might draw a marble from a sack containing thirty blue and ten red marbles, selecting the first row whenever a blue marble is drawn, the second row whenever the marble is red. (The marble must be replaced and the sack thoroughly shaken after each drawing.)

Although our present interest concerns games of strategy, the above considerations involve concepts associated with games of chance. The relative frequencies which describe a mixed strategy correspond in fact to mathematical *probabilities*. If we have had no previous experience with the random devices in the above examples, we may reason *a priori* that when a well-balanced coin is tossed, the chances for "heads" are 1 in 2, that the likelihood of drawing a blue marble from the sack described above is 3/4. The expectation is that the ratios in question will be achieved approximately in very numerous plays.

The intuitive meaning of the term "probability" derives from just such situations. In general, it is assumed that if a random experiment (like those involved in achieving mixed strategies) is repeated many times under essentially stable conditions, the relative frequency of a particular result will ultimately fluctuate only slightly, that is, will tend to a *limit* as the number of repetitions of the experiment is made greater and greater. This limiting value of the relative frequency is considered the "true" probability that the event in question will occur. (This is not a limit in the sense of the calculus, because the relative frequency is not a definite, determined function of the number of repetitions.)

The notion of a probability as the limit of a relative

frequency is at the basis of the *empirical* or *statistical* approximations so common in life insurance and other areas of vital statistics. For example, a department store can afford to double a layette gratis on the advent of twins, since the empirical probability of double births is slight. Again, when premiums are to be computed, mortality table ratios based on 100,000 cases may be considered a sufficiently good approximation to the "true" probabilities involved.

Thus for a proper understanding and handling of randomized strategies, we must make a short detour into probability theory. We shall require, in particular, one special concept from that theory if we are to formulate the Borel-von Neumann-Wald criterion for solving a rectangular game whose matrix lacks a saddle point.

Chapter 11

Probabilistic Models, Great Expectations, and Randomized Strategies

To fulfill the promise made at the close of the previous chapter, we shall now present briefly certain aspects of the theory of probability prior to resuming our discussion of games of strategy. A practical issue associated with such games was the motivation for formulating a concept of probability that is useful to the applied mathematician. But the pure mathematician sees in probability theory a methodology for the construction of "mathematical models" for a certain type of physical experiment.

A *mathematical model* (page 427) is an abstract idealization of various features of a real situation in the same sense that pure Euclidean plane geometry is the abstract counterpart of the surveyor's or the engineer's conception of physical points, lines, polygons, circles, etc. and their properties. In every model the totality of things under discussion is called the *universal set* or *universe of discourse* (Chapter 6). In a geometric model the universe of discourse may be a line or a plane or a "space," but, in any case, it is a *set of points*. In a probabilistic model the universe of discourse is also conceived to be a set of "points," where a "point" corresponds to an outcome of some "random" experiment.

Tossing a coin, rolling a die, playing bridge are all examples of what is meant by a *random experiment*. A telephone interview in connection with the rating of television programs is another example of a random experiment. Although such an experiment can be repeated many times under essentially the same conditions, the outcome will vary and no specific result can be predicted with certainty.

Nevertheless, the set of possible outcomes is known in advance. Thus one can say that these are {heads, tails} for the tossing of a coin and {1, 2, 3, 4, 5, 6} for the rolling of a die. If a telephone interview is an inquiry as to which TV channel is being observed at the time, the possible responses in a certain part of the United States are {II, IV, V, VII, IX, XI, XIII}. Such outcome sets are, of course, convenient idealizations, since, for example, a coin might land on its side, a die might bounce out of the window, and the answer to the telephone query might be, "I have no TV set."

Varied interests and purposes may lead to essentially different sets of elements for the description of the potential outcomes of one and the same random experiment. Thus, although we have used an aggregate of *six* numbers to represent the possible results of tossing a die, a gambler betting on "ace" might claim that, as far as he is concerned, the set of *two* elements {ace, not-ace} suffices. He might point out that no matter how the die falls, the outcome can be placed in one of his two categories. Again, in a situation where bets are being placed on {less than 4, equal to 4, greater than 4}, the collection of *three* categories might be considered an adequate description of all eventualities. The reader will be able to provide still other aggregates corresponding to the same totality of outcomes. One might, of course, insist on the original set of six elements by arguing that it is fundamental, since no outcome listed can be decomposed further, whereas in the other descriptions, categories like "not-ace," "less than 4," "greater than 4" are really composite and can be broken down into finer classifications.

Each aggregate describing all possible outcomes of tossing a die would be called a *sample space* of the die-tossing experiment. The terminology derives from mathematical statistics, a subject in which a random experiment is often a sampling procedure and hence an experimental outcome is a "sample." The set of possible samples is thus the sample set, or sample space. In general, a *sample space* of a random experiment is a set of elements such that any outcome of the experiment is represented by one, and only one, element of the set. Each of these elements is termed a *point* of the sample space.

In constructing a mathematical model of some random experiment, the first step is specification of the particular sample space of interest, which then becomes the *universe of discourse* or *universal set* for the model. Next, assumptions related to this abstract set of points can be formulated and deductions made. The model will be practically useful if its postulates, definitions, and theorems approximate physical realities. Since our objective is to build a *probabilistic* mathematical model, we shall begin by assigning "probabilities" on the basis of intuition or observation, with the idea of idealizing "common sense" in the axioms and definitions laid down for the abstract probabilities of the model.

Suppose, then, that the random experiment consists of tossing a single perfectly symmetric die, and that the universe of discourse is the sample space $S = \{1, 2, 3, 4, 5, 6\}$. Although a gambler does not usually define what he means by the word "probability," he might say that the probability of "ace" is 1/6, that the probability of "deuce" is 1/6, likewise for "trey," etc. If he has had no previous experience in tossing the particular die involved, it seems natural to assume that one outcome is as likely as another, that is, to assign the same "weight" to each element or point of the universe of discourse. To find the probability that the die will turn up either "5" or "6" a gambler might compute the proportion of "favorable" outcomes in the universe. Since there are six outcomes in the sample space S, only two of which favor the gambler's bet, the probability in question is 2/6. In the same way, the probability that the outcome will be less than "5" would be figured as 4/6, because there are four "favorable" outcomes, namely, $\{1, 2, 3, 4\}$. Since $2/6 = 1/6 + 1/6$, and $4/6 = 1/6 + 1/6 + 1/6 + 1/6$, one might say that the probability for the occurrence of some event is a number obtained by adding the "weights" of all the "favorable" outcomes.

We remark in passing that if our hypothetical gambler has not defined the word "probability," he has nevertheless indicated how he thinks his chances of winning should be measured. But if he holds with the statistician and conceives of a probability as the limit of a relative frequency in a long sequence of trials (see chapter 19, volume 2), he must expect that about one-third of such trials with a die would lead to "5" or "6," and about two-thirds to an outcome less than "5."

The experimental results or events to which reference has just been made can be defined by $\{5, 6\}$ and $\{1, 2, 3, 4\}$, respectively, that is, by collections of outcomes in the sample space of interest. In an abstract probability model, an *event* is defined as a set of points, one which is a *subset* of the universe of discourse (the sample space selected). An event can therefore be specified by listing the elements (outcomes) which belong to the associated subset when these are finite in number or, alternatively (and in the infinite case), by stating some property which characterizes the component outcomes.

In the die-tossing experiment it was assumed that outcomes in a certain space were equally likely and hence should be given equal weight in computing probabilities for various events. In figuring probabilities in this way, we were in fact applying the *classic* point of view of Jacques Bernoulli and Pierre-Simon Laplace. Their definition of probability stated: In the case of a random experiment with a *finite* number of possible outcomes which, by agreement, are considered *equally likely*, the probability, $P(E)$, that some event E will occur is the ratio

$$P(E) = \frac{m}{n}$$

where n is the total number of possible outcomes, and m is the number of outcomes in the subset defining the event E.

Let us apply the Bernoulli-Laplace definition once more to the same die-tossing experiment and universe of discourse considered above. If we ask, "What is the probability that the outcome will be an odd number?" the event in question can be defined by the subset {1, 3, 5}, and the probability of this event is 3/6. Similarly, the event "greater than 1" signifies any outcome or element in the subset {2, 3, 4, 5, 6}, and the required probability is 5/6.

Events that may seem special are "greater than 5," "a positive integer less than 7," "the number 17." The subset for the first of these is {6}, a singleton set or elementary event, which has probability 1/6. Since "a positive integer less than 7" means any integer in the collection {1, 2, 3, 4, 5, 6}, the "subset" in this case is the entire universe of discourse. The whole set is called an "improper" subset of itself, while other subsets are called "proper." At any rate, the probability of a positive integer less than 7 is 6/6 = 1. When a die is tossed, it is *certain* that the result will be a positive integer less than 7. Here we have an illustration of the fact that if an event is certain to occur, its probability is 1. In the same way, if one asked for the probability that the die will not turn up 75, the favorable subset would once again be the entire sample space, and the probability would be 1.

For the probability that the die will turn up 17, common sense gives *zero* as the answer. Here one would say there are no favorable outcomes, and hence the required ratio is $0/6 = 0$. But if every event, without exception, is to define a subset of the fundamental set, we shall require a subset for the event in question, or for any *impossible* event. Mathematics has available for this purpose the *null* or *empty* set, symbolized by $\emptyset$ (Chapters 1 and 6). The null set is a subset of every aggregate and hence is useful in connection with many other issues. At this point, $\emptyset$ is the subset corresponding to the event, "die will turn up 17," and since there are zero outcomes in $\emptyset$, the probability is figured to be $0/6 = 0$. Thus an impossible event has probability zero.

Even in those simplest cases we have considered, various laws of probability theory are illustrated—namely, that probabilities are real numbers between 0 and 1 inclusive, the former figure being assigned to impossibility, the latter to certainty, that is, to the empty set and the entire universe, respectively. Again, the probability that an event will occur is the sum of the weights of the outcomes (elements) in the subset which defines this event.

Another fundamental law will be illustrated if we ask, in relation to the die-tossing experiment, "What is the probability of either 'ace' or an even number?" The event in question is the subset $E = \{1, 2, 4, 6\}$, and hence its probability is $4/6$. But someone may point out that the verbal description of the event indicates that it is actually composed of *two* other events, namely, "ace" and "even," which are *mutually exclusive*, since they cannot both occur. Or, in terms of sets of outcomes, $E = \{1, 2, 4, 6\}$ is the fusion or *union* of the two *disjoint* (nonoverlapping) sets, $E_1 = \{1\}$ and $E_2 = \{2, 4, 6\}$. Symbolically, $E = E_1 \cup E_2$, where $E_1 \cap E_2 = \emptyset$. Thus our first interpretation called for $P(E)$, and the new point of view demands $P(E_1 \text{ or } E_2)$, that is, $P(E_1 \cup E_2)$. The answer must be the same whether or not E is subdivided into components. Therefore, $P(E_1 \text{ or } E_2)$ must also be equal to $4/6$. Now

$$P(\text{ace}) = P(E_1) = \frac{1}{6}$$

and

$$P(\text{even}) = P(E_2) = \frac{3}{6}$$

Therefore

$$P(E_1 \text{ or } E_2) = P(E_1) + P(E_2)$$

which is a general law of probability for a pair of mutually exclusive events.

The law illustrated is readily extended to the case of 3, 4, . . . , n, any finite number, of disjoint or mutually exclusive events, so that if E_1, E_2, E_3, . . . , E_n are disjoint, that is, if $E_1 \cap E_2 = \emptyset$, $E_1 \cap E_3 = \emptyset$, $E_2 \cap E_3 = \emptyset$, etc.

$$P(E_1 \text{ or } E_2 \text{ or } E_3 \text{ or } \ldots \text{ or } E_n)$$
$$= P(E_1) + P(E_2) + P(E_3) + \cdots + P(E_n)$$

In all the examples thus far, the Bernoulli-Laplace definition of probability, with its assumption of equal likelihood, has been applied because the classic criterion seems natural for assigning probabilities a priori (before any experimentation is carried out) in games of chance and in the case of random experiments resembling such games. But whenever the classic definition is used, it is essential to verify that equal likelihood is a realistic assumption. Thus, let us ask, "If a fair coin is tossed twice, what is the probability that it will turn up 'heads' exactly once in the two throws?" To assist us we can select as universe of discourse the sample space $S = \{HH, HT, TH, TT\}$, where TH, for example, symbolizes "tails" in the first throw, "heads" in the second. The subset describing "heads exactly once" is $\{HT, TH\}$. Therefore $m = 2$, $n = 4$, and the required probability is $2/4$ or $1/2$.

Now it is not unusual for a student to offer a different analysis. He may say that the question concerns the number of "heads," and therefore he selects as his universe of discourse the sample space $U = \{0, 1, 2\}$. Then he assumes equal likelihood for each of the three outcomes with the result that the probability of $\{1\}$ or "exactly one head" is figured as $1/3$. We tell him that his assumption is not realistic because his $\{1\}$ actually includes the *two* outcomes we labeled as HT and TH in our own analysis, whereas his $\{0\}$ and $\{2\}$ are not further decomposable. If the student insists on using $U = \{0, 1, 2\}$ as the set of possible outcomes, he must not assign equal weights. Instead, he must give twice as much weight to "heads exactly once" as to either of the other outcomes. Then he must choose the weights {1/4, 1/2, 1/4} for the respective outcomes in $U = \{0, 1, 2\}$. Observe that whatever weights are assigned to outcomes in the universal set, the sum of such weights must be equal to 1, since that set represents an event that is *certain* and hence must have probability 1.

In the above instance it was easy to justify equal likelihood for elements of one sample space, and to demonstrate that outcomes in another space were *not* equally likely. But in the case of intricate games or complicated random experiments, a formidable logical argument may be necessary. For this reason, equal likelihood is a weakness in the classic definition. The practical difficulty of reasoning about equally likely cases is not, however, the only defect in the Bernoulli-Laplace definition. Let us return, for example, to the same die-tossing experiment and the same sample space we have considered repeatedly. If we are informed that the die is loaded, how should probabilities be assigned? Thus, what would be the probability of "ace," that is, of {1}? Obviously, one can no longer apply the classic definition. It is impossible, in fact, to assign a realistic probability to {1} or to any event related to tossing a biased die if the assignment must be made a priori. But if one accepts the point of view that a probability is the limit of an empirical relative frequency in many trials, one can estimate the probability of {1} a posteriori. Thus, if "ace" should occur 29 times in 100 tosses, we might take 0.29 as a crude approximation of the ideal or "true" probability, and use this estimate for future tosses.

Again, there is the case mentioned earlier where the random experiment consists of a telephone inquiry and the sample space is $S = \{II, IV, V, VII, IX, XI, XIII\}$, the Roman numerals indicating TV channels. It would not be sensible to assign a weight of 1/7 to each response, for if viewers were as likely to be observing one TV program as another offered at the same time, what would be the purpose of TV rating schemes? Granted that the seven weights should not all be equal, it is still not possible by logical argument alone to determine the weights a priori. But if one has available considerable data from previous polls, and these show a relative frequency of 0.2 for the response "Channel II," a relative frequency of 0.15 for "Channel V," etc., such empirical results can guide the assignment of weights.

Suppose, then, that the weights based on past experience are {0.2, 0.2, 0.15, 0.15, 0.1, 0.1, 0.1}. Now one might wish to predict the likelihood of certain outcomes when a new poll is taken, for example, to ask, "What is the probability that the response will be IV or V?" Then $P(E)$ where $E = $ {IV, V} is obtained by adding the weights for IV and V. Hence $P(E) = 0.2 + 0.15 = 0.35$. Similarly, if $E = $ {II, VII, XIII}, $P(E) = 0.2 + 0.15 + 0.1 = 0.45$. The probability is zero that the response will be "I am watching Channel XXV" or "I am watching all the channels (on my one TV set) at this very instant." These two events are equivalent since both responses define $\emptyset$, the null set.

When modern probability theory is treated in formal axiomatic fashion as a mathematical science based on a system of postulates, some of the "laws" to which we have alluded can be taken as postulates (assumptions) and others can be deduced as theorems. Thus one might conceive of a probability model as having three components, namely, (1) S, the sample space selected as universe of discourse; (2) an aggregate of events, that is, of subsets of S; (3) the assignment of a real number to each event E in (2). This real number, $P(E)$, called the probability of the corresponding event, must satisfy the following axioms:

(1) $0 \leq P(E) \leq 1$. (A probability must be a positive number between 0 and 1 inclusive.)

(2) $P(S) = 1$ (If an event is *certain*, that is, describable by S, then its probability is 1.)

(3) If E_1 and E_2 are mutually exclusive events, that is, disjoint subsets,

$$P(E_1 \text{ or } E_2) = P(E_1 \cup E_2) = P(E_1) + P(E_2)$$

From these postulates one can deduce the other probabilistic laws we have mentioned. For example, to prove that an *impossible* event, that is, one definable by $\emptyset$, must have probability 0, we observe first that, obviously,

$$\emptyset \cup S = S$$

Therefore

$$P(\emptyset \cup S) = P(S) = 1, \quad \text{by axiom 2}$$

But, by axiom 3,

$$P(\emptyset \cup S) = P(\emptyset) + P(S) = P(\emptyset) + 1$$

Since the two results obtained for $P(\emptyset \cup S)$ must be equal,

$$P(\emptyset) + 1 = 1$$

and hence

$$P(\emptyset) = 0$$

It will be observed that in modern probability theory there is no postulate prescribing a specific method for assigning probabilities in a particular model. This fact makes the pure theory very general, because it permits great freedom of choice for the probabilities related to conceptual random experiments. The modern theory does *not* postulate equal likelihood, but it also does *not* forbid its use in appropriate situations. Then, if the sample space selected as universe is a *finite set*, a convenient method for specifying probabilities is as follows. First, assign positive real weights (equal *or* unequal) to the elements (points) in the universal set so that the sum of these weights is 1. Next, define the probability of any event (subset) as the sum of the weights of the elements (points) that make up this event (subset).

We digress to indicate that the above technique for assigning probabilities can be said to involve *two* functions, a *point function* for the specification of weights and a *set function* for the assignment of probabilities. As an illustration, suppose that the universe of discourse is a sample space containing *three* elements (points). Then the tabulation below represents one possible function for the assignment of weights. Its *domain* is made up of all *points* of the *universe* (hence the name "*point* function"), and its *range* is the collection of *weights*.

Point or Element	e_1	e_2	e_3
Weight	0.1	0.6	0.3

The space $S = \{e_1, e_2, e_3\}$ contains eight subsets, defining eight essentially different events. These subsets are named in the first row of the tabulation below, and the second row lists the corresponding probabilities, computed by adding weights of component elements. The table represents a function whose *domain* is a collection of *sets* (hence the term "*set* function") and whose range is an aggregate of positive real numbers between 0 and 1 inclusive.

E	$\emptyset$	S	$\{e_1\}$	$\{e_2\}$	$\{e_3\}$	$\{e_1, e_2\}$	$\{e_1, e_3\}$	$\{e_2, e_3\}$
$P(E)$	0	1	0.1	0.6	0.3	0.7	0.4	0.9

For the sake of simplicity we have restricted ourselves thus far to a consideration of *finite* sample spaces. The classic definition of probability is applicable only to such spaces, but if *unequal* positive weights are permissible, they can be applied to a sample space containing an *infinite sequence* of points. To obtain an example of such a space, let us suppose that the random experiment consists of selecting any positive integer at random, or observing the record of a Geiger counter which is counting cosmic rays. In either case, an associated sample space is the sequence of natural numbers, that is, the set $S = \{1, 2, 3, \ldots\}$.

There are, however, sample spaces corresponding to real experiments in which it is impossible to use the technique of assigning weights to individual points. For example, suppose that we are told that the length of an object lies between 2 and 3 cm., and we are asked to guess the "true length" without examining the object. A sample space for such a guess is the infinite set of all real numbers between 2 and 3. This space can be represented on a Cartesian graph (Figure 11.1) as the line segment between the points 2 and 3

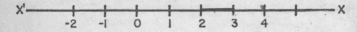

Figure 11.1   Sample space: all points of the interval (2, 3)

of the X-axis. The geometric picture will be helpful when ultimately (Chapter 14) probabilities are assigned to events in such a sample space.

In accordance with probabilistic laws, impossibility, that is, $\emptyset$, and certainty, S, *always* have probabilities of 0 and 1, respectively. In Chapter 14 we shall see that the converse statements are *false* when the universal set is a sample space like the one we have just illustrated (a *continuum*). Thus in the case of a random choice of any real number between 2 and 3, theory gives *zero* as the probability that 2.40173, say, will be selected, although it is conceivable that just that choice might be made. In this instance, zero probability does *not* imply impossibility, $\emptyset$.

Again, *any* subset of a *finite* sample space defines an *event*. But for certain sample spaces containing an infinite number of outcomes, it may be necessary to exclude some subsets from consideration as events because one cannot assign probabilities to them in consistent fashion. The mathematician is forced to limit himself to "measurable" subsets. That the "measure theory" suitable for infinite sample spaces is due in considerable part to Borel will not surprise readers. What will seem strange, however, is that Borel created the appropriate analytic concepts in his youth, many years before he decided to write on probability.

After the above detour into advanced probability theory, we shall now revert to elementary instances in order to obtain a simple formulation for a special concept due to Pascal, who was an important figure in the history of probability. In a fair lottery, it is reasonable to assume that one number is as likely to be drawn as another. Therefore, if a thousand tickets are sold and you hold just one, the probability that you will obtain the grand prize is 1/1000. If the grand prize is $500, Pascal would have said that your mathematical *expectation* is 1/1000 of $500, that is, $0.50. In a sense, that is the true value of your ticket, for it represents the amount you would get if the $500 were divided equally among the thousand ticket-holders. If you held six hundred tickets in the lottery, your expectation would be six hundred times as much as in the case of a single ticket, that is,

$$\text{expectation} = (600) \ (1/1000) \ (\$500)$$

$$= (600/1000) \ (\$500)$$

$$= (\text{probability of winning prize}) \ (\text{amount of prize})$$

In general, expectation is *defined* in this way; in other words,

$$\text{expectation} = pA$$

where A is the prize or payoff and p is the probability of winning the payoff.

In the illustration above, it was assumed that you held 600 out of 1000 lottery tickets and therefore your probability of winning the grand prize was 3/5. That probability was figured on the basis of the classic definition. If we were to reinterpret it as a *statistical* probability, it would signify a relative frequency approximated in many repetitions of the same experiment. Let us then imagine 5000 successive lotteries with a winning ticket in 3000 of the lotteries, and a losing ticket in the remaining 2000. The relative frequency of success would then be 3/5. If the grand prize is $10, the *expectation* would be $6, in accordance with the previous formula. Now the *mean* or "average" payoff in the 5000 games would be

$$\frac{\overbrace{0 + 0 + \cdots\cdots + 0}^{2000\ times} + \overbrace{10 + 10 + \cdots\cdots + 10}^{3000\ times}}{5000}$$

that is,

$$\frac{(2000)(0) + (3000)(10)}{5000}$$

which is equal to

$$(2/5)(0) + (3/5)(10) = 6$$

and this is the value of the expectation obtained by using the formula. In other words, expectation can be interpreted as the *mean* or *average* payoff in a very long series of trials.

How can you compute your expectation in a more complicated gambling situation? Suppose that you are betting on the outcome of tossing a die, and if it turns up "ace," your opponent must pay you $10; if it turns up 2 or 3 or 4, you must pay him $2; otherwise there is no exchange of money. Here the probabilities of winning $10, −$2, $0 are 1/6, 3/6, 2/6, respectively. If we consider these as relative frequencies in a long series of tosses of a die, the following tabulation would approximate the results of six thousand tosses.

Payoff	Frequency
10	1000
−2	3000
0	2000

Now interpreting the expectation as the mean or average in these very numerous trials, we have

$$\text{expectation} = \frac{(1000)(10) + (3000)(-2) + (2000)(0)}{6000}$$

$$= (1/6)(10) + (3/6)(-2) + (2/6)(0) = 2/3$$

The expected or average winning is \$⅔ per play. Now observe that each of the three terms in the sum above is itself an expectation. Thus $(1/6)(10)$ is the expectation from a lottery with prize \$10 where your chances of winning are 1 in 6. Or it is your expectation if you bet that the die will turn up "ace." Similarly, the second term in the sum above, $(3/6)(-2)$, is your expectation if you bet that the die will turn up 2 or 3 or 4, etc. Such a breakdown of the total expectation into component expectations is typical. In general, if a sample space of a random experiment contains n possible outcomes, occurring with probabilities $p_1, p_2, \ldots, p_n$, and associated with payoffs $a_1, a_2 \ldots, a_n$, then p_1a_1 is the expectation based on the first outcome, p_2a_2 the expectation based on the second, etc. The total expectation is then defined as

$$\text{expectation} = p_1a_1 + p_2a_2 + \cdots + p_na_n$$

This formula for the expectation is basic in the theory of strategic games as well as in the Wald decision theory, and will therefore be applied repeatedly. At this point it will enable us to present a criterion for the selection of optimum randomized strategies in matrix games.

If the matrix of a rectangular game has a saddle point, a solution in terms of pure strategies exists; that is, there is a best choice of row and column for a single play, and the value of the game to R is the corresponding matrix entry. The solution consists of *randomized* strategies, however, when the matrix lacks a saddle point. In that case, R and C must decide on the optimum relative frequencies for the variation in choice of rows and columns from play to play.

When the choices are varied or "mixed" in repeated plays, it would seem sensible for R and C to consider *average* payoffs. Their objectives would, of course, be diametrically opposed. R would try to maximize the average, and C would aim to make it as small as possible. Therefore, the mean payoff in a long series of plays, that is, R's *expectation* is said to be the *value* of the game to him.

In the previous chapter, it was stated (without proof) that the matrix game

$$\begin{pmatrix} 2 & 1 \\ 0 & 3 \end{pmatrix}$$

has as solution the pair of mixed strategies (3/4, 1/4) and (1/2, 1/2) for R and C, respectively. We are now ready to indicate why that choice of relative frequencies is optimum. If R selects the first row in 3/4 of all plays and C chooses the first column 1/2 the time, the payoff listed in (R_1, C_1) of the matrix will accrue to R in 3/4 of 1/2, or 3/8, of all plays. Similarly, the payoff in (R_2, C_1) will result in 1/4 of 1/2, or 1/8, of all plays, and the relative frequency or probability matrix corresponding to the given mixed strategies is

$$\begin{pmatrix} 3/8 & 3/8 \\ 1/8 & 1/8 \end{pmatrix}$$

Then R's expectation is (3/8) (2) from those plays in which (R_1, C_1) is the choice, since 2 is the gain for the corresponding position of the payoff matrix. Likewise, his expectation is (3/8) (1) from the plays in which (R_1, C_2) is the selection, etc. By what has been stated earlier, his overall expectation or average winning in the long run, that is, the value v of the game is

$$v = (3/8)(2) + (3/8)(1) + (1/8)(0) + (1/8)(3) = 3/2$$

In order to show that the mixed strategies above are truly optimum, one must consider what would happen if the relative frequencies were selected differently. If x is the long-run relative frequency (probability) for the choice of R_1, and y is that for C_1, the probability matrix for the mixed strategies is

$$\begin{pmatrix} xy & x(1-y) \\ y(1-x) & (1-x)(1-y) \end{pmatrix}$$

and the overall expectation or long-run average gain is a function of x and y which will be symbolized by $E(x, y)$. Then

$$E(x, y) = 2xy + x(1-y) + 0y(1-x) + 3(1-x)(1-y)$$

or

$$E(x, y) = 4xy - 2x - 3y + 3$$

By algebraic manipulation one can obtain the equivalent form

$$E(x, y) = 4(x - 3/4)(y - 1/2) + 3/2$$

(The reader can check this by carrying out the multiplication in the second expression.)

If $x = 3/4$ is substituted in the alternative form, the result is

$$E(3/4, y) = 4(0)(y - 1/2) + 3/2 = 3/2$$

which indicates that R's expectation from the mixed strategy $(3/4, 1/4)$ is $3/2$ *no matter what strategy* $(y, 1 - y)$ is used by C. Likewise, if C plays the mixed strategy $(1/2, 1/2)$, his expected loss to R is $3/2$, *no matter what strategy* R uses, that is,

$$E(x, 1/2) = 4(x - 3/4)(0) + 3/2 = 3/2$$

What must now be shown is that R's average winning would be *less* and C's average loss would be *greater* from a choice of strategies other than those prescribed. To see this, one should reexamine

$$E(x, y) = 4(x - 3/4)(y - 1/2) + 3/2$$

and consider the effect of substituting for x and y relative frequencies other than $3/4$ and $1/2$. If R chooses x greater than $3/4$ with the thought of possibly *adding* something to the $3/2$ of the second term, C can (if he observes that R is choosing the first row very often) counter by selecting y less than $1/2$. Then the first term above would be *negative*, and therefore the new result would be an average winning less than $3/2$ for R. (For any choice where $x > 3/4$, C's selection of $y = 0$, that is, the pure strategy $(0, 1)$, would make R's expectation the *minimum* possible for his strategy.)

Suppose, instead, that R chooses a value of x less than $3/4$. Either by chance or because he foresees R's plan, C can counter by playing y greater than $1/2$, thus making the first term negative and diminishing the expectation to a value below $3/2$. (For any choice in which $x < 3/4$, C's selection of $y = 1$, that is, the pure strategy $(1, 0)$, would make R's expectation the minimum for his strategy.)

Since R runs the risk of an average winning of *less* than $3/2$ in any strategy where $x > 3/4$ or $x < 3/4$, his best choice is $x = 3/4$, which assures him an expectation of $3/2$, no matter what C's strategy is. An analogy can be formed between R's method of selecting a mixed strategy here and his reasoning in deciding on a pure strategy in the simpler games considered in the previous chapter. There he selected a strategy that would guarantee him the *maximin* payoff. Here he selects a mixed strategy that will guarantee him the *maximin expectation* or *maximin average* winning in the long run. This was indicated earlier where, for *every* x or mixed strategy of R, it was seen that C would pick y so as to give R the *minimum* expectation for his strategy. Of all the minima for different values of x, the greatest is 3/2, corresponding to x = 3/4. Hence, (3/4, 1/4) is R's optimum strategy.

Thus far, only R's optimum mixed strategy has been determined, and it remains to select a strategy for C. If the expression for $E(x, y)$ is examined once again, it will be seen that any attempt on the part of C to diminish his loss to R below 3/2 can be countered by R. If C selects y < 1/2, R can choose x < 3/4, and thereby increase C's average loss. (By selecting x = 0, that is, by playing the pure strategy (0, 1), R can make this average loss a *maximum*.) If C selects y > 1/2, R can choose x > 3/4 and in fact can choose x = 1, that is, the pure strategy (1, 0), which will make C's average loss a *maximum*. But if C chooses y = 1/2, no strategy of R can increase C's average loss beyond 3/2, which is thus the *minimum* of the many maxima for different values of y. Then y = 1/2, or the mixed strategy (1/2, 1/2) is optimum for C, since it corresponds to 3/2, the *minimax* expected payoff to R.

To obtain some practice in solving a game where randomized strategies are involved, the reader can duplicate both the technique and the argument outlined above in order to show that in the matrix game

$$\begin{pmatrix} 1 & 3 \\ 2 & -1 \end{pmatrix}$$

the optimum strategies for R and C are (3/5, 2/5) and (4/5, 1/5), respectively, with a value of 7/5 for R. It is suggested also that the reader return to the game of matching pennies and provide *proof* that it is fair and that the common-sense strategies are actually optimum.

It was pointed out in the previous chapter that pure strategies are merely special cases of randomized strategies. Thus in the case of a 2 × 2 matrix game, R's possible pure strategies could be symbolized as the "mixed" strategies (1, 0) and (0, 1). The same is true for C. Therefore, although the rationale of the procedure in the case of mixed strategies may seem more difficult to follow, the facts in both types of game are strictly analogous. In both cases R must choose a strategy which will assure him a certain *maximin*, whereas C must direct his behavior toward a *minimax*. The equality of the maximin and the minimax makes it possible to arrive at a solution. In the more general case, the equal minimax and maximin were associated with the expectation function $E(x, y)$. But to continue the analogy further, one can say that the solution corresponds to a *saddle point* of this function. Thus in a 2×2 game, if the optimum strategies for R and C are symbolized by $(x^*, 1 - x^*)$ and $(y^*, 1 - y^*)$, the reader may imagine the surface pictured in Figure 10.1 as the graph of the function $E(x, y)$, and the point with coordinates (x^*, y^*) as the saddle point indicated in the diagram. Finally, the value of the game is an *expectation* even in the case of a solution by pure strategies; for if it corresponds to some matrix entry, this *same* payoff will be obtained in all repetitions of the game, however numerous, and will therefore be equal to the long-run average.

Most of the game-theory concepts discussed thus far were mentioned by Borel in his 1921 paper and in his subsequent publications on probability theory. But it is in the matter of general *proofs* that von Neumann went far beyond him and laid the foundation for a true mathematical theory. Von Neumann proved that *every matrix game can be solved*. This fundamental proposition is called the *minimax theorem* because the existence of a solution results from his proof that in every case

$$\underset{\text{(for all } x)}{\text{maximum}} \left[\underset{\text{(for all } y)}{\text{minimum}} E(x, y) \right]$$

and

$$\underset{\text{(for all } y)}{\text{minimum}} \left[\underset{\text{(for all } x)}{\text{maximum}} E(x, y) \right]$$

exist and are equal. The maximin or minimax is the value v of the game. The x and y corresponding to this value are such that if R selects x, he can expect to win at least an amount v; and if C selects y, he can expect to lose no more than v. This wording is in terms of 2×2 matrix games but can be extended to matrix games of *all orders*. That Borel did little more than initiate concepts is indicated by the fact that he conjectured the minimax theorem to be false for the higher-order matrix games.

The reason Borel may originally have entertained some doubts about the truth of a *general* minimax theorem is that intuitive evidence was lacking. Clues to the fact would naturally lie in finding randomized strategies for specific games of higher order. But the task of computing mixed strategies becomes more arduous as the number of rows and columns of the game matrix increases. In a proof of the minimax theorem, whether it is von Neumann's or one of the alternative demonstrations provided later on by other mathematicians, the existence of a solution is deduced from advanced mathematical theorems concerned with special types of aggregate and special kinds of function.

To obtain some idea of the larger problem, let us advance a small step further by solving the following 2×3 game:

$$\begin{pmatrix} 3 & 2 & 1 \\ -1 & 0 & 3 \end{pmatrix}$$

Examination of this matrix indicates that it has no saddle point. Therefore there is no solution prescribing pure strategies for both R and C. The minimax theorem assures us that there is a solution of some sort. Let us represent R's strategy by $(x, 1 - x)$. Now suppose, for the moment, that C does not reason about his opponent's possible moves but merely decides to select column C_1, that is, the strategy $(1, 0, 0)$. Then the probability matrix will be

$$\begin{pmatrix} 1 \cdot x & 0 \cdot x & 0 \cdot x \\ 1(1 - x) & 0(1 - x) & 0(1 - x) \end{pmatrix} = \begin{pmatrix} x & 0 & 0 \\ 1 - x & 0 & 0 \end{pmatrix}$$

and R's expectation will be

$$3x - 1(1 - x) = 4x - 1$$

Now the reader can show in the same way that if C selects the pure strategy C_2, that is, the strategy $(0, 1, 0)$, R's expectation will be $2x$, and that if C selects C_3, R's expectations will be $-2x + 3$. We shall represent the three expectation functions by

$$E_1(x) = 4x - 1$$
$$E_2(x) = 2x$$
$$E_3(x) = -2x + 3$$

where x, the relative frequency with which R chooses R_1, may have any value between 0 and 1, inclusive. The three linear expectation functions are graphed in Figure 11.2. Now suppose that R chooses the value of x corresponding to point A in the diagram. Then AB, the ordinate to the lowest intersection with the three expectation lines, represents the minimum amount which R can expect if C limits himself to pure strategies. Therefore, the heavy broken line in Figure 11.2 indicates the minimum expectations for all choices of x if C chooses pure strategies. Now if R chooses $x^* = 3/4$, represented by M in the diagram, his expectation will be $MN = 3/2$, the maximum of the minimum expectations for C's pure strategies. In addition, the diagram indicates that whether C selects C_2 or C_3, R's expectation will still be $3/2$, and if C should select C_1, R may expect a greater amount. Moreover, we shall show that even if C chooses a mixed strategy involving C_2 and C_3, R's expectation will still be $3/2$. Suppose, then, that C's strategy is $(0, y_2, y_3)$ where

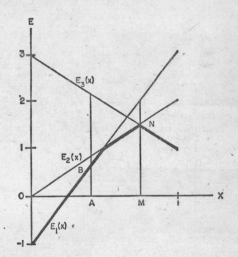

Figure 11.2   Solution of the matrix game:
$$\begin{pmatrix} 3 & 2 & 1 \\ -1 & 0 & 3 \end{pmatrix}$$

$y_2 + y_3 = 1$. Then the probability matrix when R's strategy is $(3/4, 1/4)$ will be

$$\begin{pmatrix} 0 & 3y_2/4 & 3y_3/4 \\ 0 & y_2/4 & y_3/4 \end{pmatrix}$$

and $E(x^*, y_2, y_3) = 3y_2/2 + 3y_3/4 + 3y_3/4 = 3(y_2 + y_3)/2 = 3/2$. One can show in the same way that if C uses C_1 in a mixed strategy, R's expectation will be greater than $3/2$.

Therefore, whatever C's optimum strategy is, it cannot include C_1. Moreover, $x^* = 3/4$, that is, R's mixed strategy $(3/4, 1/4)$, has the characteristic property of an optimum strategy since, whatever strategy C uses, pure or mixed, he cannot diminish R's expectation. Hence we conclude that $x^* = 3/4$ is R's optimum strategy. As far as C is concerned, the graph and the above computation indicate that C_1 must be ruled out, so that the problem reduces to solving the game

$$\begin{pmatrix} 2 & 1 \\ 0 & 3 \end{pmatrix}$$

This was the 2×2 game solved earlier in this chapter, with the result $(3/4, 1/4)$ for R, which checks with the graphic solution, and $(1/2, 1/2)$ for C, or, in terms of the 2×3 matrix, $(0, 1/2, 1/2)$.

The illustrative example is typical of any $2 \times n$ game. A

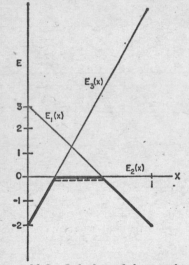

Figure 11.3   Solution of the matrix game:
$$\begin{pmatrix} -2 & 0 & 7 \\ 3 & 0 & -2 \end{pmatrix}$$
R: $(x^*, 1 - x^*)$ where $2/9 \leq x^* \leq 3/5$
C: $(0, 1, 0)$
$v = 0$

graph like Figure 11.2 will determine R's optimum strategy and eliminate all but two of C's pure strategies. Then, solution of a 2×2 game will determine C's optimum strategy. Sometimes a $2 \times n$ game will present special features. For example, Figure 11.3 corresponds to a fair game in which R has an infinite number of optimum strategies, strange as that may seem, namely, all those where x^* has any value in the interval $2/9 \leqslant x^* \leqslant 3/5$.

Next, consider the game with the 3×2 matrix

$$\begin{pmatrix} 2 & -3 \\ 0 & 0 \\ -7 & 2 \end{pmatrix}$$

The entries in the first column represent C's potential losses if he chooses C_1. But instead of speaking of losses of 2, 0, -7, one might equally well talk of *gains* of -2, 0, 7. Similarly, the second column could be conceived as containing potential *gains* for C of 3, 0, -2. Therefore, the game in question is equivalent to the 2×3 game

$$\begin{pmatrix} -2 & 0 & 7 \\ 3 & 0 & -2 \end{pmatrix}$$

This game, already solved in Figure 11.3, will provide the solution to the present game if the roles of R and C are interchanged. Thus, in the present game, it will be C who has the infinite number of optimum strategies and R who has R_2 (of the 3×2 matrix) as optimum strategy. In general, $m \times 2$ games can be solved by converting them into $2 \times m$ games in the manner illustrated.

Now to advance a step further, let us see how a *maiko* (a youthful geisha-in-training) transforms baseball into a 3×3 matrix game. Japan is a popular country for tourists nowadays, especially those from the United States. One of the festive tours includes a dinner party where several *maikos*, supervised by a senior geisha, entertain—serving *sukiyaki*, heating and pouring *sake*, playing musical instruments, singing and engaging in pantomime dances. In one of these dances, each *maiko* selects a male tourist as a partner, and the pantomime is "playing baseball." The winning "team" is determined at the end of the dance by having each partner gesture with fist, palm of the hand, or two fingers; it is simply the children's game "scissors, paper, stone" which the fourteen-year-old *maikos* are young enough to enjoy. Fist =

stone, palm = paper, fingers = scissors. Since stone sharpens scissors, scissors cut paper, and paper covers (can be wrapped around) stone, the inferior object loses and must pay off to the superior. Hence, a possible payoff matrix is

$$
\begin{array}{c}
 & \text{Scissors} & \text{Paper} & \text{Stone} \\
\begin{array}{c}\text{Scissors} \\ \text{Paper} \\ \text{Stone}\end{array} &
\left(\begin{array}{ccc}
0 & 1 & -1 \\
-1 & 0 & 1 \\
1 & -1 & 0
\end{array}\right)
\end{array}
$$

This geisha game is obviously "symmetric" because the *maiko* and her opponent, the American tourist, have the same set of pure strategies, with the same rewards attached to each choice. (The matrix is described as "skew-symmetric.") Intuition tells us that such a symmetric game must be fair, and hence $v = 0$. The fact that all penalties are equal in magnitude suggests that the optimum strategy for R or for C should be $(1/3, 1/3, 1/3)$. But how can one *prove* that this is so, and how can one solve more general 3×3 games?

If (x_1, x_2, x_3) and (y_1, y_2, y_3) represent the strategies of R and C in a 3×3 game, then $x_i \geqq 0$, $y_j \geqq 0$, where $i, j = 1, 2, 3$, and

$$
\begin{aligned}
x_1 + x_2 + x_3 &= 1 \\
y_1 + y_2 + y_3 &= 1
\end{aligned}
$$

In the matrix for "scissors, paper, stone," let us suppose that C plays the pure strategy C_1. Then the probability matrix will be

$$
\begin{pmatrix}
x_1 & 0 & 0 \\
x_2 & 0 & 0 \\
x_3 & 0 & 0
\end{pmatrix}
$$

and R's expectation will be

$$
E_1(x_1, x_2, x_3) = -x_2 + x_3
$$

Similarly, if C should play C_2 or C_3, one would have

$$
\begin{aligned}
E_2(x_1, x_2, x_3) &= x_1 - x_3 \\
E_3(x_1, x_2, x_3) &= -x_1 + x_2
\end{aligned}
$$

Now, if R's strategy is *optimum*, one of these expectations may possibly be equal to the value of the game. On the other hand, since C is selecting a pure strategy, his choice may *not* be optimum, and hence R's various expectations above may be greater than what he could expect if C used his best strategy. Therefore, $(x_1{}^*, x_2{}^*, x_3{}^*)$, R's optimum strategy, satisfies the *inequalities*

$$-x_2 + x_3 \geq v$$
$$x_1 - x_3 \geq v$$
$$-x_1 + x_2 \geq v$$

By reversing the behavior of R and C, one reaches the conclusion that $(y_1{}^*, y_2{}^*, y_3{}^*)$, C's optimum strategy, satisfies the inequalities

$$y_2 - y_3 \leq v$$
$$-y_1 + y_3 \leq v$$
$$y_1 - y_2 \leq v$$

Originally we had two equations and six inequalities which the x^*'s and y^*'s must satisfy, and now we have six more, involving the additional unknown v.

In the present specially simple example, it is easy to verify that all equations and inequalities are satisfied by the solution which intuition suggested, but matters are not so simple with nonsymmetric 3×3 matrix games, or with games whose matrices are of higher order. In such advanced cases, solutions can be provided by *linear programming*, which is a technique for finding the maximum or minimum value of a linear function subject to various constraints in the form of linear inequalities. But we shall not discuss this special numerical discipline, since it would involve considerable computational detail. Our objectives will take us elsewhere —to strategic games that are more general in scope and applicability.

Chapter 12

General Games and Statistical Decision Theory

While the von Neumann minimax theorem establishes the solvability of all two-person rectangular games, even those in which, say, a $1,000,000 \times 2,000,000$ matrix is involved, there still remains the task of considering more general games—in which there may be more than two players and each player may have several moves, etc. However, it turns out that there is no new theoretical difficulty, providing a general game is *finite*, that is, involves only a finite number of moves with a finite number of alternatives at each move. A finite game, as we shall illustrate shortly, can always be "normalized," that is, converted into an equivalent matrix game. Hence the minimax theorem and the method of solution we have discussed apply to all finite games, even the most general.

To furnish a very simple example, let us consider a game with three moves where R and C play alternately. Specifically, suppose that R makes the first move and that each move consists of a player choosing a number from the set $\{1, 2\}$, and that players are always aware of the choices made in previous moves. Thus a possible "play" of the game would be to have R choose 2 then C choose 1, then R choose 1. We shall symbolize this way of playing the game by $(2, 1, 1)$. There are other possible plays, for example, $(1, 1, 1)$, $(1, 1, 2)$, $(1, 2, 1)$, etc.

The various plays can be represented by a game *tree* (Figure 12.1), a helpful graphic device. Any complete play is pictured as a path proceeding from the root to the top of the tree. There are as many different paths as there are terminal points at the top, and it is easier to count the latter.

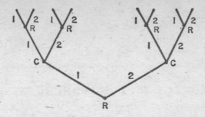

Figure 12.1   Game tree for game with three moves

In Figure 12.1 there are eight points at the top and therefore eight possible plays of the game. For each such play, the rules of the game specify the amount that C must pay to R. If (x, y, z) symbolizes a sequence of choices made by R and C in the three moves, that is, a path in the tree, then the function $M(x, y, z)$, tabulated below, is called the *payoff function* for the game.

		$M(x, y, z)$	
x	y	z	M
1	1	1	−4
1	1	2	−2
1	2	1	6
1	2	2	−8
2	1	1	10
2	1	2	4
2	2	1	4
2	2	2	12

The domain of this function consists of the eight possible paths (or sequences or ordered number triples) specified in the table, and the range consists of the eight corresponding monetary payoffs.

What meaning can be assigned to *strategy* in the game we have formulated? A pure strategy for a specified player (R or C) is conceived as a complete set of directions telling exactly what choices should be made at each of his moves under all possible circumstances that may arise, that is, for all possible sets of information about previous moves. The instructions are of the sort that could be followed by a substitute player or could be fed into a machine which would play the game in automatic fashion. In the present game, a strategy for C would concern only his move, the second, but would require a *pair* of directions—what to do if R has chosen 1 in the first move, and what to do if R has chosen 2. Thus C might plan the following strategy: If R has selected 1, choose a *D*ifferent number; if he has selected 2, pick the *S*ame number. If he were to code this strategy for convenience, he might symbolize it by DS. In effect, his strategy would select the number 2 no matter what R's first move has been. Another strategy for C would be SS, signifying that if R has chosen 1 in the first move, C will choose this *S*ame number in the second move, and that if R has chosen 2, C will choose that *S*ame number. Thus there would be *four* different pure strategies open to C, those coded as SS, SD, DD, and DS.

R's strategies are a little harder to symbolize. He might plan to select 1 in the first move and then code his contemplated behavior on the third move by using one of the four pairs above. Thus, four pure strategies available to him are 1–SS, 1–SD, 1–DD, and 1–DS. If he decides on strategy 1–DD, this means that he plans to select 1 in the first move and in the third move will apply DD on the basis of C's choice in the second move. If C has selected 1, R will choose Differently; if C has selected 2, R will choose Differently. In effect, R's total strategy consists of choosing 1 in the *first* move, and then selecting 2 or 1 in the *third* move according to whether C has picked 1 or 2 in the second move. Four additional pure strategies are available to R, namely, those where he plays 2 in the first move. In all, then, R has *eight* possible pure strategies from which to choose.

Since R and C have eight and four possible pure strategies, respectively, the game under consideration can be described by the following 8×4 matrix, and the methods of solution for matrix games can be applied. The *normalization* of the game has been accomplished.

	SS	SD	DD	DS
1–SS	-4	-4	-8	-8
1–SD	-4	-4	6	6
1–DD	-2	-2	6	6
1–DS	-2	-2	-8	-8
2–SS	12	10	10	12
2–SD	4	10	10	4
2–DD	4	4	4	4
2–DS	12	4	4	12

The payoffs in the above matrix were computed with the use of the payoff matrix $M(x, y, z)$. For example, the entry at (R_3, C_2), that is, in the third row, second column, must correspond to the strategy pair, 1–DD for R and SD for C. This means that R chooses 1, C chooses the *Same* number (hence 1), then R chooses a *Different* number from the one C picked so that the sequence of choices is (1, 1, 2) with payoff $M(1, 1, 2) = -2$. Again, (R_8, C_4) implies the sequence (2, 2, 1) with payoff $M(2, 2, 1) = 4$.

Examination of the rows of the matrix shows that R's *maximin* is a payoff of 10 occurring in the fifth row, and C's *minimax* is also 10, occurring in the second and third columns. Thus the *value* of the game to R is 10, and there are two saddle points, hence two solutions involving a pure strategy pair, namely, (R_5, C_2) and (R_5, C_3). In terms of the game, this signifies that R has one optimal strategy—to select 2 in the first move and then in the third move to choose the same number that C has picked in the second move. C, on the other hand, has two equally good strategies available. He can play SD, which amounts to choosing 1 in the move assigned to him, or else he can decide to choose the number differing from that in R's first move. Because R is planning to select 2 in the first move, either of C's strategies will compel him to select 1, and as a result, R's strategy will require him to pick 1 on the third move. Thus, although there are two solutions to the normalized game, they both result in the same optimal sequence or "path to the top," namely, (2, 1, 1), and hence to the same payoff, 10.

It will be observed that after the general game considered above was normalized, the solution was effected more easily than in some of the more elementary games we have illustrated. This was because the strategy matrix of the more complicated game had saddle points, and hence had solutions in terms of pure strategies. This relative ease of solution will always occur in any game having "perfect information," which means that at any move a player has complete knowledge of the choices made in all previous moves. A special theorem of game theory establishes the fact that in all games with perfect information the normalized form, that is, the *strategy matrix*, will have at least one saddle point and hence a solution in terms of pure strategies.

By contrast, the uncomplicated pastime of matching pennies is not a game with perfect information. If it were, the matrix would have a saddle point, and we saw this was not

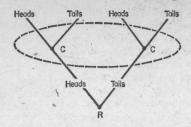

Figure 12.2   Game tree for matching pennies

the case. One can think of matching pennies as a game with two moves, where R plays the first move and C the second move (or vice versa). But one must supply an additional condition if this new form of matching pennies is used— namely, that the player in the second move is ignorant of the choice made in the first move. This additional fact is indicated in the game tree for matching pennies (Figure 12.2) by encircling the two vertices corresponding to the second move in order to indicate that C, if he is the player for that move, does *not* know at which of the vertices he is located.

Those games of several moves that we have considered may appear somewhat trivial, but after the connection between game theory and Wald's statistical decision theory has been made clear, it will be possible to provide more challenging instances of general games and also to show that the common link between the two theories is the same minimax principle which has been applied to all the strategic games illustrated up to this point.

To create an analogy with zero-sum, two-person games, Wald cast the fundamental decision process in the form of a "game against nature," in which player R is the statistician or any individual who must *decide* among alternative actions—R_1, R_2, etc.—because he is faced with an uncertain prospect whose outcome will be influenced by chance factors and may turn out to be C_1, C_2, etc., with varying consequences, monetary or otherwise, for R. In a specific example, a man is faced with the prospect that the winter ahead may be C_1 = mild, C_2 = average, or C_3 = severe. Athough he is not gambling with a real opponent, it is convenient to use the fiction of an adversary C, the one Wald called "nature," whose "states," or pure strategies, are C_1, C_2, and C_3. Suppose, then, that your decision problem, the game in which you oppose "nature," involves the choice of a strategy for purchasing and storing your winter supply of coal. Suppose that if you place your order during July and August the price is $15 per ton, but that coal ordered later costs $22 per ton. From previous experience, you know that it requires five, six, or eight tons to heat your home, depending on whether the winter is mild, average, or severe. Moreover, any coal that remains after the winter ahead will be a total loss to you because you are selling your home to people who plan to install an oil burner. If your pure strategies are orders of five, or six, or eight tons during July and August, the payoff matrix is readily computed as

	Mild	Average	Severe
(Order 5)	−75	−97	−141
(Order 6)	−90	−90	−134
(Order 8)	−120	−120	−120

Inspection of this matrix shows that the payoff, −120, for (R_3, C_3) is a maximin for rows (R's pure strategies) as well as a minimax for columns (nature's pure strategies). Therefore (R_3, C_3) is the minimax solution. This means that your best bet is to spend $120 for eight tons of coal. But it would seem to be pushing fiction too far to state that nature's optimum strategy will be to provide a severe winter, or that, in decision problems in general, she "plays" so as to give you the minimum possible or extract the maximum from you. Nevertheless, as Wald pointed out, if nature's true state is unknown to you, it is not unreasonable for you to behave *as if* she were malevolent and wished to oppose you with a minimax strategy. Put otherwise, if you are unwilling to take chances in an uncertain situation, you had better picture the worst eventuality and act accordingly.

But some theoreticians think that a decision-maker should be more optimistic.* One way he can accomplish this is to argue against the notion of complete uncertainty and say, just as Bernoulli and Laplace did, that in the absence of observational data, one must assume that nature is as likely to

---

* See Appendix to this chapter.

do one thing as another. Therefore, in the problem under consideration one would assign the a priori probabilities (1/3, 1/3, 1/3), respectively, to nature's three possible states. The assumption involved is a powerful one, for it postulates that nature is *not* maneuvering against the decision-maker, since her strategy is the *known* mixed strategy (1/3, 1/3, 1/3). The decision situation is thus reduced from a two-person game of strategy to a mere *one-person* game of chance (page 351). To solve this new game, the decision-maker would make use of the known (assumed) probabilities, and reason as follows: If pure strategy R_1 (five tons) is selected, the expectation is

$$\frac{1}{3}(-75) + \frac{1}{3}(-97) + \frac{1}{3}(-141) = -\frac{313}{3}$$

Similarly, the expectations if R_2 and R_3 are chosen can be computed to be $-314/3$ and $-360/3$, both lower than the expectation if R_1 is picked, and therefore R_1 is the best strategy. Thus, postulating equal probabilities for nature's states leads to the decision to order five tons of coal instead of the eight tons prescribed by the more conservative Wald solution.[*]

But Wald would not have approved of the arbitrary assumption of equal likelihood. He would not, however, have been averse to assuming probabilities based on experimental data compiled in the past. Thus, careful observation of many *previous* winters in the particular geographical vicinity, a long-range meteorological forecast, etc., might be combined to yield relative frequencies that would approximate the chances for the winter ahead. Then past experience might lead to approximations like (0.1, 0.6, 0.3) for the probabilities of nature's states. If these probabilities are postulated, then the expectations under R_1, R_2, R_3 are $-\$108$, $-\$103.20$, $-\$120$, respectively. Therefore, R_2 is the optimum strategy, an answer differing from the two previous solutions of the same problem.

The reader may be troubled by the fact that we have apparently obtained three different answers to the same

---

[*] The Bernoulli-Laplace assumption is only one of several alternatives to Wald's methodology. Again, see Appendix to this chapter.

problem. In fact, however, three different problems were solved. In the first instance, it was assumed that nothing whatsoever could be predicted about the winter ahead. In the second and third problems, one still had to take chances with the winter ahead but the probabilities were known, since in one case they were assigned on the basis of classic probability theory, and in the other instance they were estimated from empirical data.

In trying to make the optimum decision about ordering a coal supply for the winter ahead, the decision-maker did not carry out any special experimentation. In one solution it was assumed that he used empirical data, but the meteorological observations involved were made by others in the past and were not designed to shed light on his particular decision problem. It is much more typical of the Wald *statistical* decision procedure to design some special experiment in order to "spy" on nature and thus obtain some revealing evidence of what her true state is likely to be.

As an example, there is the sort of statistical decision process which might be used to control the quality of manufactured articles. Suppose that the statistician advises that before any lot is shipped, three items should be drawn at random and inspected, the lot to be accepted or rejected according to the outcome of this random experiment. In addition to specifying the experiment, the statistician may advise the quality-control inspector to make his decision in accordance with the following *statistical decision function*, to use Wald's terminology.

Outcome (Number of Defectives)	0	1	2	3
Action or Decision	a_1	a_1	a_2	a_2

where a_1 symbolizes "accept" and a_2 stands for "reject."

We observe that the *domain* of this statistical decision function is the sample space $S = \{0, 1, 2, 3\}$, and that the *range* is $A = \{a_1, a_2\}$, the aggregate of contemplated actions. The illustrative function would require rejection of the entire lot if the sample should contain two or three defective items. But the statistician might advise a different strategy by prescribing the following statistical decision function:

Outcome (Number of Defectives)	0	1	2	3
Action or Decision	a_1	a_1	a_1	a_2

which would permit more leniency in the control of quality. Or, if stringency is desired, he might suggest that the lot be passed only if every item in the sample is satisfactory, a policy described by the function

Outcome (Number of Defectives)	0	1	2	3
Action or Decision	a_1	a_2	a_2	a_2

The preceding example is typical, because it illustrates the fundamental role of the *statistical decision function*. Such a function can be defined as a set of ordered pairs of the form (z, a), where z is the outcome of a random experiment and a is the action or decision corresponding to this outcome.

As a further illustration, suppose that in some decision problem the statistician suggests a random experiment whose sample space $S = \{z_1, z_2, \ldots, z_5\}$ contains five possible outcomes. Suppose also that the choice of actions must be made from a set $A = \{a_1, a_2, a_3\}$. Then, in theory, there are very many different statistical decision functions which could be applied to the problem. A few of these functions are indicated by listing some of the ways actions might be assigned to outcomes:

	Outcome				
	z_1	z_2	z_3	z_4	z_5
	a_1	a_1	a_1	a_2	a_3
Action	a_1	a_1	a_1	a_3	a_2
or	a_2	a_3	a_1	a_1	a_1
Decision	a_3	a_1	a_1	a_1	a_2
	a_2	a_1	a_3	a_2	a_2

If the situation is regarded abstractly, without giving concrete meanings to the z's and the a's, there will be many other decision functions which can be applied. In fact, it can be shown that the potentially available decision functions number $3^5 = 243$ (page 410). Of course, when there are specific interpretations, like $a_1 = accept$, $a_2 = reject$, $a_3 = inspect$ *more items*, common sense would immediately eliminate some functions, for example,

Outcome	z_1	z_2	z_3	z_4	z_5
Decision	a_1	a_1	a_1	a_1	a_1

which would prescribe acceptance of a lot no matter what the results of sampling inspection should be. The number of available decision functions can be increased even beyond 243 by considering varied ways of spying on nature, that is, other random experiments and the (numerous) decision functions corresponding to each one.

With such a plethora of choice even in an apparently simple situation where the experimental outcomes and possible actions are small in number, how can a statistician advise an optimum procedure? Wald showed that once again it is a matter of playing a strategic game against nature, a somewhat subtler game than in the case of decision without experimentation. There the decision-maker's pure strategies were various courses of action. In *statistical decision*, as we have labeled the type in which experimentation may be used, it is the statistician who plays the game against nature, and his pure strategies are the (numerous) possible decision rules. Such a game can be pictured by a tree like that in Figure 12.3 where any path from the root to the top represents a possible mode of play.

In a general game with several moves, a pure strategy always signifies a complete set of directions prepared *prior* to playing the game. Then nature's pure strategy would consist of instructions for the second and fourth moves (see Figure 12.3), that is, for the experimental outcome and her actual "state."

Since the statistician (or the individual whom he is advising) plays the first and third moves (Figure 12.3), his pure strategy must specify in advance *both* the experiment to be performed in the first move and the statistical decision function which is to guide action in the third move. Hereafter we shall refer to this dual specification as a *decision rule*.

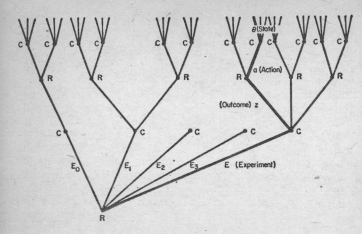

Figure 12.3 Heavy line indicates one way of playing the game. Not all paths to the top are drawn, but all those starting with E_0 (no experimentation), E_1, and E (a typical experiment) appear.

In Figure 12.3 we observe that one of the lowest branches of the tree is marked E_0. This represents a dummy experiment, that is, no experiment at all, with a dummy outcome, z_0, for the second move. The statistician may wish to start the path to the top along branch E_0, which signifies that, in actuality, only the third and fourth moves are made. In other words, he may advise a decision rule involving no special experimentation. Perhaps in certain situations it would be too costly or it might delay action unduly. Thus statistical decision includes as a special case the simple decision game without experimentation.

Although it is the *definition* of pure strategy that requires the decision rule to be selected *prior* to play, this regulation is also good common sense. If the decision-maker were not compelled to agree irrevocably to act in a specified fashion, he might change his mind if an experimental result appeared discouraging. Such behavior would be unscientific and might actually work to his disadvantage, because he would be acting contrary to what the statistician advises as the optimum procedure on the basis of the Wald theory.

Earlier it was seen that a finite game can always be normalized or converted into a matrix game in which the pure strategies of the two players correspond to rows and colums, respectively. Therefore, when any game of statistical decision is normalized, the rows represent the (numerous) decision rules—R_1, R_2, R_3, etc.,—and the columns correspond to nature's possible strategics—C_1, C_2, etc.

To illustrate such a normalized game, let us consider the following situation, where facts and figures are simplified for the sake of comprehension, and where it is assumed that preliminary screening has eliminated a great many of the possible decision rules. Suppose, then, that in the production of a certain complex object, different manufacturers hold contracts for supplying the various parts. One particular manufacturer is to produce parts of a specified type. The parts are to be packed in pairs, since two will always be needed in the construction of the object. The cost of producing one of these parts is $1, and if it is satisfactory, the manufacturer will be paid $4. If it is defective, he will be fined $2, because imperfections cause damage, delay, etc. Also, the contract calls for the scrapping of parts not shipped (to prevent the manufacturer from selling them elsewhere). Finally, if the manufacturer wishes a part to be tested for quality, this can only be done by taking it apart completely, which renders it worthless.

The manufacturer asks his statistician for advice on some sort of scheme that will insure reasonable quality in the parts shipped but will not be too costly. A statistician would actually consider a large variety of decision rules for the handling of a pair of parts, but for the sake of simplicity we assume that only four rules remain after preliminary screening, namely,

Rule 1. Ship both parts (a reasonable rule if there has been previous evidence that quality is good).

Rule 2. Select one part at random and pronounce it satisfactory. The part that remains must be scrapped, in accordance with the contract.

Rule 3. Select one part at random and test it. Judge the quality of the other part to be the same. Thus, if the part tested is good, the other part is considered to be good, too. If the test shows the part chosen to be defective, the other part is assumed to be defective and is scrapped.

Rule 4. Select one of the two parts at random and test it. Assume the other part to be opposite in quality to the one tested. Thus, if the tested part is satisfactory, the other part is assumed to be defective and is scrapped, whereas if the test shows a defective part, the other part is assumed to be satisfactory.

These decision rules are then considered as four pure strategies open to the statistician R in his game against nature C. There are three pure strategies possible for nature, namely, to have 0, 1, or 2 defectives in the package containing a pair of parts. The payoff matrix for this game is

| | | Nature (C) | |
		0 Defective	1 Defective	2 Defectives
(R)	Rule 1	6	0	−6
	Rule 2	2	−1	−4
	Rule 3	2	−3	−2
	Rule 4	−2	0	−4

The reader can readily check the entries in the payoff matrix. Those in the *first column*, for example, correspond to nature's kindest strategy, "no defective parts." Rule 1 will have the manufacturer ship both and hence receive $8. But he has spent $2 to produce the parts, and therefore his gain or payoff is $6. Under Rule 2, only one part will be shipped and the other destroyed. Hence the gain will be $4 - 2 = \$2$. Under Rule 3 the part selected will be satisfactory, and hence the other will be judged correctly as satisfactory, and shipped with a gain of $4 - 2 = \$2$. Under Rule 4 the part tested would be satisfactory, and hence the other would be judged defective and scrapped. Both parts would thus be a total loss, and the payoff therefore −$2.

The entries in the third column can be computed similarly. Some of those in the second column may require some additional explanation. For example, the entry at position (R_2, C_2) is −1, and this is figured as follows: Under Rule 2, one of the parts is selected at random. Therefore the probability of selecting the good part is 1/2, and likewise for the defective part. In the former case, there would be a gain of $4 - 2 = 2$, in the latter a loss of $-2 - 2 = -4$. For the payoff listed at (R_2, C_2), we have computed the *expectation* or *long-run average*.

$$(\tfrac{1}{2})(2) + (\tfrac{1}{2})(-4) = 1 - 2 = -1$$

Now for the solution of the game, the first column can be removed as a strategy for nature, because the corresponding entries in the last column would always be more profitable for her. There remains the matrix

$$\begin{pmatrix} 0 & -6 \\ -1 & -4 \\ -3 & -2 \\ 0 & -4 \end{pmatrix}$$

The first row of this matrix can be removed as a strategy for R, since the last row would be a better strategy. Likewise, the second row can be removed for the same reason. This leaves

$$\begin{pmatrix} -3 & -2 \\ 0 & -4 \end{pmatrix}$$

There is no saddle point and hence no solution in terms of pure strategies, because max (min of row) $= -3$ and min (max of column) $= -2$ and these numbers are not the same. The reader may use the methods of the previous chapter to show that the solution is the pair of mixed strategies $(4/5, 1/5)$, $(2/5, 3/5)$ for R and C, respectively, or, in the original matrix, $(0, 0, 4/5, 1/5)$ and $(0, 2/5, 3/5)$, with the value of the game an expected loss of \$2.40 for R. This means that as pairs of parts are submitted to the statistician (or the quality-control inspector following his advice), he should always select one part at random and test it. Sometimes he will judge the other part to be of the same quality as the one tested, and sometimes to be of the opposite quality. He uses a random device (like a sack containing forty blue and ten red marbles) to achieve the relative frequencies $(4/5, 1/5)$. The solution seems to be in accord with common sense, because it prescribes a *statistical* decision procedure where the experimentation is the sort of sampling inspection called for by either Rule 3 or Rule 4. Also, the more frequent use of Rule 3 seems rational if one thinks of the common notion of judging an entire group by means of a sample. Thus the whole group of two articles should more often than not be like the one tested.

Again, some statisticians would disagree with the preceding solution, which is based on the assumed malevolence of nature. (Thus, since the mixed strategy $(0, 2/5, 3/5)$ signifies that nature will never select C_1, one must play the game as if nature would never produce a pair of parts where both are satisfactory.) The classic viewpoint would have the statisticians use Rule 1 all the time because the first row of the matrix has the maximum total, namely zero; and hence if one were to follow Bernoulli and Laplace, he would optimistically ship both parts each time without hesitation or inspection. Another criterion (see Appendix) would lead to the exclusive use of Rule 3 where the statistician always tests one part at random and judges the quality of the other to be the same.

Still another model for this same situation will be provided in the next chapter where, after a brief return to the simpler games of chance, new concepts will present nature as a lady of infinite variety, and more general methods will enable us to adjust our behavior as best we can to her manifold moods.

The decision problems we have considered, like the games treated somewhat earlier, were presented to illustrate fundamental concepts of the von Neumann and Wald theories rather than to indicate significant applications in realistic situations. Hence one might ask whether the ideas we have discussed suffice for such applications. The answer is that the *techniques* of solution, as we have explained them, are adequate, but that issues arising in the behavioral sciences may call for something additional. The statistician or decision-maker in every case is nevertheless like the "R" of our problems, in that he must measure as best he can the relative merits of future eventualities in which chance elements will play an important role. But his evaluation of prospects may *not* be entirely a question of dollars and cents, pounds and pence, for he may wish to give weight to nonmonetary factors as well—his moral convictions, his emotional stability when risks are involved, and a host of other subjective intangibles.

Even a decision involving the simplest sort of gamble may involve subjective factors. If, for example, a friend offered the following bet, would you accept or refuse? A fair coin is to be tossed, and if it turns up "heads," he will pay you $1200. In case the result is "tails," however, you must pay him $1000. If your liquid assets are under $1000 and/or you do not like to take chances, you will doubtless refuse the bet, even though there is a chance of winning $1200 and your expectation (the criterion in the von Neumann and Wald theories) is

$$(\tfrac{1}{2})(1200) + (\tfrac{1}{2})(-1000) = \$100$$

On the other hand, a gambling addict who is already in debt would doubtless accept the wager no matter what logical arguments against such behavior were presented. A wealthy man who enjoys gambling might accept, unless the stakes seemed too small to challenge his interest. The man who considers all forms of gambling immoral would, of course, reject the wager. The sum total of the situation is that when people are faced with a gamble, their behavior is not necessarily governed by expected monetary payoff.

Decisions seem to be determined by the "true" values for an individual of the prospects or gambles which he must face. But is there any way of measuring these "true" values? Von Neumann and Morgenstern dealt with this very issue in the later editions of the *Theory of Games and Economic Behavior*. They showed that if an individual has preferences that satisfy certain assumptions, there exists a measure of (true) value, which they called *utility*.

In spite of von Neumann's proof of the existence of a utility measure, the practical task of setting up a utility scale to fit a specific situation may be an exceedingly difficult one. But suppose that in a particular problem the decision-maker has been able to assign numerical utilities to each pure strategy pair (R_i, C_j). Then the fundamental matrix becomes a *utility* payoff matrix, where the gains for R are measured in *utiles*, the units of value measurement in his special scale. The matrix governs the game, and except for the fact that its entries are to be read as utiles and not as dollars, one proceeds in exactly the fashion we have already explained.

The von Neumann utility measure provides an answer to the question of subjective values and, in addition, resolves the issue of whether or not expectation, the average payoff in very numerous trials, is a suitable criterion for a decision that is to be made just once. If the expectation formula (page 373) is applied to a matrix row of *utility* payoffs, it turns out that the result need *not* be conceived as an average based on many trials. Instead, the expectation formula is merely a prescription for figuring the "true" value or *utility* of a gamble more complicated than the basic prospects to which the decision-maker originally assigned measures. In other words, "expected" utility is just utility. If after computation of "expected," that is, *actual* utility for various gambles, the decision-maker selects what he considers an optimum strategy and claims that it is the best decision because it offers maximum utility, he will seem to be engaging in circular reasoning. As indicated earlier, his ideas of what prospects are good, better, best are supposed to precede consideration of a decision problem. Subsequently, a utility scale must be derived from these preferences. If originally he had been able to assign utility measures to *all* possible gambles that might arise in the particular problem, he would have known which eventuality he considered best. But when prospects are numerous and complicated, it is easier to rate only a few simple cases at the beginning and then to derive utilities of other prospects if and when such utility measurements are needed. Hence, in choosing a prospect after the expectation formula reveals maximum utility of the particular gamble, an individual is not reasoning in a circle but merely acting in consistent agreement with his original preferences.

As a final word, we might point to the fact that certain researchers in the behavioral sciences feel that, in addition to utility measure, *subjective* probabilities should be introduced. Since the classic and the statistical concepts of probability have already given rise to certain logical difficulties, we shall not introduce new troubles by dealing with the issue of subjective probabilities. In summary, then, utility theory will not modify our treatment of decision problems. Illustrative examples will, in general, be such that monetary payoffs are actually a suitable measure of utility. If not, it will be assumed that payoffs are in utiles, and that the term "expectation" merely signifies the utility of a mixed gamble.

In the chapters that follow we shall return to a more elementary level and consider some of the special types of decision problem that characterized mathematical statistics prior to the promulgation of Wald's theory. Before looking backward, however, it seems appropriate to conclude the present chapter with a biography of the late Abraham Wald. Two of the sources for our account are eulogies written by Morgenstern and Wolfowitz.[*]

Abraham Wald was born in Cluj, Rumania, in 1902. His grandfather was a famous rabbi, his father a small businessman with many intellectual interests. There were five other

---

[*] Oskar Morgenstern, "Abraham Wald," *Econometrica*, Vol. 19, No. 4 (October 1951), pp. 361 ff.; Jacob Wolfowitz, "Abraham Wald," *Annals of Mathematical Statistics*, Vol. 23 (1952), pp. 1–13.

children in the family. One brother, Martin, considered as gifted as Abraham, was an electrical engineer with numerous inventions to his credit.

Wald's early education did not follow the usual pattern. He was not admitted to the local *gymnasium* because, as the son of an Orthodox Jew, he would not attend school on Saturdays. Therefore he studied by himself and passed the entrance examinations of the University of Cluj. After graduation, he experienced considerable difficulty in entering the University of Vienna because of religious restrictions. Thus he spent a year at the engineering school in Vienna before he was finally permitted to study pure mathematics at the university.

In spite of his exceptional ability and the numerous research papers he wrote in the years 1931 to 1936, his religion made an academic post in Austria an impossibility. In the course of his quest for a source of income and an opportunity to work in applied mathematics, Wald met Oskar Morgenstern, who was then director of the Institute for Business Cycle Research. Morgenstern appreciated Wald's talents, employed him at the Institute, and became his lifelong friend.

Wald's research in mathematical statistics gained such renown that he was invited in 1937 to become a staff member of the United States Cowles Commission, and in 1938 to serve as a research associate at Columbia University. His decision to accept these offers was a wise one since, in the interim, the Nazis had taken control of Austria. Columbia University established a special department of mathematical statistics and named Wald as its first chairman. Students from all over the world flocked to his courses, and some of them are today's leading statisticians.

As we have already indicated, Wald's greatest achievement was the theory of statistical decision functions. But his total accomplishment included research involving more than ninety publications—both books and papers. In these many reports of his discoveries are contained some of the most decisive new ideas of modern mathematical statistics. A few of the new concepts arose from his research activities during World War II, when he was a member of the Statistical Research Group at Columbia University. One of the problems he had to solve led him to his now-famous *sequential analysis* (page 449), which was immediately applied in the war industries and saved untold millions of dollars. In fact, a visit to many American factories today will show immediately the now-familiar charts of sequential testing as indispensable tools in mass production. But sequential analysis is only a special part of Wald's broader decision theory.

Wald did not escape tragedy. At the end of the war, he learned that eight members of his immediate family, among them his parents, had been murdered by the Nazis. Even this cruel blow failed to embitter him, although a certain sadness could be felt to be with him for the rest of his life. He succeeded in bringing the sole survivor, his brother Hermann, to the United States.

In 1950 Wald received an invitation from the Indian Government to lecture at Indian universities and research centers. He accepted eagerly, and in November of that year he and his wife set out. En route, he lectured in Paris and Rome. He delivered several of his scheduled lectures in India, but the tour was not to be completed. On December 13, 1950, an airplane, lost in a fog, crashed into a peak of the Nilgiris, killing all aboard, among them Abraham Wald and his wife.

The influence of his great ideas remains, and their importance increases. Some of them have already been discussed in order to acquaint readers with the ultimate in mathematical statistics and also because the author holds Wald in particular reverence. She worked with him during World War II as a member of the Columbia University Statistical Research Group, and witnessed the development of his sequential analysis and his initial formulations in statistical decision theory.

Appendix

In addition to the Bernoulli-Laplace method and the Wald minimax principle, two other criteria have been proposed for solving games against nature. When the four criteria are applied to the game whose matrix is given below, the solutions prescribe four different strategies or decisions for R. The reader will see at once that the classic criterion would pick R_4 whereas Wald's method would select R_1.

$$\begin{pmatrix} 2 & 1 & 1 & 1 \\ 0 & 6 & 0 & 0 \\ 1 & 4 & 0 & 0 \\ 3 & 2 & 0 & 2 \end{pmatrix}$$

Professor Leonid Hurwicz has formulated a criterion whose purpose is to modify the extreme pessimism of Wald's assumption that nature will do her worst. Hurwicz suggests that R's optimism be assessed by a real number α, where $0 \leq \alpha \leq 1$. Then R must compute, for each row, the quantity $\alpha M + (1 - \alpha)m$, where M and m are the maximum and minimum payoffs in the row. Finally, R must select the row for which this quantity is greatest. We observe that if R is least optimistic or most pessimistic, $\alpha = 0$, and the quantity computed for each row is $\alpha M + (1 - \alpha)m = m$, the minimum. Thus, R will be selecting the row containing the *maximin*, and hence for $\alpha = 0$, Hurwicz's criterion reduces to Wald's. At the opposite extreme, $\alpha = 1$ when R is most optimistic. In that case, Hurwicz's index is $1M + 0m = M$, the maximum of a row. Then R will select the strategy corresponding to the maximum of row maxima if he is extremely optimistic.

In the foregoing payoff matrix, let us suppose that α is *not* extreme but has some value as yet unspecified. Then, for the first row,

$$\alpha M + (1 - \alpha)m = 2\alpha + 1(1 - \alpha) = \alpha + 1$$

Since $m = 0$ in the other rows, the Hurwicz index is seen to be 6α, 4α, and 3α, respectively. For *any* possible value of α greater than zero, 6α is the maximum of these three. It remains to compare 6α, the index for the second row, with $\alpha + 1$, the index for the first. The two strategies will be equally good if $6\alpha = \alpha + 1$, that is, if R's optimism measures $\alpha = 0.2$. If $6\alpha < \alpha + 1$, that is, if $\alpha < 0.2$, then R_1 is better than R_2, and R_1, the Wald solution, is the best of the four strategies (which seems sensible because α is close to zero). But if $6\alpha > \alpha + 1$, that is, if $\alpha > 0.2$, R_2 is the best strategy.

The fourth criterion in current use is due to Professor Leonard J. Savage, who suggests that a *regret* matrix be computed first. R's regret is defined to be the difference between the actual payoff resulting from his selection of some pure strategy and the payoff he might have received had he known what C's strategy would be. Thus if R chooses R_1 and nature chooses C_2 in the foregoing matrix, the payoff to R is 1. But if he had known nature would choose the second column, he would have played R_2 so as to obtain 6, the *maximum* payoff in that column. His *regret* is therefore $1 - 6 = -5$. In general, if R plays R_i, the ith row, and nature plays C_j, the jth column R's *regret* is the difference between the resulting payoff and the maximum payoff in the jth column. The regret matrix corresponding to the given payoff matrix is therefore

$$\begin{pmatrix} -1 & -5 & 0 & -1 \\ -3 & 0 & -1 & -2 \\ -2 & -2 & -1 & -2 \\ 0 & -4 & -1 & 0 \end{pmatrix}$$

The Savage criterion prescribes that R pick the row corresponding to the *maximin* regret. The respective minima for rows are -5, -3, -2, and -4. Therefore -2 is the maximin and R_3 the best strategy. We observe that regrets are either zero or negative in value, and therefore the minima actually correspond to the regret of *greatest* magnitude attached to each strategy. When R seeks the maximum of the minimum regrets, he is in fact trying to diminish the magnitude of his regret by bringing it as close to zero (no regret) as possible.

Here R's use of the maximum strategy for the regret matrix has him proceed as if he were applying the Wald criterion to this matrix. There is one difference, however. The choice of R_3 in the above regret matrix does *not* signify that there is a saddle point in the third row. The minimum regret in the third row, namely, -2, occurs in three different positions. In no one of these positions is it true that the entry -2 is also the maximum of its column. Naturally, -2 cannot be the maximum of a column since that must always be zero (no regret). Thus, the Wald criterion would have called for a solution in terms of mixed strategies. Savage, however, does not accept the fundamental assumption used by Wald, namely, that R must proceed as if nature were actually maneuvering against him. Savage sees nature as an opponent with no known objectives or prejudices. Thus, in the present problem all that can be assumed is that nature's strategy is unknown, and therefore R must act so as to have least regret, no matter what she does.

In summary, the four different criteria lead to four different solutions:

Bernoulli-Laplace	R_4
Wald	R_1
Hurwicz	R_2 if $\alpha > 0.2$
Savage	R_3

This situation places the problem squarely in the hands of the practicing statistician. In the case of a particular problem, he will have to use the criterion which seems most suitable for the given facts.

If the Bernoulli-Laplace assumption of equal likelihood is gratuitous and the Wald principle is pessimistic, mathematicians are able to point out that the Hurwicz and Savage philosophies for solution of a decision problem also have shortcomings. Hence, at the present time no criterion has all the characteristics that will satisfy both the pure mathematician and the practical decision-maker.

Chapter 13

From Dice to Quantum Theory and Quality Control

Statistical decision theory as formulated by Wald might be described as mathematical statistics considered from an advanced point of view. Since one of our objectives is to present mathematical subject matter as it exists today, it has seemed best to present the all-encompassing picture first and fill in special technical details later on. As a result, it has not been possible to provide challenging problems of statistical decision, because they usually require special concepts from probability theory or from the earlier less general species of mathematical statistics. For the sake of significant applications, we must now backtrack. Therefore, the present chapter will resume the discussion of probability theory initiated in Chapter 11, and Chapter 14 will treat some of the basic notions of the twentieth-century mathematical statistics which Wald incorporated into his theory. In both chapters the historic evolution of ideas will be presented, and concepts will be related both to theoretical science and to practical problems of statistical decision.

For the reasons cited, it will be necessary to start the story of probability anew. How did it all begin? It is conjectured that the infinitesimal germs of those notions that were to blossom into the work of Borel, von Neumann, Morgenstern, and Wald may have existed even 40,000 years ago. It now appears that games of chance were already in vogue in that early era and that *astragali*, the knucklebones (hucklebones) of animals, served as dice. The *astragalus* is a small bone in the ankle, just under the heel bone or *talus*. The matter of ancient dice-rolling and the entire history of games of chance have been investigated thoroughly by Dr. F. N. David of the University College, London, who has presented the results in a most interesting and significant paper. She tells us:*

The astragali of animals with hooves are different from those with feet, such as man, dog, and cat. From the comparison in Figure 13.1, we note how in the case of the dog the astragalus is developed on one side to allow for the support of the bones of the feet. The astragalus of the hooved animal is almost symmetrical about a longitudinal axis, and it is a pleasant toy to play with. In France and Greece, children still play games with astragali, and it is possible to buy pieces of metal fashioned into idealized shapes but still recognizable as astragali.

Sheep

Dog

Figure 13.1   Drawings of the astragali in sheep and dog

Dr. David states that many early games of chance probably originated in Egypt and did not start in Greece as is often claimed. She writes: "However, Herodotus, the first Greek historian, like his present-day counterparts, was willing to believe that the Greeks (or allied peoples) had invented nearly everything."

She quotes Herodotus' account of the famine in Lydia (*ca.* 1500 B.C.):

For some time the Lydians bore the affliction patiently, but finding that it did not pass away, they set to work to devise remedies for the evil. Various expedients were discovered by various persons; dice and hucklebones (i.e., astragali) and ball and all such games were invented, except tables (backgammon), the invention of which they do not claim as theirs. The plan adopted against famine was to engage in games on one day so

* F. N. David, "Studies in the History of Probability and Statistics I," *Biometrika*, Vol. 42 (1955), pp. 1–15. See also, F. N. David, *Games, Gods, and Gambling*, Hafner, New York, 1962.

entirely as not to feel any craving for food, and the next day to eat and abstain from games. In this way passed eighteen years.

It is Dr. David's opinion that some sort of theory of probability might have developed early in history if dice had not been associated with divination rather than with mathematics. This was true in classical Greece and Rome, and still holds among the Buddhists in Tibet. Even as late as 1737, John Wesley decided by the drawing of lots whether to marry or not.

Allusions to gambling with knucklebones and dice appear in the literature of all lands throughout the ages. The existence of various gamblers' handbooks, and the evidence of the constant warfare of the Christian Church against the vices associated with gaming, are proof that variants of the early games of chance continued on and on. Be that as it may, there was no genuine mathematical analysis of such games until Cardano's *Liber de Ludo Aleae* (Manual on Games of Chance), written *ca.* 1526, but not published until 1663, almost a century after the algebraist's death.

Cardano's distinction as a physician and the contributions to algebra that made him the leading mathematician of his day are emphasized in histories of science, but he is rarely given the credit he deserves for founding a *theory* of probability. The great Galileo added a few additional theoretical notions in his own work on dice, *Sopra le Scoperte de i Dadi* (On Discoveries About Dice), first published in 1718, although written much earlier. Galileo's manual is remarkably lucid in style, with explanations so thorough and simple as to read like those offered to high school students today. But Cardano's major role and Galileo's interest in probability have suffered neglect by the historians, and it has become traditional to attribute the creation of probability theory to Pascal and Fermat.

It is true that the two French mathematicians contributed to the theory in the course of a correspondence initiated by a gambling problem of Antoine Gombaud, Chevalier de Méré (1607–1684). In 1654 Pascal wrote to Fermat: "Monsieur le Chevalier de Méré is very bright, but he is no mathematician, and that, as you know, is a very grave defect."

De Méré (as he is usually called) knew that the odds favored the appearance of at least one "6" in 4 throws of a single die. His analysis alluded to 36 possible outcomes of rolling a pair of dice, or six times as many as in the case of a single die. Hence he felt that six times as many tosses, that is, 24, should be carried out with a *pair* of dice, and then *"double* 6" would be favored. When he discovered, however, that this was *not* the case, he declaimed loudly that "mathematical theorems are not always true and mathematics is self-contradictory." He put the problem to Pascal and asked for an explanation. Pascal wrote to Fermat about the matter, and in the ensuing correspondence both mathematicians demonstrated, each in a different fashion, that in 4 throws with one die, the odds are 671 to 625 in favor of having at least one "6" turn up, but that the probability of a "double 6" at least once in 24 throws is only about 0.49. A method of arriving at this conclusion will be indicated shortly.

It must be remarked that with Pascal, Fermat, and others who contributed to the development of probability theory, such work was merely incidental to broader scientific activity. So it was with Christiaan Huygens who, as a young man of twenty-seven, not yet the monumental figure who ranked close to Newton in the quality of his discoveries in mechanics, optics, astronomy, and mathematics, wrote a small tract, *De Ratiociniis in Aleae Ludo* (On Reasoning in the Game of Dice). This appeared in 1657 as an appendix to Frans van Schooten's *Exercitationes Mathematicae*. The date was prior to that of publication of Cardano's and Galileo's texts. Hence Huygens' was the *first* printed work on the theory of games of chance, and in this sense he must be considered a founder of probability theory.

Since, by 1500, the human race has been indulging in games of chance for at least four thousand years and possibly for much longer, why was there no probability *theory* until Cardano made a small beginning in his gamblers' handbook *ca.* 1526? One explanation, and it may indicate the major factor, is to be found in religious beliefs and ethical principles. If gambling is considered immoral, then it is also sinful to use games of chance as models of scientific situations.

But after Cardano, Galileo, Fermat, Pascal, and Huygens had made successive contributions to a theory of probability, why was progress still slow? The answer is that general issues and worthwhile applications could not be treated until there was a fully formulated methodology for determining, without resort to enumeration, the number of elements in the large (but finite) aggregates to which probabilistic reasoning may apply. At certain points in previous discussions, the reader must have been aware of this problem. For example, when there were three possible actions, $\{a_1, a_2, a_3\}$, from which to choose in formulating a decision function associated with five possible outcomes, it was asserted that there would be 243 different ways of assigning actions to outcomes. But the only verification suggested was enumeration of all the varied possibilities—$a_1a_1a_1a_1a_1$, $a_2a_2a_2a_2a_2$, $a_1a_1a_1a_2a_3$, $a_2a_1a_3a_1a_3$, etc.

The reader is thus somewhat in the same position as the early probabilists and must therefore consider the elements of the *combinatorial* algebra or combinatorial analysis they began to develop, that is, he must study principles which substitute reasoning for enumeration. As a very simple example, suppose that a man plans to travel from Chicago to London, stopping at New York City en route. He can journey from Chicago to New York via one of five convenient flights, $\{A, B, C, D, E\}$. Next he has three choices—the *Queen Elizabeth 2* the *France*, or a transoceanic jet. Let us symbolize these possibilities as $\{1, 2, 3\}$. In how many different ways can he plan his trip? One might list all the possible plans—$A1$, $A2$, $A3$, $B1$, . . . etc., and then count them. But in order to arrive at a general principle, let us consider the planning of the trip as if it were a game with two moves, the first a choice of *letter* and the second a selection of *number*. This "game" can be pictured as a tree in which each path from root to top is a possible plan. Since there are 15 paths (Figure 13.2), as many as terminal

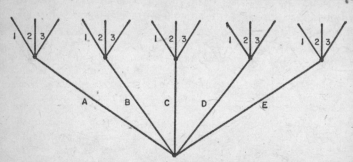

Figure 13.2   Tree for possible trips from Chicago to London via New York

vertices at the top of the tree, there are 15 possible plans. But to help us obtain a general rule, we observe the pattern of the tree. Each lower branch is topped by three branches, so that the paths subdivide into sets of three. Thus if it is planned to take flight A, the paths or possible journeys to London are $\{A1, A2, A3\}$. Similarly, if one were to take flight B, the paths or possible trips would be $\{B1, B2, B3\}$, etc. There would be 5 such sets of three because there are 5 ways of starting out. Hence there are $5 \times 3 = 15$ paths or possible trips.

Now suppose that there had been 7 suitable flights and 4 choices for transoceanic travel. Then the tree for this situation would exhibit paths in sets of *four* like $\{A1, A2, A3, A4\}$, $\{B1, B2, B3, B4\}$, etc., and since there would be 7 ways of starting the journey, there would be 7 such sets, and hence $7 \times 4 = 28$ paths or possible trips. And, in general, if there were m ways of starting out and n ways of continuing, there would be mn possibilities for the entire journey.

Suppose now that the original travel plan is extended so that following a stay in England, our voyager will go on to the Continent. He considers the following countries as possibilities for his next stop—Belgium, Holland, France, Switzerland. In how many ways can he plan the new three-stage journey? To answer, one need only permit the original tree to grow taller. Let us label the countries listed as $\{a, b, c, d\}$. In Figure 13.3 part of the taller tree is pictured, and the diagram indicates that the paths to the top (trips from Chicago to the Continent via New York and London) fall into sets of *four*. Each path in the original tree (trip to London) is topped by four new branches. Because trip $A1$

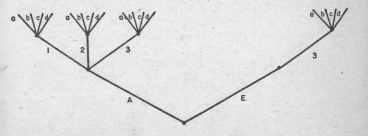

Figure 13.3   Part of tree for three-stage trip

can be completed in four different ways, one has the four paths to the top, $\{A1a, A1b, A1c, A1d\}$. Similarly, journey $A2$ can be rounded out into the trips $\{A2a, A2b, A2c, A2d\}$, etc. Finally, $E3$ can be completed in one of the four ways $\{E3a, E3b, E3c, E3d\}$. There will be $5 \times 3 = 15$ such sets of four, because each set corresponds to a path of the original tree (possible way of traveling to London), and it was shown that there are 15 such paths. Hence, the paths of the taller tree, the three-branch paths, will number $5 \times 3 \times 4 = 60$, that is, there are 60 possible ways of making the three-stage journey. In general, if there are n_1 choices for the first lap of the journey, n_2 for the second, and n_3 for the third, then the trip to London can be planned in $n_1 n_2$ ways, and the entire journey can be planned in $n_1 n_2 n_3$ ways. One can generalize this further by picturing a trip with four or five or six, etc., successive stages. And one can go still further by considering other sequences of actions, in no way connected with planning a trip.

Therefore, by analogy with the cases illustrated, a completely *general* principle for counting is as follows: If one thing can be done in n_1 different ways, and after this is done, a second thing can be done in n_2 ways, and subsequently, a third thing can be done in n_3 ways, a fourth thing in n_4 ways, etc., then the number of ways in which the sequence of things can be done is the *product*, $n_1 n_2 n_3 n_4 \ldots$.

Let us apply the general principle to the problem previously considered, where one had to assign an action or decision to each of five outcomes, and each action had to be chosen from the set $\{a_1, a_2, a_3\}$. To find the number of possible assignments, we can say that $n_1 = 3$, because the action corresponding to the first outcome can be chosen to be a_1 or a_2 or a_3. Next, $n_2 = 3$, because the same choice is available. Then $n_3 = 3$, $n_4 = 3$, $n_5 = 3$. Hence the five choices can be made in $n_1 n_2 n_3 n_4 n_5 = 3 \cdot 3 \cdot 3 \cdot 3 \cdot 3 = 3^5 = 243$ ways. This was the claim made previously, but never proved.

To provide another example, suppose that 6 persons in a theater party have consecutive seats in the same row. In how many different ways can they arrange themselves? Since the first to arrive has a choice of 6 seats, the second a choice of 5, the third a choice of 4, and so on, the answer is $6 \cdot 5 \cdot 4 \cdot 3 \cdot 2 \cdot 1 = 720$, offering an unexpectedly large number of social complications.

Each of the 720 different seating arrangements would be described as a *permutation* of the 6 persons, and, in general, the term "permutation" signifies an arrangement of a finite set of things in a particular order. To obtain other permutations related to the members of our theater party, let us suppose that they are celebrities and that, during an intermission, a newspaper photographer arrives with the request that any 4 members of the group stand side by side to pose for a picture. In how many different ways could this be done? There are 6 possible volunteers for the first position in the lineup, and after someone has filled this position, there are 5 possibilities for the second position, thereafter 4 possibilities for the third position, etc. Then there are $6 \cdot 5 \cdot 4 \cdot 3 = 360$ different ways of satisfying the photographer's request. Each of these represents a permutation, that is, an ordered arrangement of *four* members of the group. If we symbolize the members as $\{A_1, A_2, A_3, A_4, A_5, A_6\}$, then the 360 permutations or possible photographs include arangements like

$$A_1A_2A_3A_4, \; A_2A_1A_3A_4, \; A_4A_1A_3A_2, \; \ldots$$
$$A_2A_1A_5A_6, \; A_6A_2A_5A_1, \; A_5A_2A_6A_1, \; \ldots$$
$$A_2A_3A_4A_6, \; A_4A_3A_6A_2, \text{ etc.}$$

We have applied a fundamental combinatorial principle in order to avoid the need for such enumeration, but nevertheless have listed a few of the possible permutations in order to indicate that *any* subset of size 4 might be drawn from the entire set of 6 persons and that the individuals in such a subset could be arranged in any conceivable order. Therefore, the figure 360 gives the totality of all permutations of all subsets of size 4 which can be formed using members of the entire set of six.

There is a convenient notation for representing answers to some permutation problems. Instead of saying that there are $6 \cdot 5 \cdot 4 \cdot 3 \cdot 2 \cdot 1$ permutations of members of the theater party, one would describe the number as *factorial* 6, symbolized by 6!. Thus, 6! signifies the product of the first six positive integers. If members $\{A_1, A_2, A_3, A_4\}$ volunteer for the requested photograph, then the photographer can permute this group of 4 persons in $4 \cdot 3 \cdot 2 \cdot 1 = 4!$, that is, *factorial* 4 ways. The reasoning which led to 6! and 4! shows that for any set of 6 distinguishable elements (4 elements), whether these be persons, pictures, coins, books, symbols, etc., the number of permutations is 6! (4!). If 10 distinguishable elements are to be permuted, there would be 10 choices for the first position, 9 for the second, 8 for the third, etc., and hence 10! permutations. In general, if there are n distinguishable elements in a set, the number of permutations of these elements is $n!$.

Instead of considering a set of 6 persons, let us return again to a sample space for the rolling of a die, $S = \{1, 2, 3, 4, 5, 6\}$, in order to explain the answers given by Pascal and Fermat to the classic questions raised by the Chevalier de Méré (page 409). At first the Chevalier was concerned with tossing a single fair die 4 times. Let us describe the possible outcomes by sequences like 1-2-6-4, 2-6-6-6, 4-5-2-2, 3-3-3-3, 6-1-6-4, 6-6-6-6, 4-3-5-1, etc. Since De Méré was betting on the occurrence of a "6" at least once in 4 throws, the favorable sequences in the above list would be 1-2-6-4, 2-6-6-6, 6-1-6-4, 6-6-6-6. What is the total number of sequences, and how many favor De Méré's bet? There are 6 possibilities for the first toss of the die (first number in the sequence), 6 for the second toss, etc., so that there would be $6 \cdot 6 \cdot 6 \cdot 6 = 1296$ possible sequences, all considered *equally likely* in classic probability theory. To find how many of these are "favorable," it is easier to compute the number of *unfavorable* outcomes and subtract from the total. For each toss (position in the sequence) there are 5 unfavorable possibilities, namely any of the numbers $\{1, 2, 3, 4, 5\}$. So failure for a "6" to appear could occur in $5 \cdot 5 \cdot 5 \cdot 5 = 625$ different ways. Since $1296 - 625 = 671$, a "6" would appear once or oftener in 671 games out of 1296, so that the probability is $671 \div 1296 = 0.52$, and the odds are 671 to 625 in favor of having a "6" turn up at least once.

Now the second of De Méré's wagers concerned a pair of dice. Let us describe the possible outcomes as 1-1, 1-2, 1-3, 1-4, 1-5, 1-6, 2-1, 2-2, 2-3, etc. If the reader wishes to distinguish between outcomes like 1-2 and 2-1, for example, he can think of rolling a pair of dice of different colors, say, black and white. Then "black 1, white 2" is a different outcome from "black 2, white 1." Since there are 6 different ways in which the black die can turn up and the same is true of the white die, there should be $6 \times 6 = 36$ terms in the above list of potential outcomes. But the pair of dice is to be rolled 24 times. Since there are 36 possibilities for the first toss, 36 for the second, 36 for the third, etc., the total number of possible sequences for the 24 tosses is $(36)^{24}$. Because De Méré's bet was on "double 6," that is, 6-6, the other 35 ordered number pairs can be considered unfavorable. Then there are $(35)^{24}$ unfavorable results in 24 tosses of a pair of dice, and the probability that "double 6" will never appear in the course of these 24 trials is $(35)^{24}/(36)^{24}$ = 0.51. (This approximation can be obtained by using logarithms.) Therefore the probability that "double 6" will appear one or more times is 0.49, the fact that seemed so utterly puzzling to De Méré.

De Méré's difficulties may have stimulated Pascal and Fermat to formulate combinatorial principles, but a much more innocent situation will help to explain an important probabilistic concept which will, in turn, make it possible to prove a fundamental law. Let us, then, return to consideration of the random device decribed at the end of Chapter 10, namely, a sack containing 30 blue and 10 red marbles. If a marble is drawn at random, the probabilities are $P(\text{blue}) = 3/4$ and $P(\text{red}) = 1/4$. If we are now told that 32 of the marbles are small and 8 large, we can compute $P(\text{small}) = 4/5$ and $P(\text{large}) = 1/5$. Suppose that the complete classification according to color and size is

	Blue	Red	Total
Small	27	5	32
Large	3	5	8
Total	30	10	40

This tabulation makes it possible to compute $P(\text{small and blue}) = 27/40$. $P(\text{large and red}) = 5/40$, etc.

Imagine that someone draws a marble from the sack, informs you that it is *large*, and asks you to make a bet about its color. To figure your chances, you wish to assign a value to $P(\text{blue} \mid \text{large})$, which is read as "the probability of *blue*, given *large*." Then you must consider only the 8 large marbles to which the second row of the tabulation refers. Since 3 of those marbles are blue, $P(\text{blue} \mid \text{large}) = 3/8$ and $P(\text{red} \mid \text{large}) = 5/8$.

Each of these figures is described as a *conditional* probability, in contrast with the original "unconditional" or "absolute" probabilities. We observe in the example above that the conditional probabilities for *blue* and *red* (3/8, 5/8)

are less and greater, respectively, than the corresponding unconditional probabilities (3/4, 1/4). Thus the concept of conditional probability makes a species of "statistical inference" possible, because the revision of the original probability estimates is a conclusion based on experimental evidence (in the illustration, the fact that the marble drawn is large).

The example considered also shows that a conditional probability results from a reduction in the original sample space. The absolute probabilities for *blue* and *red* were based on a sample space of 40 elements, whereas the conditional probabilities referred to a set of only 8 elements, which was a *proper subset* of the original sample space.

To make sure that the reader understands the concept of conditional probability, he should proceed as follows.

(1) Interpret symbols like $P(\text{red} \mid \text{small}) =$ "the probability of *red*, given *small*."

(2) Evaluate some conditional probabilities like $P(\text{red} \mid \text{small})$, $P(\text{large} \mid \text{blue})$, $P(\text{small} \mid \text{red})$. (The answers are 5/32, 1/10, 1/2.)

(3) Observe that the reduced sample spaces in (2) contain 32, 30, 10 elements, respectively.

(4) Compare the answers in (2) with the corresponding unconditional probabilities, 1/4, 1/5, 4/5.

Let us now make a more detailed analysis of the computation of a conditional probability. For example,

$$P(\text{blue} \mid \text{large}) = \frac{3}{8} = \frac{3/40}{8/40} = \frac{P(\text{large and blue})}{P(\text{large})}$$

This equation expresses a conditional probability as the quotient of two unconditional probabilities and suggests the general definition: The conditional probability of E_2, given E_1, is symbolized by $P(E_2|E_1)$ and is expressed by the formula

$$P(E_2 \mid E_1) = \frac{P(E_1 \text{ and } E_2)}{P(E_1)}$$

providing $P(E_1) \neq 0$. (In those cases where E_1 has probability zero, a conditional probability cannot be defined.) But if

$P(E_1) \neq 0$, we can multiply both sides of the above equation by this probability to obtain

$$P(E_1 \text{ and } E_2) = P(E_1) \cdot P(E_2 \mid E_1)$$

a theorem expressing the important *multiplication law* of probability theory. Although we have proved the multiplication formula only for the case where $P(E_1) \neq 0$, it is valid even when $P(E_1) = 0$, if it is agreed that the product in the right member of the formula is zero whatever the value of $P(E_2 \mid E_1)$.

In Chapter 11 it was emphasized that an event can be defined by a set of points which is a subset of the sample space of interest. Then if two events, E_1 and E_2, are defined by such point sets, the event "E_1 and E_2" is the *intersection* of the two sets. This intersection is customarily symbolized by $E_1 \cap E_2$. The intersection of two sets consists of all points (elements) common to those two sets. But the present discussion will employ the terminology "E_1 and E_2" rather than the symbolism $E_1 \cap E_2$, partly because events will usually be defined by verbal statements and partly because we wish to avoid confusion with $E_1 \cup E_2$, the *union* of two sets (pages 48 and 365), which corresponds to "E_1 and/or E_2."

The multiplication law given above is a formula for the probability of $E_1 \cap E_2$. It is useful for assigning probabilities in problems like: A sack contains 10 blue and 15 red marbles. One marble is drawn at random, and then a second marble is drawn at random from the remaining marbles. What is the probability that the first marble is red and the second blue? Here $E_1 =$ "first red" and $E_2 =$ "second blue." Then

$P(\text{first red and second blue}) =$
$$P(\text{first red}) \, P(\text{second blue}|\text{first red})$$

$$= \left(\frac{15}{25}\right)\left(\frac{10}{24}\right) = \frac{1}{4}$$

In our illustrations the conditional probabilities have all differed from the corresponding absolute or unconditional probabilities. But a conditional probability may in some instances be equal to the original "absolute" probability. For example, consider the case where a coin is tossed and then a die is rolled. If the possible outcomes are described by the sample space $S = \{H1, H2, .., H6, T1, .., T6\}$, the probability that the die will turn up deuce, that is, the probability of the event $\{H2, T2\}$, is $P(\text{deuce}) = 2/12 = 1/6$. Suppose that the experimenter tells us that the coin has turned up "heads." This information leads to the reduced sample space $S_1 = \{H1, H2, \ldots, H6\}$, containing only 6 outcomes, and in this space the event, "die will turn up deuce" is described by $\{H2\}$. Hence the *conditional probability* $P(\text{deuce}|\text{heads}) = 1/6$, which is equal to the original "unconditional" probability for deuce. This result is not surprising, because the additional information that the coin has turned up "heads" seems to have no bearing on the behavior of the die. One would say that the event "die turns up deuce" is *independent* of the event "coin turns up heads," a fact borne out by the equality of the conditional and "absolute" probabilities computed above.

In general, if $P(E_2|E_1) = P(E_2)$, event E_2 is said to be *independent* of E_1. In that case, substitution of $P(E_2)$ for $P(E_2|E_1)$ in the *multiplication law* gives

$$P(E_1 \text{ and } E_2) = P(E_1) \, P(E_2)$$

as the condition for E_2 to be independent of E_1. Now, if $P(E_1) = 0$, the conditional probability $P(E_2|E_1)$ is undefined, as explained earlier. Hence we could not compare it with the unconditional probability $P(E_2)$ in order to test for independence, nor could we carry out a substitution in the multiplication law, as specified above. Nevertheless, it is customary to accept the above equation as a criterion of independence even when $P(E_1) = 0$.

In summary, then, if

$$P(E_1 \text{ and } E_2) = P(E_1) \cdot P(E_2)$$

E_2 is said to be independent of E_1. Observe that this equation can also be written in the form

$$P(E_2 \text{ and } E_1) = P(E_2) \cdot P(E_1)$$

because the order of factors in the right member is immaterial, and because the event $(E_2 \text{ and } E_1)$ is obviously the same as $(E_1 \text{ and } E_2)$. But the alternative form of the equation expresses the condition for E_1 to be independent of E_2. Hence, if E_2 is independent of E_1, then E_1 is also independent of E_2. Thus, independence is a symmetrical relation which makes it possible to speak of a *pair* of independent events.

The equation formulated repeatedly above therefore

provides a *definition* for two independent events, E_1 and E_2. In other words, two events are said to be independent if, and only if, the probability of their joint occurrence is equal to the product of their absolute probabilities.

To apply this definition, consider the experiment where one card is drawn at random from a bridge deck. Are the events E_1, a spade, and E_2, a picture card, independent? We see that $P(E_1) = 13/52 = 1/4$ and $P(E_2) = 12/52 = 3/13$. Now the event "spade and picture" is $(E_1 \text{ and } E_2) = \{$king of spades, queen of spades, jack of spades$\}$, and thus $P(E_1 \text{ and } E_2) = 3/52$. Since

$$\frac{3}{52} = \left(\frac{1}{4}\right)\left(\frac{3}{13}\right)$$

$$P(E_1 \text{ and } E_2) = P(E_1) \cdot P(E_2)$$

and therefore events E_1 and E_2 are independent. One might have anticipated this result on intuitive grounds, because the fact that a card is a spade gives no clue whatsoever as to whether or not it is a picture card, and vice versa.

With reference to the same random experiment, what is the probability that a card will be either a spade or a picture card, or both? What we seek, then, is $P(E_1 \text{ and/or } E_2)$, that is, $P(E_1 \cup E_2)$. To count favorable cases, one might compute

13 spades + 12 picture cards

But this would include the king, queen, and jack of spades twice. Therefore one must subtract the three cases that are *both* spades and picture cards, so that

$$P(E_1 \text{ and/or } E_2) = \frac{13 + 12 - 3}{52}$$

$$= \frac{13}{52} + \frac{12}{52} - \frac{3}{52}$$

From the results of the previous example, we recognize that the three fractions in the right member are $P(E_1)$, $P(E_2)$, $P(E_1 \text{ and } E_2)$, respectively, so that the equation expresses the fact that

$$P(E_1 \text{ and/or } E_2) = P(E_1) + P(E_2) - P(E_1 \text{ and } E_2)$$

The answer to the problem is $22/52 = 11/26$, but we are much more interested in the fact that the last equation above expresses a general law, one which includes as a special case the axiom applicable to mutually exclusive events (page

368). Thus, if one uses the general formula to compute the probability that a card drawn from a deck is E_1, a spade, or E_2, the queen of diamonds, then $P(E_1 \text{ and } E_2) = 0$, since a card cannot be both a spade and a diamond. Therefore the required probability is

$$\frac{13}{52} + \frac{1}{52} = \frac{14}{52} = \frac{7}{26}$$

If E_1 and E_2 cannot both occur, that is, if $P(E_1 \text{ and } E_2) = 0$, the general formula reduces to that for mutually exclusive events, namely,

$$P(E_1 \text{ or } E_2) = P(E_1) + P(E_2)$$

To apply some of the above probabilistic principles to a problem related to statistical decision, we shall consider an example similar to a hypothetical situation described in the previous chapter. There we pictured that weather data would yield empirical probabilities for the occurrence of a mild, average, or severe winter, or else that, lacking such data, one might possibly assume equal likelihood for the occurrence of each state of nature in the winter ahead. In either case the probabilities would be assigned *prior* to the experimentation associated with the statistical decision problem. The incorporation into the formula for conditional probability of some of the probabilistic laws discussed above leads to an important principle of statistical inference, called *Bayes' rule*, which provides a method of reassessing probabilities *after* the experimentation associated with statistical decisions is carried out. We remark in passing that the principle was formulated in 1763 by the Reverend Thomas Bayes, a British clergyman with a strong bent for mathematics.

For a specific example of the Bayes technique, let us consider a question that would arise in a statistical decision problem related to production in a small factory having only two machines A and B. Suppose that past experience indicates that A produces 30 per cent of the articles with about 1 per cent defective, and that among the 70 per cent produced by B, about 3 per cent are defective. The experimentation to be carried out consists in selecting a package of items at random, and inspecting one article drawn at random from it. If the article turns out to be defective, what is the probability that it was manufactured by A?

What is sought is $P(A \mid \text{defective})$, and by the definition of conditional probability,

$$P(A \mid \text{defective}) = \frac{P(A \text{ and defective})}{P(\text{defective})}$$

Now the multiplication law can be applied to the numerator of the fraction on the right to yield

$$P(A \text{ and defective}) = P(A)\, P(\text{defective} \mid A)$$
$$= (0.3)(0.01) = 0.003$$

But the denominator, $P(\text{defective})$, concerns an event that can occur in two *mutually exclusive* ways, namely, as the result of manufacture by A or by B. Therefore,

$$P(\text{defective}) = P(A \text{ and defective}) + P(B \text{ and defective})$$
$$= 0.003 + (0.7)(0.03)$$
$$= 0.003 + 0.021 = 0.024$$

Substituting the numerical values just obtained, we have

$$P(A \mid \text{defective}) = \frac{0.003}{0.024} = \frac{1}{8}$$

Thus the probabilities for manufacture by A or B are $1/8$ and $7/8$, respectively. If we imagine that the "states of nature" in the decision problem refer to manufacture by A or by B, then we have here a reassessment of the probabilities for these states of nature, since they were given a priori as 0.3 and 0.7, respectively.

The above computation of revised probability estimates involved substitution (with the aid of two fundamental principles) in the formula for conditional probability. Now Bayes' rule is nothing but a formulation of this procedure. To use the customary symbolism for the above problem, it is usual to say that one has two states of nature or two "hypotheses"—H_1 and H_2—and that the experiment has resulted in the event E. Then the computations carried out above can be formulated as

$$P(H_1 \mid E) = \frac{P(H_1)\, P(E \mid H_1)}{P(H_1)\, P(E \mid H_1) + P(H_2)\, P(E \mid H_2)}$$

with a similar formula for $P(H_2 \mid E)$. The pair of formulas constitutes Bayes' rule when there are two states of nature. The expression of Bayes' rule where there are n, any finite number of states, consists of n formulas like the above, with

n terms in the denominator of each. This rule is considered the first instance in mathematical history of a specific method of statistical inference.

Let us now leave the macrocosm within which Bayes operated in order to examine further details of the microcosm of combinatorial analysis. A little earlier, we spoke of a theater party of 6 persons and showed that they could take their seats in 6! ways. During the first intermission at the theater, 4 persons were to volunteer for a photograph, and we saw that this gave rise to $6 \cdot 5 \cdot 4 \cdot 3 = 360$ possibilities. During the second intermission, which is lengthy, members of the group have time to talk about all sorts of things—impressions of the play, personal matters, etc. Someone mentions that an organization to which they all belong has asked for a committee of 4 volunteers to serve in a fundraising drive. "Since A_1, A_2, A_3, and A_4 will appear in a newspaper picture, they will become better known and would therefore be a good committee for the special purpose," A_5 comments. But the others disagree. Hence a natural question is: In how many different ways could a committee of 4 be selected from the 6 members of the theater party?

The number of potential committees is *not* 360, since the issue is *not* a question of permutation. The 4 committee members need not be named in one particular order. Members A_1, A_2, A_3, A_4 may have posed for the picture in the order named or in any one of the 4! different orders in which these 4 individuals can be lined up. They would nevertheless constitute only a *single committee*. The same fact could be asserted about $\{A_3, A_4, A_5, A_6\}$, or about $\{A_1, A_3, A_4, A_5\}$, or any subset of 4 members. Each such subset would constitute one committee but would provide 4! or 24 permutations. Therefore there are 24 times as many permutations of 4 members as there are committees, and the number of different committees of four is $360 \div 24 = 15$. In general, if a set contains 6 elements of any nature, there are 15 different *unordered* subsets containing 4 elements.

The symbol $\binom{6}{4}$ is often used to represent the number of unordered subsets of 4 elements that can be selected from a set of 6 elements. Such unordered subsets were formerly called *combinations* to distinguish them from permutations, which are *ordered* subsets. The name "combination" is the origin of the term *combinatorial analysis (algebra)*.

If the committee or subset selected is $\{A_1, A_2, A_3, A_4\}$, there is a subset containing the *two* members omitted, namely, $\{A_5, A_6\}$. Again, if $\{A_1, A_3, A_5, A_6\}$ is the subset picked, then the subset $\{A_2, A_4\}$ contains the *two* members not selected. Therefore each selection of a committee or subset of 4 members is inevitably accompanied by the simultaneous designation of a residual subset of 2 members. One could reverse the procedure and thus observe that selecting a committee of 2 members involves the simultaneous choice of a subset of 4. Therefore

$$\binom{6}{4} = \binom{6}{2} = 15$$

One can verify this last result by computing $\binom{6}{2}$ directly.

Instead of saying that a selection of a subset of 4 elements from a set of 6 leaves a residual subset of 2 elements, one can say that the act of choice effects a *partition* of the entire set into subsets containing 4 and 2 elements, respectively. The number of partitions of this type is symbolized by

$$\binom{6}{4,\,2}$$

and therefore

$$\binom{6}{4,\,2} = \binom{6}{4} = \binom{6}{2} = 15$$

To obtain some practice in evaluating and interpreting "combinations," consider

$$\binom{9}{6} = \binom{9}{3} = \binom{9}{6,\,3}$$

These symbols represent the number of subsets of size 6 in a set of size 9, the number of subsets of size 3, and the number of partitions into subsets containing 6 and 3, respectively. These numbers, moreover, are equal to one another. Let us evaluate $\binom{9}{3}$ by imitating the procedure followed in the earlier illustration. Then we must first treat the problem as if it were a question of finding permutations of 3 elements chosen from the entire set of 9 elements. There would be

$9 \times 8 \times 7$ such permutations. But a subset like $\{A_1, A_2, A_3\}$ or any other subset of 3 elements would give rise to 3! permutations. Therefore the number of permutations is 6 times as large as the number of combinations and

$$\binom{9}{3} = \frac{9 \cdot 8 \cdot 7}{3!} = \frac{9 \cdot 8 \cdot 7}{1 \cdot 2 \cdot 3} = 84$$

Because any selection of a subset of size 3 leaves a residual subset of size 6, and vice versa,

$$\binom{9}{6} = \binom{9}{3} = 84$$

The concepts of partition and combination are useful in those areas of modern quantum mechanics which require that the elementary particles of a mechanical system be assigned at random to small "cells" or regions of an (abstract) space. In issues involving electrons, protons, neutrons, and all particles with "fractional spin," the *Fermi-Dirac statistical mechanics*, named after Enrico Fermi (1901–1955) and Professor Paul Dirac of Cambridge University, is a suitable model. In that subject the particles are considered indistinguishable, and only one may be assigned to a cell. Particles thus restricted are called *fermions*, a term used in combinatorial algebra for indistinguishable elements of *any* sort when these are to be placed in various categories, with a maximum of one element in any category. Suppose that there are 6 fermions and 20 cells. Then it is a matter of choosing from the entire set of 20 cells the subset of 6 cells that is to be occupied by the fermions. Reasoning in the fashion explained above,

$$\binom{20}{6} = \frac{20 \cdot 19 \cdot 18 \cdot 17 \cdot 16 \cdot 15}{1 \cdot 2 \cdot 3 \cdot 4 \cdot 5 \cdot 6} = 38{,}760$$

possible ways of assigning the fermions.

In the quantum mechanics of those particles which have "whole number spin," namely, photons, pions, and K-mesons, the *Bose-Einstein statistical mechanics* applies. The *bosons*, so named after the Indian mathematical physicist S. N. Bose, are like fermions in being indistinguishable, but differ from the latter in that any number may occupy a cell. Again, in combinatorial problems, the term *boson* is applied to *any* indistinguishable elements which are to be distributed into categories with no limitations on the number per category. Thus, if there are 3 bosons and 6 cells, one possible interpretation is the problem of how to present 3 identical coins to 6 children, and another is the question of what stops may occur when 3 passengers are to be discharged from an elevator which can stop at 6 floors. Some of the possible distributions of 3 bosons into 6 cells are

$$
\begin{array}{c|c|c|c|c}
\begin{array}{c} b \\ bb \end{array} & & & \begin{array}{c} b \\ bb \end{array} & \begin{array}{c} b \\ b \end{array} \\
& b & & & \\
& & bbb & & bbb \\
\end{array}
$$

From these it is seen that 8 positions are involved, namely, those of the 3 bosons and the 5 bars separating the 6 cells. Then the problem becomes that of selecting from 8 positions the 3 positions in which the bosons should be placed. If it were a matter of permutation, there would be 8 choices of position for the first boson, 7 choices for the second, 6 for the third, so that there would be $8 \times 7 \times 6$ arrangements possible. But the principle of combinations rules that this figure must be divided by 3!. Therefore the number of different groups of 3 positions, or the number of ways the bosons can be distributed, is

$$
\frac{8 \cdot 7 \cdot 6}{1 \cdot 2 \cdot 3} = 56
$$

This problem might have been interpreted in terms of the dividing bars: From 8 possible positions, how many different ways can a combination of 5 be selected for the 5 dividing bars? The answer would be $\binom{8}{5} = 56$, which must, of course, be the same as the previous result. Moreover, if the problem were to place 5 bosons in 4 cells, there would still be 56 possible ways of accomplishing this, since there would again be 8 positions, this time for 5 bosons and 3 bars dividing the 4 cells, and one would have to choose either the 5 boson positions or the 3 for bars so that the number of placements would be figured either as $\binom{8}{5}$ or $\binom{8}{3}$.

Because boson analysis is not limited to quantum mechanics, one of the preceding results says that there are 56 ways of distributing 3 identical coins among 6 children (if a child may be given one or more coins) and 56 ways an elevator may discharge 3 passengers when stops on 6 floors are possible. Again, one can apply the same analysis to dice-rolling. If 3 dice are tossed, there are $6 \times 6 \times 6 = 216$ possible permutations. If the 3 dice were different in color or size, these 216 permutations would be distinguishable. Thus {red 1, black 2, white 6} would appear as a different occurrence from {red 2, black 1, white 6} or {red 6, black 1, white 2}. If the dice are alike, however, these occurrences are indistinguishable, and gamblers eventually discovered that there are only 56 distinguishable tosses. To reason this out combinatorially instead of by enumeration, one can think of 6 cells (or *categories* corresponding to the 6 ways any die can turn up), and then consider the 3 dice as bosons. This is permissible since they are indistinguishable, and several of them may turn up the same way, that is, be in the same category or "cell." Then, since there are 3 bosons and 6 cells, this is the same instance already considered and hence it can be figured, as previously, that there are 56 distinguishable occurrences.

In the early gambling era of probability theory, this figure was computed and applied to matters very different from Bose-Einstein statistical mechanics. In fact, around 1000 A.D., a bishop, Wibold of Cambray, applied the problem of three dice to clerical purposes. A description is given by the British mathematical statistician M. G. Kendall.[*]

Wibold enumerated 56 virtues—one corresponding to each of the ways in which three dice can be thrown, irrespective of order. Apparently a monk threw a die three times, or threw three dice, and hence chose a virtue which he was to practice during the next twenty-four hours. It does not sound like much of a game, but the important point is that the falls of dice were correctly counted. There was no attempt at assessing relative probabilities.

The use of dice for the purpose of choosing among a number of possibilities may well be much older than Wibold and continued for long after his time. There exist several medieval poems in English, setting out the interpretations to be placed on the throws of three dice. The best known is the "Chaunce of the Dyse" which is in rhyme royal; one verse for each of the 56 possible throws of three dice.

The earliest approach to the counting of the number of ways in which three dice can fall (permutations included) appears to occur in a Latin poem *De Vetula*. This remarkable work was re-

* M. G. Kendall, "Studies in the History of Probability and Statistics II," *Biometrika*, Vol. 43 (1956), pp. 1–14.

garded as Ovid's for some time, and is included among certain medieval editions of his poems. It is, however, suppositious, and several candidates have been proposed for authorship. The relevant passage may be briefly and freely construed as follows:

If all three numbers are alike, there are six possibilities; if two are alike and the other different, there are 30 cases, because the pair can be chosen in 6 ways and the other in 5; and if all three are different, there are 20 ways, because $30 \times 4 = 120$, but each possibility arises in 6 ways. There are 56 possibilities.

Perhaps the reader may find this explanation in *De Vetula* easier to understand than the boson method used earlier. At any rate, before we leave the question, its relevance to probability theory must be pointed out. The assumption in rolling fair dice is that each of the 216 *permutations* is equally likely to occur, or that each has the probability of occurrence $1/216$. This reasoning treats the permutations as if they were distinguishable. Thus a throw of $\{1, 3, 5\}$ can occur in 6 ways {red 1, black 3, white 5}, {red 1, white 5, black 3}, etc., so that the probability of such a throw is $6/216 = 1/36$ and a throw of $\{1, 1, 3\} = $ {red 1, black 1, white 3}, {red 1, black 3, white 1}, {red 3, black 1, white 1} can occur in 3 ways, so that the probability of such a throw is $3/216 = 1/72$. In the "classical" Maxwell-Boltzmann-Gibbs statistical mechanics (Chapter 15), devised for thermodynamic application, the assumptions made concerning equal likelihood are similar to those in dice-rolling.

But the Fermi-Dirac and Bose-Einstein types of statistical mechanics are models based on experimentation related to the various particles of modern quantum theory, and empirical results justify the assumption of equal likelihood *not* for the permutations, but for the various *distinguishable* groupings of fermions or bosons. Thus, since there are 56 distinguishable distributions of 3 bosons over 6 cells, any one of these would be assumed to have a probability of $1/56$. Referring to the case of 3 dice where there are also 56 distinguishable cases, the probability of $\{1, 3, 5\}$ was seen to be $1/36$. The toss $\{1, 3, 5\}$ can be interpreted as a die in category or "cell" 1, another in "cell" 3, another in "cell" 5. But the probability that the quantum bosons will occupy cells 1, 3, 5 is equal to $1/56$. Here we see a difference between the model for fair dice and the Bose-Einstein model for certain types of particles. Again, take the dice throw $\{1, 1, 1\}$, whose probability is $1/216$. For the quantum bosons, this would mean that all three are in the first cell, an occurrence with probability 1/56. To see the difference among the models for dice (Maxwell-Boltzmann-Gibbs), bosons, and fermions, consider the distribution of 3 fermions over 6 cells. Then the dice throw or boson placement {1, 1, 1} is impossible for fermions; that is, such placement has probability 0 for fermions, because one fermion at most may occupy a cell, and the presence of all three in the first cell cannot occur. Thus three different probabilities for the same event, namely, 1/216, 1/56, and 0, have been obtained in the three different models. If this fact appears puzzling, one must recall that the theorems of a mathematical model, whether it is geometry or statistical mechanics, are deduced from the axioms or assumptions. In the three kinds of statistical mechanics, in order to describe properly the elements involved, there is a difference in the selection of the postulate concerning equal likelihood. This is logically permissible, just as, in the case of Euclidean, Lobachevskian, and Riemannian geometries, there are different parallel postulates.

As a somewhat different application of combinatorial analysis, consider a "single sampling inspection" scheme where the manufacturer ships items in lots of 50 and tests quality by selecting 2 items at random from each lot. He applies a *decision function* prescribing that if both articles are defective, the lot is to be rejected, otherwise it is to be accepted. In the technical language of quality control, the *acceptance number* is 1, which means that if the number of defectives does not exceed 1, the lot is to be accepted. One might ask: What is the probability that a lot 30 per cent defective, that is, containing 15 defective items, will be accepted?

First, one can readily figure the probability that the lot will be rejected. By combinatorial algebra, there are $(50 \cdot 49)/1 \cdot 2) \Rightarrow 1225$ different possible ways a sample of size 2 can be selected, and among these there will be $(15 \cdot 14)/(1 \cdot 2) = 105$ samples in which both items are defective. Hence, the probability of rejection is $105/1225 = 3/35$, and therefore the probability of acceptance is 32/35, that is, the chances are better than 9 in 10 that the lot will be accepted.

In the study of the different decision functions associated with various sampling schemes, an *operating characteristic* function may be helpful. This function indicates how the probability of acceptance depends on the *quality* of the lot, that is, the proportion of defective items. If p represents the proportion defective in the lot, then, as in the preceding example, the number defective is $50p$; the probability of rejection is

$$\frac{50p(50p - 1)}{50 \cdot 49}$$

and if y represents the probability of acceptance,

$$y = 1 - \frac{50p(50p - 1)}{50 \cdot 49}$$

or

$$y = 1 + \frac{p}{49} - \frac{50p^2}{49}$$

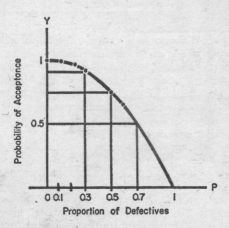

Figure 13.4   Operating characteristic (*OC*) curve for sampling inspection scheme

This equation is called the *operating characteristic* of the particular sampling scheme and its graph (Figure 13.4) is called the corresponding *OC* curve.

There may be 1 or 2 or 3 or . . . 50 defectives in a lot, and hence p may have the value 0.02 or 0.04 or 0.06 or . . . 1. Hence, although the *OC* curve appears to be continuous, strictly speaking, only those 50 points which correspond to the above values of p have meaning for sampling inspection of lots of size 50. In most industrial situations there are many more items in a lot—500 or 1000, say—and therefore 500 or 1000 pertinent points, very close to one another on the OC curve. For the sake of convenience, this curve is graphed as a continuum and not as a set of 50 or 500 or 1000 "discrete" points.

The OC curve of Figure 13.4 shows that if quality is standardized at $p = 0.3$, that is, if all lots with p less than 0.3 are considered "good" and all others "bad," then the chance of acceptance of any "good" lot is greater than 0.9. But "bad" lots, unless they are very bad, have a good chance of passing inspection. For example, the OC curve indicates that lots that are 50 per cent defective have a probability of 0.75, or 3 chances in 4, of being accepted, and even those that are 70 per cent defective have a 50-50 chance of acceptance.

Figure 13.5 shows the *ideal* form for the OC curve of a

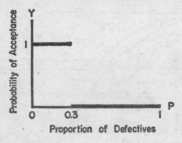

Figure 13.5   Ideal *OC* curve if quality is standardized at $p = 0.3$

sampling scheme if quantity is standardized at $p = 0.3$. This ideal OC curve would guarantee acceptance for "good" lots (probability 1) and assure rejection (probability of acceptance = 0) for "bad" lots. No decision function associated with a sampling plan will lead to an OC curve exactly like that of Figure 13.5, but the more closely the curve approximates the ideal, the better the decision rule. The OC curve of Figure 13.4 approximates the ideal up to $p = 0.3$, and therefore the sampling plan it represents is a satisfactory one, providing the quality of production is good. But this OC curve is very far from the ideal for values of p between

0.3 and 1. Figure 13.6a and 13.6b show the effect on an *OC* curve of some single sampling scheme if the acceptance number is decreased or the sample size is increased. Common sense, as well as an examination of Figure 13.6b, would lead to an increase in the size of the sample inspected as a remedy for the specific weakness which Figure 13.4 indicated in the original decision rule.

By taking some clues from the comparison of *OC* curves, we can furnish a more realistic solution to a statistical decision problem considered in the preceding chapter (pages 395–397). There we treated the question as a two-person game in which there is a theoretical conflict between the statistician and nature. But instead of imagining that nature is maneuvering against the statistician, one might merely assume that she has selected a definite strategy which is either

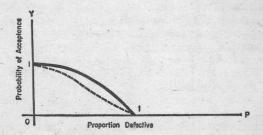

Figure 13.6(a) Effect on *OC* curve of decrease in acceptance number (--- represents *OC* curve corresponding to smaller acceptance number)

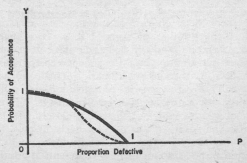

Figure 13.6(b)   Effect on *OC* curve of increase in sample size (--- represents *OC* curve corresponding to larger sample)

completely unknown to the statistician or which, on the other hand, he may be able to estimate by means of observation. If the latter situation obtains, then nature's strategy becomes known, and the problem is reduced to a one-person game, that is, a simple game of chance. An *OC* function makes the merit of a particular decision rule dependent on the relative frequency of defective items in the manufacturing process. Using this same idea, we shall now consider nature's pure strategy to be p, the proportion of defective items she "chooses" to produce.

Up to this point, we have followed the pattern used in formulating an *OC* function. Now we depart in order to include a factor which the *OC* function neglects, namely, the question of gain or loss, an important feature of game theory and the Wald decision process. For each possible strategy of nature, that is, for each value of p, a decision rule will assign a specific expected payoff or gain, and thus an *expected gain function* is defined. Figure 13.7 gives the four gain functions for the four decision rules of the previous chapter. The combinatorial analysis involved in deriving these gain functions will be explained subsequently. At this point, Figure 13.7 will be applied to the selection of optimum decision rules.

First, let us imagine a manufacturing process which is in its early stages, so that not much empirical data is available for the estimation of p. Since p (in the mathematical model) can be any real number between 0 and 1, inclusive, nature's available pure strategies are infinite in number and, in theory, form a *continuum*.

Thus we picture the statistician R as playing a two-person game of strategy against nature, C. Then in Figure 13.7 the graph for each decision rule is analogous to a matrix row, except that the number of payoffs in a "row" cannot, in the present case, be read off one after the other, since they constitute a continuum. For the same reason, one cannot draw all the matrix "columns" in Figure 13.7, but whenever we wish to indicate a particular pure strategy of nature, that is, a specific value of p, we shall indicate the "column" in question by drawing the corresponding line parallel to the Y-axis.

It will now be seen that the infinite-columned "matrix" has a saddle point, that is, a point representing R's maximin and C's minimax. Examining each graph of Figure 13.7 *in toto*, the minimum expected gains for Rules 1, 2, 3, and 4 are -6, -4, $-13/6$, -4, respectively. The maximum of the four minima, that is, R's maximin, is $-13/6$, corresponding to Rule 3. The broken line in Figure 13.7 represents the maximum "payoff" that nature would have to accord the statistician for each value of p. Her minimax is $-13/6$, corresponding to a strategy which can be read as $p = 0.83$ (approximately) in Figure 13.7. The exact value which can be computed from the equations to be formulated later (page 438) is $p = 5/6$. At any rate, since $-13/6$ is both R's maximin and C's minimax, the game has the solution (Rule 3,

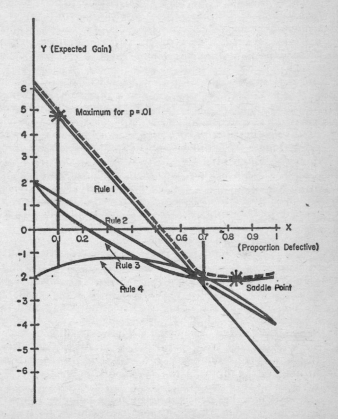

Figure 13.7   Expected gain functions for the four decision rules in the statistical decision game of Chapter 12

$p = 5/6$). Nature's "choice" of $p = 5/6$ is a pessimistic fiction, but in accordance with the Wald theory, Rule 3 is the optimum selection for the statistician.

If the manufacturing process is in a state of *statistical control* so that quality has been stabilized except for small fluctuations, and if enough previous sampling has been done to show that p is approximately 0.1, then nature's strategy is uniquely specified and R plays a one-person game by examining Figure 13.7 and observing that Rule 1 is the best, since it would provide the maximum expected gain (4.8) for the given value of p. Suppose, on the other hand, that the manufacturing process has just begun and it is felt that quality is exceedingly poor, the proportion of defectives being about 70 per cent. Then the diagram indicates that it would make little difference which decision rule is used.

In order to see just how the gain functions of Figure 13.7 have been computed, it will be necessary to return to combinatorial analysis once again, and it is inevitable that games of chance should provide helpful idealizations or models. In the present case, the simplest of all games of chance, coin-tossing, will serve. It is worth noting that problems concerned with the tossing of several coins were considered in the Orient 3000 years ago. In the *I-king*, one of the oldest Chinese mathematical classics, whose probable date is about 1150 B.C., there appear the "two principles": the male *yang*, and the female *ying*. From these were formed the *Sz'Siang* or "four figures," the 4 permutations possible with 2 forms choosing 2 at a time, repetition being allowed. This question is the equivalent of tossing 2 coins, and the four figures correspond to HH, TH, HT, TT. The Chinese also formed the *Pa-kua*, or 8 trigrams, the 8 permutations of the male and female forms taken 3 at a time, repetition being allowed. This is equivalent to tossing 3 coins, since the first coin can fall in 2 ways, the second in 2, the third in 2, and the total number of possibilities is $2 \times 2 \times 2 = 8$.

The *Pa-kua* were invested with various symbolic properties by the Chinese and have been used from the time of invention to the present day for purposes of divination. They are found on the compasses used by Chinese diviners and on amulets, charms, fans, vases, and many other objects from China and India. Figure 13.8 shows the *Pa-kua* or 8 trigrams, also the meaning and direction connected with each in the *I-king*. Three males stood for heaven, three females for earth, a female followed by two males for steam, a female between two males for fire, etc.

But our present purpose is merely to associate the ancient figures with the results of tossing modern coins. One might describe the outcomes of coin-tossing as

1 coin	H	T					
2 coins	HH	HT	TH	TT			
3 coins	HHH	HHT	HTH	THH	TTH	THT	HTT	TTT

If the exponential symbolism is used, $HH = H^2, HHT = H^2T$, etc. Then an alternative to the above is

1 coin	H	T					
2 coins	H^2	HT	TH	T^2			
3 coins	H^3	H^2T	TH^2	TH^2	T^2H	T^2H	HT^2	T^3

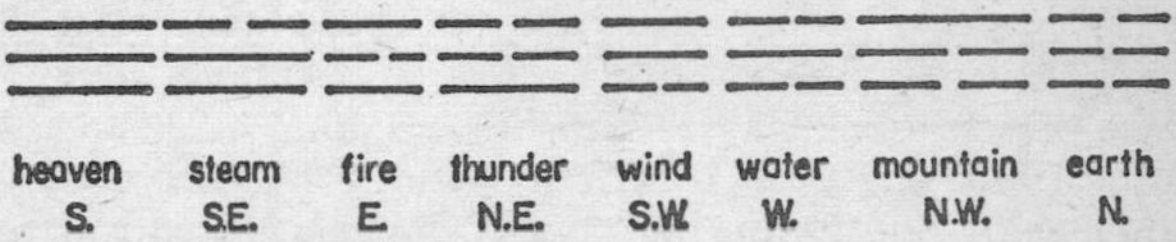

heaven	steam	fire	thunder	wind	water	mountain	earth
S.	S.E.	E.	N.E.	S.W.	W.	N.W.	N.

Figure 13.8   The Pa-kua or eight trigrams

As far as most games of chance are concerned, $HT = TH$, $HHT = HTH$, etc., for the person making a wager on the coins is not usually interested in the arrangement but merely in the actual number of heads or tails. Therefore a third listing of the same facts is

1 coin	H	T	
2 coins	H^2	$2HT$	T^2
3 coins	H^3	$3H^2T$	$3HT^2$	T^3

These are readily recognized as the terms of the algebraic expansions of $(H + T)^1$, $(H + T)^2$, and $(H + T)^3$, respectively. Therefore it may seem reasonable to conjecture that the situation for 4 coins will be symbolized by the terms of $(H + T)^4$, and for any number n of coins by $(H + T)^n$. This fact can actually be proved by the method of "mathematical induction." If the reader will apply the "boson technique" to coin-tossing, he will see that the number of distinguishable occurrences with 3 coins is a matter of distributing 3 bosons (the coins) into 2 categories or "cells" (H or T). This calls for 3 bosons and 1 dividing bar or 4 positions from which 3 (or 1) must be chosen. Therefore, 4 distinguishable occurrences are possible, namely, H^3, H^2T, HT^2, T^3. Similarly with n coins, there are $n + 1$ possibilities. Hence $(H + T)^n$ must have $n + 1$ terms.

In connection with this area of probability theory, Pascal made considerable use of the famous *arithmetic triangle*, pictured below.

$$
\begin{array}{ccccccccccc}
 & & & & & 1 & & & & & \\
 & & & & 1 & & 1 & & & & \\
 & & & 1 & & 2 & & 1 & & & \\
 & & 1 & & 3 & & 3 & & 1 & & \\
 & 1 & & 4 & & 6 & & 4 & & 1 & \\
1 & & 5 & & 10 & & 10 & & 5 & & 1 \\
\end{array}
$$
etc.

For this reason, he is often credited with originating the device, but it now appears that Tartaglia (Chapter 5) and subsequently Cardano were among the first Europeans to consider its properties. (It was known to the Chinese much earlier.) In the triangle, the numbers in any row after the first two are obtained from those in the preceding row by copying the terminal 1's and adding together the successive pairs of numbers from left to right to give the new row. Thus to get the fourth row, put a 1 at each end, and, looking at the third row, say $1 + 2 = 3$, $2 + 1 = 3$ to get the other numbers; for the fifth row, place a 1 at each end and, to obtain the other numbers put $1 + 3 = 4$, $3 + 3 = 6$, $3 + 1 = 4$. Moreover, the first row represents $(H + T)^0$, the second row gives the coefficients for $(H + T)^1$, the third for $(H + T)^2$, the fourth for $(H + T)^3$, etc. Using the fifth line, we can write $(H + T)^4 = H^4 + 4H^3T + 6H^2T^2 + 4HT^3 + T^4$ and get the probabilities for tossing 4 coins. The expansion shows 1 case of 4 heads, 4 cases of 3 heads and 1 tail, 6 cases of 2 heads and 2 tails, etc., out of a total of 16 outcomes considered equally likely in classic probability theory. Thus one obtains the (relative) *frequency function* for the number of heads when 4 fair coins are tossed (or one fair coin is tossed four times). The tabulation of this frequency function is

Number of Heads	0	1	2	3	4
(Long-Run) Relative Frequency or Probability	1/16	4/16	6/16	4/16	1/16

The probabilities in this table could have been obtained merely by substituting $H = 1/2$, $T = 1/2$ in the successive terms of the expansion of $(H + T)^4$, and in the same way the probabilities for the number of heads in tossing a fair coin n times can be obtained from $(H + T)^n$.

The binomial expansion* can furnish the appropriate frequency function even when the coin is not fair. Suppose, for example, that the coin is heavily loaded to favor tails and the probability of heads on a single toss is 0.2 (and hence the probability of tails 0.8); the substitution of $H = 0.2$, $T = 0.8$ in $H^2 + 2HT + T^2 = (0.2)^2 + 2 (0.2) (0.8) + (0.8)^2$ will give the *frequency function* for the number of heads in 2 tosses of the unfair coin, as

Number of Heads	0	1	2
(Long-Run) Relative Frequency or Probability	0.64	0.32	0.04

This frequency function can be applied to the inspection sampling of 2 items from a manufacturing process leading to 20 per cent defective and 80 per cent satisfactory merely by substituting "number of defectives" for "number of heads" in the preceding tabulation. In the more general case mentioned earlier, where the relative frequency of defectives is unknown because it cannot be specified exactly, the probability that an article will be defective can be represented by p, and the probability that it will be satisfactory by $1 - p$. Then $H^2 + 2HT + T^2 = p^2 + 2p(1 - p) + (1 - p)^2$, which provides the frequency function for Rule 1 (page 396). This frequency function and the payoff or gain associated with each number of defectives in accordance with the rule is

Number of Defectives	0	1	2
(Long-Run) Relative Frequency or Probability	$(1 - p)^2$	$2p(1 - p)$	p^2
Payoff or Gain (in dollars)	6	0	−6

For the graphs of Figure 13.7, the expected or long-run average gain was used, and in the present case the expected gain for Rule 1 is $6(1 - p)^2 + 0 \cdot 2p(1 - p) - 6p^2 = 6 - 12p$. Therefore the gain function for Rule 1 appears as the straight-line graph $E_1 (p) = 6 - 12p$ in Figure 13.7. The gain functions for the other three rules are found in similar fashion. For example, the payoffs for Rule 3, as listed in the matrix for the decision game (page 396), are 2, −3, −2, respectively. Therefore

$$E_3(p) = 2(1 - p)^2 - 3 \cdot 2p(1 - p) - 2p^2$$
$$= 2 - 10p + 6p^2$$

In summary, the four expected gain functions are

$$E_1(p) = 6 - 12p$$
$$E_2(p) = 2 - 6p$$
$$E_3(p) = 2 - 10p + 6p^2$$
$$E_4(p) = -2 + 4p - 6p^2$$

Chapter 14

Realm of Random Variables

"What is geometry?" This was a question put to Oswald Veblen (1880–1960), the renowned American geometer. "Geometry is what geometers do," he responded in all seriousness. If, by analogy, modern mathematical statistics is what a modern statistician does, then a discussion of Wald's very general statistical theory does not give an adequate picture of the facts. One must fill in the details of the broad outline by explaining the elements of the early twentieth-century statistics developed by W. S. Gosset (1876–1947), Jerzy Neyman, Egon Pearson and, above all, by that world leader in mathematical statistics, Sir Ronald Aylmer Fisher (1890–1962).

Although the roots of probability theory go back to primitive man, the origins of modern mathematical statistics are more recent. The subject was fostered by applied mathematicians like the Belgian L. A. J. Quételet (1796–1874), director of the royal observatory at Brussels, who in 1829 designed and analyzed the first Belgian census. Next came Sir Francis Galton (1822–1911), a cousin of Darwin and, like him, a student of heredity. Modern mathematical statistics took its first giant stride in the contributions of Karl Pearson (1857–1936), British mathematician and biometrician.

Statisticians from Karl Pearson to R. A. Fisher have considered mathematical statistics as a sort of adjunct to the traditional "scientific method." Francis Bacon broke that technique down into a series of steps among which were experimentation, the drawing of tentative conclusions from the observations obtained (formation of hypotheses), and the determination whether the conclusions agree with observed facts. In connection with the first step, the modern statistician has a theory of the proper *design of experiments*. The second and third steps involve the entire issue of *statistical inference*, a subject concerned with the major difficulty in all inductive reasoning, namely, the uncertainty attendant upon forming generalizations on the basis of a limited number of observations.

Of course, one may be able to collect *all* the information about the phenomenon in which one is interested—the ages of all workers in a certain factory, the number of children in every family in a particular small town, the grades of all freshman students in the final examination in mathematics at a certain college. The data might be tabulated, graphed, and summarized by giving the mean or median figure and the range. Such procedures are referred to as *descriptive statistics*. Any inductions like "The men in the factory range from twenty-one to fifty-two years of age" or "All freshman final grades in mathematics were lower than 95 per cent" are trivial in the sense that they are merely summaries.

Descriptive facts become important only if the aggregate being described is *not* the entire set associated with a phenomenon but a random *sample* (proper subset) of a larger *population*. There is inductive inference if one concludes that various attributes of the sample also apply to the population as a whole. Or one engages in *inductive behavior*, Professor Neyman's term, when one takes an action (makes a decision) which a Wald decision function associates with the particular sample observation. As we have said, one purpose of the theory of statistical inference is to *measure* the uncertainty attached to inductive generalization or inductive behavior. Thus, once again there is the matter of assigning appropriate probabilities.

We are now ready to tell what a modern practical statistician does. He may design random experiments and/or he may carry out such experiments, draw conclusions from the results, and measure the fallibility of these conclusions. In particular, he tests statistical hypotheses and estimates population "parameters" on the basis of sample observations.

There are certain basic theoretical concepts associated with all activities of the statistician. First and foremost is the notion of a *random variable*. The number of heads obtained in coin-tossing, the number of defectives in a sample, the number of dollars of payoff or gain in the tabulation on page 437, and the number of aces in repeated throws of a single die are all examples of what the statistician calls a *random variable*. It is evident that throughout our discussion of probability and game theory we made use of random variables without mentioning the fact. Whenever a unique number x is associated with each possible outcome of a random experiment, the number x is called a random variable. Let us illustrate different random variables which might be associated with the same simple random experiment, namely, the one where a coin is tossed twice. An associated sample space is $S = \{HH, HT, TH, TT\}$. If we are interested in the number of heads, the values of the relevant random variable x are

Outcome	HH	HT	TH	TT
Value of x	2	1	1	0

If we were interested in the number of tails, the respective values of the random variable would be 0, 1; 1, 2. Suppose that we are playing a game against nature and are to receive 5 cents if the outcome is HH, pay the bank 10 cents if the outcome is TT, and otherwise incur neither a gain nor a loss. In that case, the random variable x, whose values are tabulated below, is the sort of payoff function which appeared repeatedly in our earlier discussion of strategic games and decisions.

Outcome	HH	HT	TH	TT
Value of x	5	0	0	-10

The term "function" was used to describe this example of a random variable, but the other random variables illustrated were also functions. In each case, a sample space formed the *domain* of the function and the set of values of x constituted the *range*. In general, then, a random variable is a *function* whose *domain* is a sample space of some random experiment and whose *range* is a set of real numbers. In general, too, different random variables can be associated with the same experiment. In tossing a single die five times, for example, the number of aces is one random variable, the number of 6's is another random variable, the number of times a throw results in less than 5 another, the number of times the result of a throw is greater than 2 another; then a gambler's gain in betting connected with each of these random variables is also a random variable. Thus, if the outcome of five tosses of a die is the sequence 2—1—6—1—5, the respective values of the first four random variables described above would be 2, 1, 3, 2.

What the random variable accomplishes, in effect, is the substitution of a *number* for the verbal description (possibly lengthy) of an outcome of some random experiment. Then, instead of having to deal with a sample space or aggregate of possible outcomes, one can handle a *set of numbers*, namely the *range of the random variable*. In the previous chapters, there was much discussion of how to assign weights to the outcomes in a sample space—whether to use empirical relative frequencies, whether to assume equal likelihood, etc. Such weights will now be associated with the values of the random variable which replace the basic outcomes. The result will be a *frequency function* like those used in the previous chapter (pages 436–438).

For an immediate example of such a function, let us picture a game in which a marble is to be drawn from a bag containing 3 red, 4 white, 1 blue, and 2 black marbles. Let us suppose that the following payoffs are the values of the random variable of interest:

Outcome	Red	White	Blue	Black
Value of x	−2	0	1	2

Since the probabilities of drawing marbles of the various colors are 0.3, 0.4, 0.1, and 0.2, respectively, the *frequency function* for the random variable is

x	−2	0	1	2
$f(x)$	0.3	0.4	0.1	0.2

There is a frequency function associated with every random variable; this is the most important aspect of such a variable, since it is this function which provides the probabilities required by the statistician. The frequency function, also known as the *probability density function* (because one physical interpretation links it with density of mass), has the set of possible values of the random variable as its domain and the corresponding probabilities as its range.

Thus the number of heads in coin-tossing is a random variable with a *binomial* density function, so called because the probabilities are given by the terms of a binomial expansion (page 435). The number of defectives in sampling from a large population of items also has a binomial frequency function and, in general, the same is true of the number of "successes" in a sequence of *independent* trials where the probability of occurrence of some event is *constant* from trial to trial. Because Bernoulli made a profound study of such sequences, it is customary to call them *Bernoulli trials* and also to describe a binomial frequency function as Bernoullian. The frequency functions considered in the previous chapter were all of the Bernoulli type.

In the present chapter, two different random variables were associated with tossing a coin twice. In both cases, probabilities would be given by the terms of the binomial expansion, $(H + T)^2 = H^2 + 2HT + T^2$. If the coin is fair and the random variable represents the number of heads, the frequency function would be

x	0	1	2
$f(x)$	¼	½	¼

In the case where the values of the random variable are payoffs of -10, 0, 5, respectively, the frequency function would be

x	-10	0	5
$f(x)$	¼	½	¼

If the coin is unfair, and the probability of "heads" is 0.6, the values of $f(x)$ in both frequency functions above would be replaced by 0.16, 0.48, 0.36.

The binomial probability density function is one of the fundamental types considered in mathematical statistics. But in *theory*, if not in practice, there can be infinite variety among probability density functions. For example, the following tabulation would qualify.

x	-4	-3	-2	0	2
$f(x)$	0.43	0.18	0.14	0.21	0.04

We leave to the reader the task of devising a random experiment or a game with cards, marbles, etc., for which the preceding tabulation would be a suitable frequency function. We shall discuss more significant frequency functions later in the chapter but, in theory, a tabulation like the last one is always a possibility, providing it has two major properties which will be seen to exist in all the illustrative examples we have furnished. First, since the values of $f(x)$ are *probabilities*, they must be numbers between 0 and 1, inclusive. Second, since some outcome or other in the sample space is *certain* to occur, some one of the values of x within its range must be observed, and therefore the probabilities represented by $f(x)$ must have a total sum equal to 1. This is in accordance with probability theory, since events that are certain to occur correspond to S, the sample space selected as the universal set, and $P(S) = 1$.

But now we must see how a mathematical statistician *applies* frequency functions to problems of inductive inference. As we have said, one part of Bacon's scientific method consisted of formulating tentative hypotheses and observing how well their consequences would agree with subsequent observations. In mathematical statistics, however, one does not deal with general hypotheses such as "Cancer is caused by a virus" or "There is life on Mars." A *statistical hypothesis* is an assumption about the *frequency function* of a random variable. For example, there is the following: In a sample survey, the number of people who will favor candidate Jones is a random variable with a *binomial frequency function* in which the probability of success is 0.7. Or again: The number of cases in which Brand A toothpaste will prevent cavities is a binomial variable with $p = 0.5$.

During the years 1928–1933, Professor Jerzy Neyman, in collaboration with Karl Pearson's son, Professor Egon S. Pearson, developed a theory for testing statistical hypotheses. The two statisticians devised a method which was later seen to be a special case of Wald's decision process. To explain the elements of the Neyman-Pearson theory, we shall once more draw examples from games of chance. Therefore, let us now imagine that a gambler has observed a certain coin-tossing game and suspects that the coin being used is unfair and is, in fact, strongly biased in favor of "heads." The bank thinks otherwise, maintaining in effect the truth of the *statistical hypothesis:* The frequency function for the number of "heads" is *binomial,* with $p = \frac{1}{2}$. The gambler proposes to test this hypothesis by having the particular coin tossed 10 times in succession. If it turns up "heads" each time, the hypothesis is to be rejected. Now even if the hypothesis is true, that is, even if the coin is perfectly fair, it may happen *by chance* that 10 "heads" in a row will result. The probability of that event is $H^{10} = (\frac{1}{2})^{10} = 1/1024$. What this signifies is that if many such tests with fair coins were to be carried out, about once in every 1000 tests the freak phenomenon would be observed and the hypothesis would be unjustly rejected.

Another gambler, who has observed even more coin-tossing games, feels very sure that the bias exists. He says that the hypothesis should be rejected even if there are only 8 or 9 "heads" among the 10 tosses. What would be the risk of faulty judgment in that case? The coin is to be pronounced unfair if 8 or 9 or 10 "heads" occur. In case the coin is in actuality absolutely fair, the probability that one of those outcomes will result is

$$H^{10} + 10H^9T + 45H^8T^2 = \left(\frac{1}{2}\right)^{10} + 10\left(\frac{1}{2}\right)^{10} + 45\left(\frac{1}{2}\right)^{10} = \frac{56}{1024}$$
$$= 0.05 \text{ (approximately)}$$

One might then say that the probability of an erroneous judgment is 0.05.

Now a third gambler appears on the scene. He believes the coin is unfair because he has heard rumors to that effect. However, he is not certain whether the bias is in favor of "heads" or "tails." Therefore, he suggests rejection of the hypothesis if there are extremes in either direction—9 or 10 "heads," 9 or 10 "tails." In that case, the probability of a chance occurrence of the phenomenon is obtained by substitution in $H^{10} + 10H^9T + 10HT^9 + T^{10}$ and is readily computed to be about 0.02. Again, this figure measures the risk of erroneous rejection of the "fairness" hypothesis.

Even when more serious statistical hypotheses are subjected to test, it is because there is some uncertainty about the frequency function of a random variable, just as in the case of the tosses of a coin. Also, there will be the same sort of risk in pronouncing judgment on the hypothesis at the conclusion of an experiment designed to test it. The usual situation fits into the mold of decision theory. One must choose between two alternative hypotheses or else weigh a specific hypothesis against a whole set of possible alternatives.

To furnish an illustration analogous to that of coin-tossing, suppose that past experience with the use of a certain drug for a particular malady has shown that it is effective in about 50 per cent of all cases. A pharmaceutical firm offers a new drug for the same ailment with the claim that sufficient experimentation has been carried out to prove it will effect cures in 70 per cent of all cases. In one hospital it is decided to subject the new drug to test prior to considering it as a possible replacement for the older palliative. The doctors formulate a "null" hypothesis, as is usually the procedure in the Neyman-Pearson theory: The new drug is *no better* than the old; that is, the probability that it will cure is merely 0.5, and not 0.7 as claimed. There is good reason for framing statistical hypotheses in this negative form. In discussing the limitations of inductive reasoning, it is customary to point out that millions, even billions, of repetitions of a phenomenon cannot constitute an absolute proof. But to show that some claim is false, only a single counterexample is needed. Hence it is customary to devise a test that may lead to the rejection of some "null" hypothesis and thus lend credence to the acceptance of some alternative hypothesis, the latter being one for which researchers claim to have substantiating evidence.

To be specific on the Neyman-Pearson technique, suppose that in the example under consideration the alternative assumptions and the test procedure agreed upon in advance by the hospital staff are

Null hypothesis $p = 0.5$ for new drug (see above)
Alternative hypothesis $p = 0.7$ for new drug (as claimed)
Decision rule
  (a) *Experimental test:* Give new drug to 10 patients selected at random from those suffering from the particular ailment.
  (b) *Decision function:*

Number of Cures	0–9	10
Decision or Action	Accept null hypothesis	Reject null hypothesis and accept alternative (as a new working hypothesis)

When the new drug is given to the patients, the cure of all 10 may result even though the drug is no more effective than the old, for a "freak" once-in-a-thousand occurrence is always possible. But the doctors have designed the experiment in advance with the understanding that they are willing to risk such a chance, and hence should the entire group of patients be cured, they will reject the null hypothesis and accept its alternative, in this case the assertion that the probability of a cure with the new drug is 0.7.

The Neyman–Pearson theory, like the more general Wald theory, always weighs the risks involved in testing a statistical hypothesis. As indicated, one kind of error may be committed by rejecting a (null) hypothesis when in actuality it is true. Neyman and Pearson call this a Type I error. If on the other hand the (null) hypothesis is false (and some alternative true), a Type II error is committed if the (null) hypothesis is accepted. What is called for in mathematical statistics is to give a numerical measure of the risk of committing either kind of error. In the foregoing illustration, the probability of occurrence of a Type I error is the probability of the "freak" event, and this measures 0.001 (approximately). Usually the design of an experiment includes the maximum risk that will be tolerated for a Type I error, and this is called the *level of significance*. In the present case this level $= 0.001$.

To compute the chance of a Type II error in the example under consideration, one must find the probability that if the alternative hypothesis $(p = 0.7)$ is true and the null hypothesis $(p = 0.5)$ false, the latter will nevertheless be accepted. This type of error will occur if, although $p = 0.7$, fewer than 10 cures occur. If $p = 0.7$, the probability of 10 cures would be $(0.7)^{10} = 0.028$. Therefore the probability of fewer than 10 cures is $1 - 0.028 = 0.972$, which is the chance of a Type II error. About 97 chances in 100 seems like a large risk to take. Can it be diminished?

The desired decrease in risk can be accomplished by altering the decision function associated with the experiment. Thus, suppose that the level of significance is set at 0.05, which means that the probability of a Type I error must not exceed 0.05. It might then be specified at the outset that the null hypothesis will be rejected if the new drug should cure 8 or 9 or 10 of the group of 10 patients. To show that this meets the prescribed level of significance, one can substitute $H = 0.5$, $T = 0.5$ in $H^{10} + 10H^9T + 45H^8T^2$. (See the eleventh line of the "arithmetical triangle" (page 436) for the coefficients in this expansion.) The result is

$$(0.5)^{10} + 10(0.5)^9(0.5) + 45(0.5)^8(0.5)^2 = 0.05 \text{ (approximately)}$$

If one substitutes $H = 0.7$, $T = 0.3$ instead, with the result 0.382, this figure is the probability of 8 or 9 or 10 heads if the alternative hypothesis is true. But the Type II error would then occur should that hypothesis be rejected, that is, should the number of cures be fewer than 8. The probability of that occurrence is $1 - 0.382 = 0.618$. A risk of 62 in 100 is considerably less than the 97 in 100 of the original design. Hence by running a greater risk of a Type I error (0.05 rather than 0.001), the risk of a Type II error has been diminished.

The situation just illustrated is typical. If the size of the sample group subjected to a test is kept the same, the probability of a Type II error can only be decreased by increasing the risk of committing a Type I error, and the experimenter who is limited in the matter of sample size must weigh the risks in accordance with the situation. In the example considered, doctors eager to retain the old drug and dubious about the new one should design a test in which the chance of a Type I error is slight. If on the other hand they are not satisfied with the old drug and are eager to replace it by one that may possibly be better, they should diminish the probability of a Type II error and run a greater risk of the opposite sort of mistake.

If the size of the sample subjected to the test can be enlarged, then *both* risks can be diminished. For example, if the new drug can be administered to 100 patients suffering from the malady it purports to cure, and if the doctors decide in advance to reject the null hypothesis if 60 or more cures should be effected, the probabilities of Type I and Type II errors can both be diminished to about 0.02 each. (The computation involved in proving this would be arduous for the reader. It is usually carried out by a process of approximation which will be treated later in the present chapter.)

In the preceding example a choice was to be made between two specific statistical hypotheses, but in actual practice one may have a whole set of possible alternatives to the null hypothesis. Thus the hypothesis that $p = 0.5$ for the new drug might be compared with the possibility that p has *any* value greater than 0.5. Then the null hypothesis would still be the assumption that the number of cures is a binomial variable with $p = 0.5$, and the alternative would be that the number of cures is a binomial variable where p has some value greater than 0.5 (and, of course, equal to or less than 1).

The testing of a statistical hypothesis illustrates a very special type of statistical decision function, one where the range of actions contains *only two* values, namely, "accept" or "reject." The Neyman-Pearson technique is also restricted by the fact that implicitly the decision rules are such that the cost of experimentation is a certain *fixed* amount, whether this be measured in dollars or utiles. Wald indicated another reason the traditional testing of statistical hypotheses is less general than his own decision procedure, namely, that related experimentation must be carried out in a single stage. He implied that use of his notion of *sequential analysis* would make the Neyman-Pearson procedure less specialized.

Thus, in the illustration where a new drug was under examination, a single experiment was to be carried out, and the size of the sample to be tested was fixed at ten *prior* to the performance of the experiment. Setting the size of a sample in advance was standard statistical procedure until Wald proposed a modification. In his sequential technique, size is made dependent upon the course of the test, and criteria are determined by the observations as they occur. The sequential method can be described thus: A rule is given for making one of the following three decisions at any stage of an experiment: (a) to take action 1; (b) to take action 2; (c) to continue the experiment by making an additional observation. Wald proved that observations will not have to continue indefinitely, but that, on the contrary, the size of the sample required in order to arrive at a terminal decision is, as a rule, far smaller than where the standard technique of fixed sample size is employed.

At any rate, whatever sampling technique is followed, whatever the problem of statistical decision, one must specify the frequency function of some random variable. In the tests considered earlier, we knew that the associated random variable had a binomial frequency function, but our information was incomplete because we did not have the exact value of the basic *parameter* p. In the examples given, the tests weighed one value of p against another. In mathematical statistics, there are other decision procedures for handling the same problem. One of them will give a specific *estimate* of p on the basis of observed values of the random variable. For example, if a coin is tossed 100 times and it turns up "heads" 47 times, one might give 0.47 as an estimate of the true value of p, the probability of heads. Thus, if one uses the relative frequency as the estimate, the associated decision function assigns a specific estimate to each possible experimental outcome. Increasing or decreasing the number of observations would vary the decision rule. Or one might decide to estimate p by using some aspect of the observations other than the relative frequency of "heads." Choosing the *optimum* method of estimation would once again be a case of choice among decision rules, that is, a typical Wald game of statistical decision would be called for. Much more statistical theory, in particular much more discussion of the frequency functions of random variables, is needed before one can play this last sophisticated game.

Still another method of solving the same problem is to obtain an *interval* estimate of p, for example, (0.42, 0.62). In such a case experimental data might enable us to state that our "confidence" is 0.9 that the true value of p lies within the interval named. Or the observed values of the random variable might lead us to state, with "confidence" 0.8, that p must have a value in the interval (0.47, 0.57). Just what "confidence" means in this connection and just how the intervals are obtained call for the same sort of statistical theory as in the case of making specific numerical estimates of the parameter p. Again, we have instances of the decision process—decision functions which assign interval estimates to experimental outcomes, and general decision "games" where one selects the optimum rule for obtaining the interval estimate.

The testing of statistical hypotheses as well as "point" and interval estimation represented the most typical instances of statistical decision prior to Wald's theory. They remain important and, as we have stated, we cannot handle them without a more varied knowledge of frequency functions and their attributes.

Just how its frequency function characterizes a random variable will become apparent gradually. In the case of a specific binomial variable, for example, the frequency function provides the *probabilities* for various events. It is not necessary, therefore, to limit a discussion of coin-tossing to absolutely fair coins for which the outcomes are equally likely. The assumption that a particular binomial frequency function fits the situation where coins are unfair (or where the probability of a defective item is *not* 1/2, but 0.03, say) will enable us to assign probabilities to the different events in which we may be interested. As we study other types of random variable, we shall find that, in general, it is the frequency function which determines the probabilities. Postulating a particular frequency function to fit a special situation is a *modern replacement* for assumptions like *equal likelihood*.

In statistical problems, we may be interested not only in probabilities but also in other aspects of a random variable. Thus, although the frequency function may tell us that some values of a random variable are more likely to occur than others, we might like an overall picture. In games of chance and games of strategy, the *expectation* or long-run *mean* provides part of such a picture. For a random variable with a finite range, the formula for the mean μ is the same as that for the expectation (page 373), namely,

$$\mu = p_1 x_1 + p_2 x_2 + \cdots + p_n x_n$$

Let us apply this formula to find the mean or expected value of a binomial variable with $p = 1/2$ and $n = 3$. Substitution in $(H + T)^3$ leads to the frequency function

Number of Heads (x)	0	1	2	3
Probability	1/8	3/8	3/8	1/8

Then the mean is

$$\mu = p_1 x_1 + p_2 x_2 + p_3 x_3 + p_4 x_4$$

$$= \left(\frac{1}{8}\right)(0) + \left(\frac{3}{8}\right)(1) + \left(\frac{3}{8}\right)(2) + \left(\frac{1}{8}\right)(3)$$

$$= \frac{12}{8} = \frac{3}{2} = 1.5$$

The mean $\mu = 1.5$ gives an overall picture by telling us that although in many repetitions of a certain coin-tossing experiment, results will vary at random between 0 and 3, respectively, they can be characterized as 1.5 on the average. It will be observed that, in the example, $1.5 = (3)(1/2) =$

np. It can be proved that, in general, the mean or expectation for a binomial variable is given by the formula

$$\mu = np$$

Hence in a manufacturing process where the proportion of defective items is $p = 0.04$ and articles are shipped in lots of fifty ($n = 50$), the average or expected number of defectives per lot is

$$\mu = np = (50)(0.04) = 2$$

But one may desire something more than the range and the mean to give an overall picture of how the values of the random variable will be distributed about the mean in repeated experimentation. Using the preceding figures, the mean number of defectives per lot is 2. But the range of the random variable is 0, 1, 2, 3, 4, . . . , 50. Thus, although the average is 2, it is possible that the number of defectives in some lots might be high. Then the manufacturer would want to know whether the average 2 is the result of many occurrences of, say, 0, 1, 2, 3, 4, or whether it comes about because many lots with 20 defectives, say, are balanced by an enormous number with no defectives at all. Envisioning the latter situation might cause the manufacturer some anxiety, because he would have trouble with the many customers receiving the unsatisfactory lots.

To see how one might measure the dispersion or spread of values, imagine that the following values of a random variable (arranged in order of magnitude) were obtained in 10 repetitions of a random experiment: {4, 6, 8, 8, 8, 8, 9, 9, 10, 10}. This aggregate is a *sample* taken from the *population* of values which one would obtain by repeating the same experiment again and again indefinitely. The mean of the sample, $m = 8$, is readily computed. (It will be noted that m, the sample mean, is to be distinguished from μ, the population mean or expectation of the random variable.) Now we wish to study how the sample values are dispersed about the sample mean. One way of indicating this scatter would be to state that the sample values range from 4 to 10. Another would be to list the size of the deviation of each value from the sample mean, namely, {4, 2, 0, 0, 0, 0, 1, 1, 2, 2}, and then average these deviations. The average, 1.2, would be called the "mean deviation from the mean." In actuality, the first two of the above deviations were negative, but the mean deviation uses only the *magnitude* and not the direction of the deviations.

Another way of avoiding negative numbers is to *square* the deviations, and this is done in defining the *variance: The variance is the mean square deviation from the mean.* The variance of the preceding sample, symbolized by s^2, would therefore be equal to

$$s^2 = \left(\frac{1}{10}\right)(16 + 4 + 0 + 0 + 0 + 0 + 1 + 1 + 4 + 4) = 3$$

If the values of the random variable were lengths expressed in inches, then the deviations would be measured in inches, the squares of the deviations and hence the variance in square inches. Therefore, if one seeks a measure of variability with the same dimensionality as the values of the random variable, one can take the square root of the variance to obtain the *standard deviation*, sometimes called by the more descriptive name *root mean square* (deviation from the mean). In the present instance,

$$\text{standard deviation} = s = \sqrt{3} = 1.7 \text{ (approximately)}$$

The values of the random variable (or any linear function of them) can be compared directly with the standard deviation, which thus forms a sort of "standard" or unit of linear measurement for a specific random variable. For example, in the present case, one might state that the highest value in the sample is roughly $6s$, or that the mean deviation from the mean is about $0.7s$.

The equation which gave the value of s^2 could be expressed in the form

$$s^2 = \left(\frac{1}{10}\right)(4)^2 + \left(\frac{1}{10}\right)(2)^2 + \left(\frac{4}{10}\right)(0)^2$$
$$+ \left(\frac{2}{10}\right)(1)^2 + \left(\frac{2}{10}\right)(2)^2$$

Here the fractional coefficients are the relative frequencies of the sample values. Each relative frequency is multiplied by the square of a deviation from the sample mean. If a sample is very large, that is, if the random experiment is repeated many times, the relative frequencies approximate true probabilities. This fact suggests why the definition of the population variance, σ^2, is analogous in form to the preceding equation. In fact,

$$\sigma^2 = p_1d_1{}^2 + p_2d_2{}^2 + \cdots + p_nd_n{}^2$$

where $p_1p_2, \ldots, p_n$ are the probabilities which the frequency function assigns to the occurrence of $\{x_1\}$, $\{x_2\}$, ..., $\{x_n\}$, respectively, and $d_1, d_2, \ldots, d_n$ are the corresponding deviations from the population mean or expectation,

$$\mu = p_1x_1 + p_2x_2 + \cdots + p_nx_n$$

The reader will observe the similarity in form in the formulas for μ and σ^2. This occurs because both measures are *expectations* or long-run averages, that is,

$$\mu = E(x)$$
$$\sigma^2 = E(d^2) = E(x - \mu)^2$$

The reader can think of μ and σ^2 as if they were computed in the same way as m and s^2, except that the relative frequencies are obtained from an enormous number of experimental repetitions.

The definitions given for population mean and variance apply to the case where the range of the random variable contains only a *finite* number of values. When the number of possible values is infinite, questions of mathematical analysis are involved—the convergence of a series or the existence and evaluation of a definite integral. But in every case the mean is a measure of "location" or "central tendency," and the variance or the standard deviation is a measure of dispersion. Special properties of certain types of random variable will be related to these measures. Thus, let us mention in passing that in the case of a *binomial* variable, it can be proved that

$$\sigma^2 = np(1 - p)$$

where n is the number of trials and p is the probability of "success" at each trial.

The binomial random variable will now lead us to an even more important species. Returning once again to the tossing of a fair coin, let us consider the frequency function for the number of heads when such a coin is tossed 20 times. Figure 14.1, which represents this frequency function, is usually described as a *probability* or *frequency polygon*.

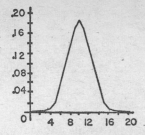

Figure 14.1 Probability or frequency polygon of $(H+T)^{20}$

Note the resemblance of the polygon to a smooth curve. If the number of trials with the coin is made greater, this resemblance to a smooth curve becomes more marked. In fact, as the number of tosses of the coin becomes greater and greater, the corresponding frequency polygon approaches a certain curve as a *limit*. This curve (Figure 14.2), bell-shaped in appearance, is called the *normal probability curve*, and its equation (in standard form) is

$$y = \frac{1}{\sqrt{2\pi}} e^{-x^2/2}$$

where e is the natural logarithmic base.

The approach of the binomial frequency polygon to the normal curve was discovered by Abraham de Moivre (1667–1754). French by birth, De Moivre emigrated to England after the revocation of the Edict of Nantes had made France less tolerant toward Protestants. He spent part of his life in England among the gamblers of a London coffeehouse and, like Cardano, wrote a gambler's manual, *The Doctrine of*

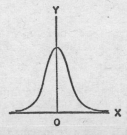

Figure 14.2 Normal probability curve

Chances. The limit theorem which he proved became the prototype for other limit theorems which are at the heart of probability theory and mathematical statistics today. Until recently, Laplace, and not De Moivre, was credited with being the first to relate the binomial and the normal frequency functions. Laplace did contribute notably to the theory of the normal probability curve, and later Gauss, the mathematical giant of the nineteenth century, made a thorough study of its properties. For this reason, one often finds this important frequency function called the law of Laplace, or the Gaussian curve.

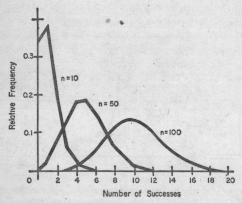

Figure 14.3   Frequency polygon of $(0.1 + 0.9)^n$
for increasing values of *n*

De Moivre's limit theorem indicates that the normal curve, or more practically, tabulations of the normal frequency function, can be used to provide *approximate* probabilities when a fair coin is tossed a very large number of times. In fact, the normal law is a good approximation for the probabilities of "success" in the case of *any* Bernoulli sequence with very numerous trials. This is suggested by Figure 14.3, which represents $(H + T)^n$ with $H = 0.1$, $T = 0.9$, for increasing values of *n*. The diagram shows how the frequency polygon for tossing an *unfair* coin approaches a normal density function as the number of trials increases. In many different situations which have nothing to do with coin-tossing, empirical frequency functions approximate a normal density. This is the case with vital statistics, anthropometry, psychological or educational tests, and the like. Figure 14.4 furnishes an example. The reason that numerical measurements from so many varied fields conform to the frequency function of one particular type of random variable and that the normal frequency function plays a major role in theoretical statistics will appear presently. At this point, it should be remarked that a minor algebraic modification of the

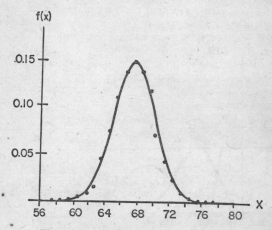

Figure 14.4 Fitting of normal curve to the empirical frequency function of heights of adult males in a large random sample. Mean = 67.5 in. Standard deviation = 2.6 in.

standard normal formula makes it more suitable for specific statistical problems. Thus, although the standard curve has the equation

$$y = \frac{1}{\sqrt{2\pi}} e^{-x^2/2}$$

the formula for the normal curve of Figure 14.4 is

$$y = \frac{1}{2.6\sqrt{2\pi}} e^{-\frac{1}{2}\left(\frac{x-67.5}{2.6}\right)^2}$$

This substitutes $(x - 67.5)/2.6$ for x in the original formula and introduces the additional factor $1/2.6$. The reader will observe that the mean height, 67.5 in., appears in the modified formula. The effect of introducing this mean value in the foregoing manner is to produce a normal curve that is symmetric about $x = 67.5$ instead of $x = 0$, as in the standard curve. The numerical quantity, 2.6 in., is the *standard deviation*, whereas $(2.6)^2$ is the *variance* of the population of heights.

As we have already stated, the variance and standard deviation measure whether the heights are concentrated close to the mean or widely spread out to right and left. A smaller standard deviation would have indicated a greater concentration of the heights represented in a diagram like Figure 14.4, and a larger standard deviation would have indicated a greater dispersion above and below the mean height. Thus statistical applications make use of a whole *family* of normal curves,

$$y = \frac{1}{\sigma\sqrt{2\pi}} e^{-\frac{1}{2}\left(\frac{x-\mu}{\sigma}\right)^2}$$

one curve for each pair (μ, σ^2).

As an example, let us consider the member of this family which would approximate the frequency polygon graphed in Figure 14.1. The polygon corresponds to the experiment of tossing a fair coin 20 times. Hence, $p = \frac{1}{2}$, $n = 20$, and by the formulas for the mean and variance of a binomial variable, $\mu = np = (20)(\frac{1}{2}) = 10$, and $\sigma^2 = np(1 - p) = (20)(\frac{1}{2})(\frac{1}{2}) = 5$. Substitution in the formula for the normal family yields the normal frequency function

$$f(x) = \frac{1}{\sqrt{10\pi}} e^{-\frac{(x-10)^2}{10}}$$

The reader can check, by substituting various values of x, that this curve is a good fit for the polygon of Figure 14.1. For example, if $x = 10$,

$$\frac{1}{\sqrt{10\pi}} e^0 = \frac{1}{\sqrt{10\pi}} = 0.18 \text{ (approximately)}$$

which is close to the reading for $f(10)$ in Figure 14.1. Again, substitution of either $x = 5$ or $x = 15$ yields

$$f(5) = f(15) = \frac{1}{\sqrt{10\pi}} e^{-2.5} = 0.18e^{-2.5}$$

Numerical tables give the approximation $e^{-2.5} = 0.082$. Therefore, $f(5) = f(15) = 0.015$ (approximately), which is just about the value of the ordinates corresponding to $x = 5$ and $x = 15$ in Figure 14.1.

The typical decision procedures that were discussed in the case of a binomial frequency function apply to normal densities as well. One can test a statistical hypothesis where the assumed frequency function is normal. If the value of μ is known, one may use "point" or interval estimation to approximate σ^2. Or one may use these types of estimation to approximate both μ and σ^2. And again more theory would be needed to explain our measure of "confidence" in interval estimates, or our selection of an optimum decision rule for point estimates.

Many special properties of a normal variable were studied by Laplace and Gauss. For example, they showed that the probability is approximately 2/3 that a normal variable will not differ from its mean by more than σ. In the population of heights previously considered, this would signify that about 2/3 of the men must have heights between $67.5 - 2.6 = 64.9$ in. and $67.5 + 2.6 = 70.1$ in. Furthermore, in a normal population about 95 per cent of all cases must lie in the range $(\mu - 2\sigma, \mu + 2\sigma)$ and practically all cases in the range $(\mu - 3\sigma, \mu + 3\sigma)$. All these properties of a normal variable are approximately true for a binomial variable when n is large, since the frequency function of the latter approximates a normal curve.

If we consider a binominal variable where $p = 0.1$ and $n = 100$, its frequency function will be described by one of the frequency polygons in Figure 14.3. For this case,

$$\mu = np = 10$$
$$\sigma^2 = np(1 - p) = 9$$
$$\sigma = 3$$

Then, in accordance with what was stated earlier, practically all experimental results should lie between $10 - 3\sigma$ and $10 + 3\sigma$, that is, between 1 and 19. The diagram confirms this fact by indicating negligible relative frequencies for $x > 19$. A variety of interpretations can be provided. In the first case, if we think of an experiment where 100 unfair coins with $H = 0.1$ are tossed, numerous repetitions of this experiment will practically never lead to more than 19 "heads" or fewer than 1. If we think of a manufacturing process where 10 per cent of all items produced have some minor defects and articles are packed in lots of 100, there will hardly ever be more than 19 defectives in a lot even though the quality of production is so poor. Again, if it is known from past experience that about 10 per cent of the people who reserve theater tickets over the telephone do not call for them at the box office, a policy where 100 such reservations are accepted for each performance entails, at worst, a possible loss on 19 sets of tickets for some (few) performances.

Since so much has been said about binomial and normal frequency functions, it is necessary to emphasize that there are many other types of probability density function. It would not be feasible to discuss the latter in great detail, but it will be worthwhile to make some general statements about random variables and then to give examples that are neither binominal nor normal.

In the first place, there is a distinction among random variables that was implied in our initial discussion of probability theory when we illustrated both finite and infinite sample spaces. Just as *cardinal numbers* like 1 or 2 or 3 or 4 or 5, etc., tell how many outcomes are contained in a finite sample space, there are *transfinite* cardinal numbers for infinite sets. The theory of such numbers was developed by a leading mathematician of the modern era, Georg Cantor. Instead of saying that the aggregate of natural numbers is *countably infinite* (see Chapter 24), one can use Cantor's symbolism and state that its cardinal number is $\aleph_0$ (read *aleph null*). A higher transfinite cardinal, which Cantor symbolized by C, is assigned to an infinite set which is a *continuum*, an aggregate like the totality of points in a continuous line segment of any length—an interval on the X-axis, say, or the entire X-axis.

Now the range of a random variable may also be a finite set, a countably infinite set, or a continuum.* For example, in those cases where a different value of the random variable is assigned to each outcome in a sample space, there will be as many values as outcomes, and hence the range of the

---

* In advanced statistics, the range can also be mixed in type, containing both a continuum and a set of isolated points; for example, the values might be 0, 1, 2, and any real number in the interval from 4 to 5 on the X-axis.

random variable will be a finite aggregate, a countably infinite set, or a continuum according as the sample space is one of these three types. In statistics a random variable is described as *discrete* (Chapter 2) if its range is finite or countably infinite, since in either case the values in the range can be arranged as a *sequence*. A *continuous* random variable is one whose range is a continuum. A *binominal* random variable is *discrete* because its range is finite. A *normal* variable is *continuous* because its range is the set of all real numbers, that is, the whole X-axis, which is a continuum.

We have not as yet illustrated a discrete random variable with a countably infinite range. Let us then consider the discrete random variable whose range is the set of natural numbers and whose frequency function is

$$f(x) = \frac{1}{2^x}$$

which can be tabulated

Value of x	1	2	3	4 . . . n . . .
$f(x)$	$\frac{1}{2}$	$\frac{1}{2^2}$	$\frac{1}{2^3}$	$\frac{1}{2^4} \cdots \frac{1}{2^n} \cdots$

In this instance, one possible interpretation is that the random experiment consists of tossing a fair coin until it turns up "heads" for the first time. Then x is the number of tosses required, and could therefore have one of the values 1, 2, 3, 4, 5, etc. In theory, one might have to toss the coin many times before obtaining "heads." That this does not happen often in practice is indicated by the probabilities which the frequency function assigns. Thus the probability that a dozen tosses will be needed ($x = 12$) is $1/2^{12} = 1/4096$. In other words, in very numerous repetitions of a random experiment, only once in about 4000 times would a dozen tosses be required before the appearance of "heads." If x is, say 1,000,000 or more, the probability is so very small that it is extremely unlikely (even if possible) that such a large number of tosses would be needed.

The illustration can be used to review probabilistic issues treated in Chapter 11. There we indicated that if an event is certain to occur, its probability must be equal to 1 whether the sample space is finite or infinite. Let us use the preceding function to compute the probability that "heads" will appear on some toss, whether it is the first or the second or the third or the billionth, etc., and see whether the answer is equal to 1, as it should be. Originally, an event was defined as a subset (proper or improper) of the sample space. But such a subset of the *domain* of the random variable corresponds to a subset of the *range*, and the frequency function assigns probabilities to the latter. Hence the event "heads in some toss" can be described by the *improper* subset of the range $E = \{1, 2, 3, 4, \ldots \text{ forever}\}$; that is, the event E corresponds to the entire range, and $P(E)$ is the sum of the respective weights assigned to the values 1, 2, 3, 4, etc., in accordance with another fundamental law of probability theory. Then

$$P(E) = f(1) + f(2) + f(3) + \cdots + f(n) + \cdots$$

and

$$P(E) = \frac{1}{2} + \frac{1}{2^2} + \frac{1}{2^3} + \cdots + \frac{1}{2^n} + \cdots$$

The infinite series in the right member is *convergent*. It is, in fact, a *geometric* series, and the reader will have no difficulty in showing that its sum is equal to 1, which is consistent with probabilistic law.

What we observe is that, in general, for any random variable with a countable infinity of values, it is necessary that the probabilities assigned by the frequency function form a *convergent* infinite series whose sum is 1. We can see why the classic assumption of equal likelihood cannot apply to a countably infinite sample space, for if one assigns the same probability p, however small, to each outcome or to the corresponding value of the random variable, then the infinite series, $p + p + p + p + \ldots$, would diverge, because the sum of the first n terms would be np, which could be made to exceed all bounds by making n sufficiently large.

It was Bernoulli who studied the most important type of random variable with a *finite* discrete range, namely, the binomial. De Moivre and Laplace provided the properties of the frequency function par excellence for continuous random variables, namely, the normal. And now the French mathematician and mathematical physicist Siméon Denis Poisson (1781–1840) must be credited with an analogous contribution for random variables whose range is countably infinite. The three fundamental types of random variable are related, moreover, since both the normal and the Poisson frequency functions are special limiting cases of the frequency function for a binomial variable. A Poisson probability density is a good approximation to the binominal when p, the probability of "success," is small and n, the number of trials, is large, but the product np is moderate in size. The formula for a Poisson frequency function is

$$f(x) = \frac{e^{-\mu}\mu^x}{x!}$$

where x, the random variable, has the countably infinite range $\{0, 1, 2, 3, 4, \ldots$ forever$\}$, e is the base of natural logarithms, and $\mu = np$, n and p being the number of trials and the probability of "success" for the related binominal variable. Figure 14.5 indicates how good an approximation a Poisson density can furnish even when p is not so very small or n so very large.

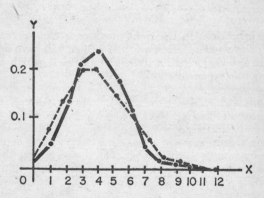

**Figure 14.5   Binomial (——) and
Poisson (- - -) frequency polygons
for $n = 12$, $p = 1/3$, and $\mu = 4$**

To see how the Poisson approximation can make the computation of probabilities less arduous, suppose that for a binomial variable, $p = 0.02$ and $n = 200$. Then $np = 4$, which seems "moderate" in size. These figures might be interpreted as giving $p = 0.02$, the proportion of defective items in a manufacturing process under control where articles are packed in lots of 200 (with a mean or expectation of $np = 4$ defective items). Then, if one wished to know the probabilities that a lot would contain 0 or 1 or 2 or 3 or 4, etc., defective items, one would evaluate successive terms of the binomial expansion

$$[(1 - p) + p]^n = [(0.98) + (0.02)]^{200}$$

a lengthy and tedious computational procedure. Instead, let us use the Poisson formula to *approximate* the probability that the number of defectives will be less than 4. We must find the probabilities for the outcomes 0, 1, 2, 3, and add them. We seek

$$\frac{e^{-4}4^0}{0!} + \frac{e^{-4}4^1}{1!} + \frac{e^{-4}4^2}{2!} + \frac{e^{-4}4^3}{3!} = e^{-4}\left(1 + 4 + 8 + \frac{32}{3}\right)$$

where $0! = 1$ in accordance with a mathematical convention. From numerical tables, one can obtain $e^{-4} = 0.0183$. Hence the required probability is $(0.0183)(71/3) = 0.433$. The more arduous computation using the binomial expansion gives the result 0.437, showing once more the closeness of the Poisson approximation.

But the Poisson frequency function is *not* limited to the purpose of approximating binomial densities. It exists in its own right and, like the normal density, seems to be applicable to numerous and varied situations in the real world. As an example, we shall indicate how well a Poisson density will fit the empirical frequency function for the occurrence of vacancies in the United States Supreme Court during the years 1837–1932.

Number of Vacancies per Year (x)	0	1	2	3
Relative Frequency (empirical probability)	59/96 (0.61)	27/96 (0.28)	9/96 (0.09)	1/96 (0.01)

The mean number of vacancies per year would be

$$\left(\frac{59}{96}\right)(0) + \left(\frac{27}{96}\right)(1) + \left(\frac{9}{96}\right)(2) + \left(\frac{1}{96}\right)(3) = \left(\frac{48}{96}\right) = 0.5$$

The corresponding Poisson frequency function is

$$f(x) = \frac{e^{-0.5}(0.5)^x}{x!}$$

To show that it fits the preceding tabulation *approximately*, one can substitute $x = 0$ and obtain $f(0) = e^{-0.5} = 0.61$ (from numerical tables), which agrees with the frequency for $x = 0$ in the tabulation; if $x = 1$, $f(1) = e^{-0.5} (0.5)/1 = 0.30$, which approximates the tabulated value, 0.28; if $x = 2$, $f(2) = 0.61(0.5)^2/2! = 0.08$ (the tabulation has 0.09); $f(3) = 0.61 (0.5)^3/3! = 0.01$; $f(4) = 0.001$; and the probabilities for $x = 5$, $x = 6$, etc. are still smaller. It will be observed that the empirical tabulation has a zero relative frequency for $x > 3$ so that the probabilities of 0.001 or less *approximate* the tabular values. A *theoretical* Poisson variable can, of course, assume any one of the infinite set of values 0, 1, 2, 3, 4, . . . forever.

As a final point, let us show that the sum of the weights assigned by a Poisson frequency function is equal to 1. Once again this is necessary because it is *certain* that $x = 0$ or 1 or 2 or 3 or some other positive integer, and probabilistic law requires that such an event have probability 1. Under the Poisson formula the probability of $E = \{0, 1, 2, 3, 4, . . . ,$ forever$\}$ is

$$\frac{\mu^0 e^{-\mu}}{0!} + \frac{\mu^1 e^{-\mu}}{1!} + \frac{\mu^2 e^{-\mu}}{2!} + \frac{\mu^3 e^{-\mu}}{3!} + \cdots$$

$$= e^{-\mu}\left(1 + \mu + \frac{\mu^2}{2!} + \frac{\mu^3}{3!} + \cdots\right)$$

Now it is shown in the theory of infinite series that the expression within parentheses is equal to e^μ. Therefore the required probability is $e^{-\mu} e^\mu = e^0 = 1$, which is the desired result.

By this stage of our story it is becoming increasingly evident that the statistician assigns probabilities by postulating suitable frequency functions. Usually it is past experience or present observation which provides the justification for the assumption. Thus, alternative frequency functions might be tested by the Neyman-Pearson theory. But how can probabilities be assigned when empirical evidence is lacking? In the case of a *finite* sample space, one can always revert to classic theory and assign equal likelihood to outcomes. There is something analogous for a *continuous* random variable whose range is a finite interval. Suppose, for example, that a telephone answering service has failed to record the exact time for some incoming call and that the operator knows only that she received it at some time between noon and 2 P.M. What is the probability that the call came at 1:15 P.M., that is, between 1:15 and 1:16 P.M.? Complete ignorance compels us to assume that any one-minute interval is as likely as another, and since there are 120 one-minute intervals between noon and 2 P.M., the answer is 1/120. On the same basis, the probability that the call came between 12:30 and 1 P.M. would be 30/120 = 1/4. If the timing of a call could be carried out with a high-precision instrument, the exact moment might be measured as 18.347 minutes after noon, for example. Therefore an idealized model for the situation would treat x, the number of minutes after noon, as a *continuous* random variable whose range is the continuous interval (0, 120) and whose frequency function is $f(x) = 1/120$ (Figure 14.6). Such a frequency function is

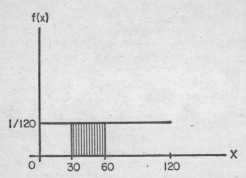

Figure 14.6   Uniform or rectangular frequency function
$f(x) = 1/120$ in the interval (0, 120)

described as *uniform* or *rectangular*. In Figure 14.6, the shaded rectangular area represents the probability that the call came in between 12:30 and 1 P.M. The probability that it came in during the 1/4-minute interval after 1 P.M. would be represented by a rectangle with base 1/4, height 1/120, and area 1/480. In general, in the case of *continuous* random variables, *events* are pictured as *intervals* or *sets of intervals* within the range of the variable, and the probabilities can be pictured by areas, as in the present case. It will be observed that we did *not* ask for the probability that the call would arrive at *exactly* 1 P.M., but phrased the question in terms of a short interval thereafter. To make the time closer to 1 P.M., one might consider the length of the interval (base of the rectangle) as, say, only 0.01 minute. Then the corresponding probability would be only 1/12,000. The rectangle which measures probability would have very little area. If one insisted, even though the concept of an event forbids it, on the probability of a call at exactly 1 P.M., there would be an interval of zero length, and the area of the probability rectangle would be $(1/120)(0) = 0$. The probability of occurrence on the dot, whether it is 1 P.M. or 12:15 P.M. or any other instant, is *zero*. Although it is unlikely or physically inconceivable that calls would arrive at *exactly* these moments (if we could measure the time very precisely), it is *not* abstractly impossible. This illustrates a statement we made in our first treatment of probabilistic concepts, that in the case of infinite continuous sample spaces an impossible event must have probability zero, whereas the converse is false. Zero probability does *not* imply absolute impossibility. As the complementary fact, a probability measuring 1 does not imply certainty.

In general, the formula for a uniform or rectangular frequency function is

$$f(x) = \frac{1}{c}$$

where the range of the random variable x is the interval $(0, c)$. This density function assumes "equal likelihood," as it were, except that the random variable associated with outcomes has a continuous range because its values are distances, intervals of time, or the like. Thus the foregoing formula would provide the probabilities in roulette if the wheel is fair and has circumference c. In that case the random variable x would be the distance at which the wheel would stop.

It has been stressed repeatedly that the properties of a random variable are related to its frequency function. But it is necessary to mention that the *cumulative distribution function* (or briefly, the *distribution function*), is more suitable to the purposes of advanced probability and statistics than the frequency function. The term referred originally to the distribution of a total probability of 1 over the range of the random variable. Associated with the following empirical frequency function (first tabulation) for the intelligence quotients of a group of 200 students, there is (second tabulation) a *cumulative* relative frequency function (the empirical distribution function).

Intelligence Quotient	88–92	93–97	98–102	103–107	108–112	113–117	118–122	123–127	128–132	133–137	138–142	143–147
Relative Frequency	0.01	0.03	0.065	0.13	0.16	0.20	0.16	0.12	0.07	0.025	0.02	0.01
Intelligence Quotient	87.5	92.5	97.5	102.5	107.5	112.5	117.5	122.5	127.5	132.5	137.5	142.5	147.5
Cumulative Relative Frequency	0	0.01	0.04	0.105	0.235	0.395	0.595	0.755	0.875	0.945	0.97	0.99	1.00

The cumulative table refers to the proportion of students whose I.Q. does not exceed a specific I.Q. Thus 23.5 per cent of the students have I.Q.'s not exceeding 107.5, and 97 per cent have I.Q.'s not exceeding 137.5. In accordance with mathematical usage, an I.Q. of 92 signifies a *measurement* made to the nearest integer, which means that it is not exactly 92 but nearer to 92 than to 91 or 93, that is, a measurement equal to or greater than 91.5 but less than 92.5. This explains the entries for intelligence quotients in the cumulative table. Thus 0.04 or 4 per cent of the I.Q.'s are 97 or less, and since an I.Q. of 97 actually signifies a measurement equal to or greater than 96.5 but less than 97.5, the cumulative table more properly indicates that 97.5 is an upper bound for 4 per cent of the I.Q.'s. Figure 14.7 is the cumulative frequency polygon corresponding to the foregoing tabulation. Figure 14.8 is the cumulative normal distribution graph. Figure 14.9 is the distribution graph corresponding to a uniform frequency function, and the step graph of Figure 14.10 represents the cumulative distribution for the tossing of a single die. A step function is typical for discrete

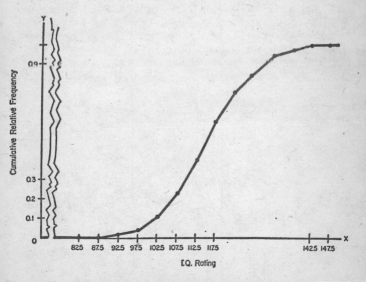

Figure 14.7   Cumulative frequency polygon for an empirical distribution of I.Q.'s

random variables. Apropos of the present subject, the reader must be warned that the term "distribution" is used rather loosely in mathematical writing and may refer either to the frequency function or the cumulative distribution function.

To give one instance of how a distribution function may solve a problem more easily than a frequency function, we return to the case of a continuous random variable where an event, as we have stated, is represented by an interval or a set of intervals on the X-axis, and the probability that this event will occur is represented by a geometric area like that in Figure 14.11, an area under the curve representing the frequency function of the random variable. In general, there would therefore be a question concerning the existence and evaluation of a definite integral. The case previously considered, where the frequency function was uniform (Figure 14.6), was specially simple because the required area was rectangular. But suppose that one is given a *distribution function* of some continuous random variable, for example, $F(x) = \sin x$ where the range of x is $(0, \pi/2)$, and one seeks the probability of the event represented by the interval $(\pi/6, \pi/2)$. Since $F(\pi/2)$ is the probability that $x \leq \pi/2$ and $F(\pi/6)$ is the probability that $x \leq \pi/6$, therefore $F(\pi/2) - F(\pi/6) = \sin \pi/2 - \sin \pi/6 = 1 - 1/2 = 1/2$ is the probability that x lies in the interval $(\pi/6, \pi/2)$. Thus it was possible to obtain the probability of the event in question without requiring the reader to have a knowledge of

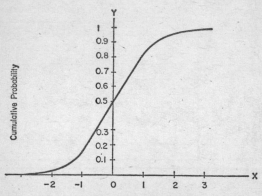

**Figure 14.8   Cumulative distribution function
for a normal variable**

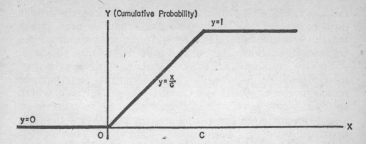

Figure 14.9 Cumulative distribution function corresponding to a uniform frequency function

integral calculus. Probabilities can be derived from the distribution function by simple substitution.

Although the statistician is free to assume any sort of frequency or distribution function to fit a particular situation, it must be stated that the normal frequency and distribution functions (and other functions derived from them) are the most important types for the *theoretical* purposes of mathematical statistics. The reason this is so will now be explained. That so many empirical phenomena fit into the normal mold, and that so many different species of random variable have distributions that are normal in the limit, is the result

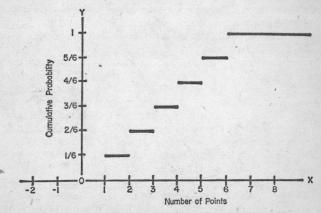

Figure 14.10 Cumulative distribution function for the tossing of a fair die

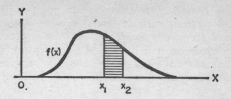

Figure 14.11   Area representing probability of occurrence of an event

of a modern *limit theorem*, a major generalization of De Moivre's limit theorem. The conceptual background for the more inclusive proposition is to be found in the point of view of Laplace and Gauss, who believed that the normal law must of necessity be almost universal for data describing natural phenomena. Their prescription for any departures from the standard frequency function was to gather more and more data, because adequate observation was supposed inevitably to banish irregularities and smooth figures into the normal pattern.

To Laplace and Gauss, normal curves were *curves of error* like those obtained from tabulations of fine measurements of some physical entity, where any random deviation from the true measurement is an error. In other kinds of statistical data, the "errors" were taken to be the differences between the values of the random variable and its mean or average value. Thus the amounts by which the heights represented in Figure 14.4 differ from 5 ft. 7.5 in. can be interpreted as nature's "errors." It is assumed that gross or coarse errors as well as systematic errors have been removed from the results of measurement and that only random effects remain. Such random errors can be considered as the total effect of numerous smaller components—slight defects in different parts of the apparatus, small variations in temperature and pressure, imperfections in the vision of the observer, random factors affecting the manual dexterity of the observer and his general alertness, unconscious bias of the observer, and so on. Each of these components is itself a random variable which does not usually influence the other components, and the total "error" is the sum of numerous random variables, usually statistically independent of one another.

The *central limit theorem* of probability theory asserts that a random variable which is such a sum must have a *normal* frequency function. A rigorous statement of this basic theorem or a discussion of its proof would take the reader into advanced issues. Suffice it to say that in very broad terms the theorem in its most general form signifies that any random variable whose numerical value is influenced by a large number of independent causes, each contributing a small "impulse" to the total effect, must be approximately normal. This is the logical justification for the frequent occurrence of normal variables in statistical applications to so many different fields.

The central limit theorem explains the use of the normal frequency function in what statisticians call *large sample theory*. If, for example, one is drawing a large sample at random from a very large set of people (the "population") and tabulating heights in order to obtain a frequency table like that graphed in Figure 14.4, the height of the first person whose name is drawn is a random variable. This means that if a sample of size 100 is drawn, and then another such sample is drawn again and again, the *first* height obtained will vary in random fashion from sample to sample and there will be a frequency function for the set of all possible first heights. The same is true of the *second* height, the *third* height, etc. Naming these random variables x_1, x_2, x_3, . . . , x_{100}, respectively, the central limit theorem demonstrates that y, the sum of these variables, will have a frequency function that is approximately normal. Thus the normal variable is

$$y = x_1 + \cdots + x_{100}$$

Dividing both sides by 100,

$$\frac{y}{100} = \frac{x_1 + c_2 + \cdots + x_{100}}{100}$$

yields the *sample* mean, and since it is one-hundredth of the variable that is normally distributed, its values from sample to sample will be proportional to those of the normal variable y. Hence, on intuitive grounds, the sample mean should have a normal frequency function.

As an example of the application of the properties of the normal distribution to large sample theory, suppose that measurements (idealized here for the sake of simplicity) taken over a long period show that the mean gross weight of individuals departing from a particular airport is 165 lb., and that the distribution of weights is approximately normal, with a standard deviation equal to 23.3 lb. Then very few (in fact less than 0.3 per cent) of the passengers would have had weights differing from the mean weight by more than three times the standard deviation, that is, 70 lb. Thus, almost all passengers would have had gross weights between 95 lb. and 235 lb. Now the central limit theorem implies that the mean weights for all flights carrying a full passenger load of, say, 80, would fluctuate normally about the "grand mean" of 165 lb. with a standard deviation of $23.3/\sqrt{80}$ and that practically all the mean weights would differ from this grand mean by less than $70/\sqrt{80} = 7.8$ lb. (For flights of size n, the standard deviation would be $23.3/\sqrt{n}$ and the maximum difference from the grand mean $70/\sqrt{n}$ lb.) Therefore it could be safely assumed that the mean weight of passengers from flight to flight in 80-passenger planes would rarely exceed 173 lb., and the total passenger weight would hardly ever be more than 13,840 lb., or about 7 tons.

Even if the gross weights recorded over a long period were not to follow a normal distribution, the central limit theorem implies that the means from flight to flight would nevertheless be distributed normally about the grand mean in all cases where n, the number of passengers, is sufficiently large. The standard deviation of the population of passenger weights is substituted in the formula $\sigma/\sqrt{n}$, and $3\sigma/\sqrt{n}$ is subtracted from and added to the grand mean in a way analogous to the foregoing in order to estimate the range in mean weight from flight to flight.

As a second application, let us use large sample theory to obtain a *confidence interval* for the mean of a population. Suppose that a random sample of 100 observations is drawn from a population with unknown mean μ and known standard deviation $\sigma = 3$. By virtue of the central limit theorem, the sample means of all the possible samples of size 100 will be distributed normally about the population mean with a standard deviation equal to $\sigma/\sqrt{n} = 3/\sqrt{100} = 0.3$. As stated earlier, about 95 per cent of the observed values of a normal variable will differ from the population mean by less than 2 standard deviations. Therefore, in the present case, 95 per cent of all sample means will lie in the interval ($\mu - 0.6$, $\mu + 0.6$). Suppose that the mean in the particular sample observed is 14.2. We might imagine that this mean value falls in the above interval, but to be conservative, we can picture the observed mean at one of the ends of the interval so that it deviates from the true mean by the maximum amount of any number in the interval. In that case, either

$$\mu - 0.6 = 14.2 \quad \text{and} \quad \mu = 14.8$$

or

$$\mu + 0.6 = 14.2 \quad \text{and} \quad \mu = 13.6$$

The two extremes lead us to say that (13.6, 14.8) is a 95 per cent *confidence interval* for μ, or that our confidence is 0.95 that the true value of μ will lie in this interval. The exact probabilistic meaning of the statement is: In repeated sampling from the specified population, the different sample means will lead to various confidence intervals computed in the preceding manner. About 95 per cent of the confidence intervals so obtained will contain the true value of μ, the population mean.

In sampling situations where sample size is small and in other statistical problems where the random variable is not normally distributed, nonnormal distributions come into use. Figure 14.12 shows the "Student"* t-distribution (t-frequency function) used for a sample of size 16. Its appearance is not too different from that of the normal curve. The other "Student" curves in Figure 14.12 are for smaller samples. The theory of the t-distribution makes it possible to use a small sample to obtain a confidence interval for the mean of a normal population when neither this mean nor the standard deviation of the population is known.

Random variables and their frequency functions have been related to various problems of statistical inference, and these in turn have been considered as special instances of Wald's general decision process. But the particular objectives and the limited size of the present work have made it necessary to restrict discussion to the elementary aspects of mathematical statistics and the inclusive theory of decision. Thus there are *multivariate* problems where more than one

* "Student" was the pseudonym of William Sealy Gosset, who discovered the relationship of the t-curves to *small* sample theory, a field he investigated as early as 1908. He was a statistical consultant to the Guiness brewery in Dublin. A ruling of that firm forbade its employees to publish the results of research, but the regulation was relaxed to permit Gosset to write under a pen name.

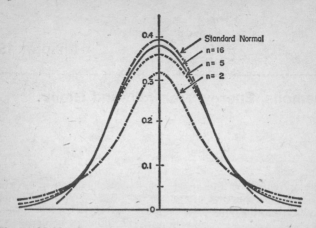

Figure 14.12   Student t-distributions (frequency functions) compared with standard normal density

random variable is associated with an experiment, as we shall illustrate in our next chapter. Then one would obtain probabilities from frequency functions like $f(x, y)$ or, say, $f(x_1, x_2, x_3, x_4)$, or distribution functions like $F(x, y)$ or $F(x_1, x_2, x_3, x_4)$. Although the underlying notions remain the same, *mutatis mutandis*, some new issues arise; for example, the question whether the random variables are statistically independent of one another. Then there is an area of inference involving functional relationships between random and nonrandom (controlled) variables. There is also the matter of designing the experiments associated with the subtler problems of statistical decisions. A new methodology being developed at the present time is called *distribution-free* or *nonparametric inference*. Its purpose is to avoid the traditional pattern explained in this chapter, where inference always involves the assumption that the random variable has a specific type of frequency function—binomial, normal, Poisson, etc. In spite of all such unexplored territory, the author believes that the reader has been offered a maximum minimum of those fundamental concepts which are invariant in the more extended theories and which can therefore provide an avenue of approach to their comprehension.

Chapter 15

Demons, Energy, Maxwell, and Gibbs

Just as regular as the appearance of angle-trisectors on the mathematical horizon are the periodic attempts of someone in the world of letters to prove that Shakespeare was Bacon, Marlowe, Raleigh, Jonson, or even Queen Elizabeth I. To the sophisticated it does not matter whether the Bard who gave the world its greatest poetry and drama is a legendary figure or someone who can be labeled with a name, date, profession, geographical habitat, scholastic degree. But, we assure ourselves, it couldn't happen now. A creator of immortal work can no longer remain unknown to his contemporaries. Yet let any "inquiring reporter" quiz the man on the street or, for that matter, the man on the campus, on the identity of Josiah Willard Gibbs (1839–1903). It is a safe conjecture that few will recognize the name of the foremost native American mathematical physicist.

Gibbs's greatest discovery, *statistical mechanics*, links his research with the subject matter of the preceding chapters, where the fundamentals of probability and statistics were presented. Why and how did Gibbs's selection of one particular branch of mathematical physics come about, and why did that subject require the use of modern probabilistic concepts? To answer these questions, part of the present chapter must be concerned with some pre-Gibbsian concepts and also with the ideas of James Clerk Maxwell (1831–1879), the renowned Scottish mathematical physicist who terminated one classical line of thought in physics and founded the new era of statistical physics. He was a contemporary of Gibbs, and one of the few leading scientists of the day to understand the latter's ideas and to appreciate the genius they disclosed.

Maxwell is best known for the electromagnetic "field equations," the set of differential equations governing electrodynamics (Chapter 9) in the same way that Hamilton's canonical equations rule ordinary dynamics. But Maxwell was also interested in the kinetic theory of gases, and he found in that subject a possible source of conflict with traditional thermodynamic principles, namely, with ideas originally set forth by Sadi Carnot (1796–1832), the founder of modern thermodynamics.

Carnot had assumed that heat energy cannot "spontaneously," "naturally," of its own accord, flow from a colder to a hotter body. In modern refrigerators, heat energy does pass from the colder interior to the warmer kitchen, but this is *not* spontaneous, since there is an additional external supply of energy, namely electrical. If one disconnects this external factor, the refrigerator defrosts, with the natural passage of heat energy from the hotter room to the cooler icebox.

Maxwell lived long before the electric comforts that were direct or indirect consequences of his electromagnetic equations, but he was aware of many examples confirming Carnot's postulate. However, one *counterexample* that Maxwell offered has become famous. If his predecessors had their assumptions, he saw no reason why he could not himself postulate a situation where *intelligence* could contradict Carnot's principle. In Maxwell's illustration an ideal gas fills a vessel that is divided into two compartments, the temperature of the left compartment being higher than that of the right. According to the kinetic theory, temperature is an average effect, so that the very, very numerous individual gas molecules in both compartments vary in speed and direction of their motions, the average effect of those in the left compartment being higher than the average in the right. Now Maxwell imagined a highly intelligent, skillful, "sorting demon" to be placed at a tiny trapdoor between the compartments. At the approach of a very slow-moving particle in the left chamber, the demon opened the door to permit passage of the particle to the right chamber; whenever an exceptionally speedy molecule in the right chamber came near, the little "devil" placed the shutter the other way so that the rapid molecule would pass into the left compartment. Moreover, this was done effortlessly, that is, without the expenditure of energy. By such repeated sorting and sifting, a great many slow particles were concentrated in the right, and a large proportion of the rapid molecules in the left compartment. Heat energy of a gas is measured by the mean kinetic energy ($\frac{1}{2}mv^2$) of the gas molecules. If two molecules with speeds of 800 and 200 meters per second are exchanged, an exchange in kinetic energy proportional to $640,000 - 40,000 = 600,000$ is effected, and thus there is an increase in the mean kinetic energy of the left chamber, with a corresponding decrease on the right. Such exchanges would increase and decrease the left and right average effects, respectively, so that Maxwell's sorting demon could, by means of numerous exchanges, transfer considerable heat energy from the cooler right to the warmer left. Maxwell stated that it is *highly probable* that heat energy will pass from a hotter to a colder body, but that the reverse is *not* impossible, merely unlikely, and that if such a phenomenon has never been observed, it may be because the probability of its occurrence is so small. Perhaps it can occur only once in a million years.

The above statements suggest that a thermodynamic law may be a probabilistic rather than an absolute principle. In fact, in 1859 Maxwell asserted in precise form the first major natural law that is *statistical*, and not absolute, deterministic, causal. It was connected with the kinetic theory of gases. In that subject it is assumed that, in a fixed volume of gas in thermal equilibrium (at constant temperature), the individual molecules will be fairly uniformly distributed through-

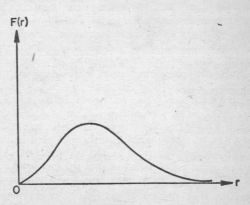

Figure 15.1   Maxwell-Boltzmann distribution of molecular speeds

out the containing vessel and will be moving in all possible directions with different speeds. Maxwell's statistical law is a frequency or density function of a random variable (Chapter 14), namely, molecular speed. Therefore the law enables one to find the proportion or relative frequency of molecules moving at different speeds—close to zero, at about 500 meters per second, or much higher, etc. Figure 15.1 represents this frequency function. In the diagram, we see that relative frequencies or probabilities are small for low or high speeds. Stripped of all technicalities, Maxwell's formula is a *frequency function,*

$$f(r) = ar^2e^{-b^2r^2}$$

Here r represents molecular speed. The physical constants, a and b, depend on the particular gas and its absolute temperature. Subsequently we shall see how Maxwell derived his law.

By making assumptions concerning molecular collisions and applying certain other postulates, the Austrian Ludwig Boltzmann (1844–1906) was able to improve the mathematical rigor in Maxwell's derivations, and subsequently it became the custom to speak of the above law as the Maxwell-Boltzmann distribution of molecular speeds.* Émile Borel, that leader in analysis, pure mathematical probability, and game theory, whose role was discussed in Chapter 10, called this law "one of the most beautiful and fruitful of all applications of probability theory to physics." The Maxwell-Boltzmann distribution was a purely theoretical construction, but around 1930 apparatus became available for obtaining actual experimental measurements of molecular speeds, and the resulting figures were in close agreement with the hypothetical ones obtained from the Maxwell-Boltzmann law.

Up to this point we have emphasized only molecular *speed*, that is, the magnitude of molecular *velocity*, without considering the *direction* of molecular motion. A velocity is a *vector*, however, having both direction and size. In space, such a vector (Figure 4.3) can be considered as the resultant or "sum" of three components parallel to the three coordinate axes, respectively (Chapter 4). Maxwell's line of

---

* As pointed out in Chapter 14, physicists sometimes use the term *distribution* where mathematicians prefer *frequency* or *density* function, reserving the term "distribution" for the *cumulative* frequency function.

thought led him to the assumption that the x-component of the velocity would have a normal frequency function,

$$f(x) = \frac{1}{\sigma\sqrt{2\pi}} e^{-x^2/2\sigma^2}$$

and the y and z components would also be distributed by the same normal frequency function, that is,

$$f(y) = \frac{1}{\sigma\sqrt{2\pi}} e^{-y^2/2\sigma^2}, \qquad f(z) = \frac{1}{\sigma\sqrt{2\pi}} e^{-z^2/2\sigma^2}$$

Here $\sigma^2 = kT/m$, where T represents the absolute temperature of the particular volume of gas, m is the mass of a molecule of this gas, and the proportionality factor k is an exceedingly important physical constant, called *Boltzmann's constant*.

The value of the variance σ^2 indicates whether the set of velocity components is concentrated fairly close to the mean or is spread out. The mean of each of the above distributions is *zero*. Therefore a small value for σ^2 (and hence a low absolute temperature, since σ^2 is proportional to T) signifies that the x-components of molecular velocity will, on the whole, be close to zero, that is, very small. The same will be true of y and z components, so that the resultant velocities may have *any* direction but will, on the whole, be small in magnitude at low temperatures and much more varied in size at high temperatures.

Maxwell's logic in probabilistic proofs was brilliantly intuitive but lacking in mathematical rigor. For example, he assumed that molecular velocity components are statistically independent of one another, and in this case, probability theory permits the multiplication of respective probabilities to obtain the joint frequency function,

$$f(x, y, z) = \left(\frac{1}{\sigma\sqrt{2\pi}} e^{-x^2/2\sigma^2}\right)\left(\frac{1}{\sigma\sqrt{2\pi}} e^{-y^2/2\sigma^2}\right)\left(\frac{1}{\sigma\sqrt{2\pi}} e^{-z^2/2\sigma^2}\right)$$

$$= \frac{1}{2\pi\sigma^3\sqrt{2\pi}} e^{-(x^2+y^2+z^2)/2\sigma^2}$$

The above function can be applied to answer questions like the following: In a certain volume of nitrogen gas at $0°C$ (or absolute temperature $T = 273°$), what proportion of molecules would have *velocities* with components $x = 200$

(meters per second), $y = 300$, $z = 250$?* Since T, m (mass of a nitrogen molecule) and k (Boltzmann's constant) are known, $\sigma^2 = kT/m$ can be computed. Then the values of σ^2, x, y, and z are substituted in the formula above. Numerical tables can be used to evaluate the right member of this formula, and thus the desired probability or relative frequency can be determined.

The first statistical concept illustrated by the density function $f(x, y, z)$ is that of a *multivariate* frequency or density function, that is, one where two or more random variables are involved. The distribution above is one type of multivariate *normal* function. There are three random variables, namely, x, y, and z, the velocity components. But interest may center in the *speed*, that is, the magnitude of velocity, (without regard for the direction of motion). For studying speeds one can take the multivariate distribution of velocities and from it derive the Maxwell-Boltzmann univariate distribution of molecular speeds. The procedure would be as follows.

Banishing technicalities, one can consider the above multivariate formula as

$$f(x, y, z) = Ae^{-b^2 r^2}$$

where $r^2 = x^2 + y^2 + z^2$ (see Figure 4.3), and the positive value of r is the molecular *speed* (not velocity). But then one must be careful to interpret this formula correctly. For example, in the problem about a small volume of nitrogen gas, $r^2 = 192{,}500$, or the speed, $r = 439$ meters per second (approximately) would be substituted. Now one could use the very same substitution to answer a great many different questions, for example, to obtain the proportion of molecules whose velocity components are $x = -200$, $y = 300$, $z = 250$, or the proportion of those for which $x = 200$, $y = -300$, $z = -250$, etc. In the last two instances the velocity is different from that of the original problem, but the speed is the same; the difference in velocity is due to a difference in the *direction* of motion. Again, the substitution, and hence the answer, would be the same because r, the speed, is the same, but the velocity would be different if $x = -300$, $y = 250$, $z = -200$, or $x = -250$, $y = -300$, $z =$

---

* Since the frequency function is of the *continuous* type, the question is interpreted to mean that x is in the *interval* (199.5, 200.5), y in the interval (299.5, 300.5), z in the interval (249.5, 250.5).

−200, and it would be approximately the same if $x = 248$, $y = -305$, $z = 200$, etc. There are countless sets of different components, that is, different velocities all corresponding to the *same* speed, about 439 meters per second. The original multivariate density function gives the same answer for any single velocity in this infinite set.

If one were to draw a sphere with center at the origin and radius equal to 439, all the vectors drawn from the origin to the surface of this sphere would represent all the different velocities with this same speed. Then, if one were not interested in velocities, but merely in speed, one might ask the question: What proportion of the nitrogen molecules have speeds approximately equal to 439? This would require a summation of all the relative frequencies corresponding to the vectors drawn to all points of the sphere. The number of relative frequencies (or vectors) is infinite, and the summation is carried out by integral calculus. In general, one would be performing a summation of frequencies corresponding to all vectors whose end-points are on a sphere of radius r. This is similar to the summation used in obtaining the area of a sphere, and the result in the latter case is $4\pi r^2$. Therefore it seems logical that, if the individual frequency corresponding to one vector or one point of the sphere is $Ae^{-b^2r^2}$, the total frequency should be $4\pi r^2$ times as great, and hence that the frequency function for speeds should be

$$f(r) = 4\pi r^2 \cdot \frac{1}{2\pi\sigma^3\sqrt{2\pi}}\, e^{-b^2r^2} = \frac{1}{\sigma^3}\sqrt{\frac{2}{\pi}}\, r^2 e^{-b^2r^2}$$

or

$$f(r) = ar^2 e^{-b^2r^2}$$

This is exactly the formula for the Maxwell-Boltzmann distribution of molecular speeds (page 480).

The thermodynamics of Maxwell and Boltzmann, with its three random variables, extends the concept of univariate distribution emphasized in the previous chapters. But more profound thermodynamic issues require much further generalization, since a study of molecular motion may involve as many as 10^{24} variables, or even more, as the present chapter will indicate. When the number of variables is so enormous, it would be wise to offer some simpler method for presenting thermodynamic theory. A more elementary approach was sought and ultimately achieved in the statistical mechanics of Josiah Willard Gibbs.

Each year since 1923, when the American Mathematical Society established the Josiah Willard Gibbs Lectureship, there is simultaneous recognition of the work of Gibbs and that of the distinguished mathematician who is invited to deliver a memorial address on a mathematical topic of current interest. In 1930 Edwin Bidwell Wilson (1879–1964) was asked to talk about Gibbs himself, and subsequently we shall quote from Wilson's "Reminiscences of Gibbs by a Student and Colleague." In 1934 it was Einstein and a decade thereafter John von Neumann who were Gibbs lecturers, and others whose mathematical research has been or will be discussed in the present book gave the special addresses in other years: James Pierpont, G. H. Hardy, Hermann Weyl, Norbert Wiener, Kurt Gödel, Marston Morse, and Eugene P. Wigner.

Not enough of this sort of reverence was accorded to Gibbs during his lifetime (1839–1903), most of which was spent at Yale University (first as son of a professor of divinity, then as a student, then as a professor of mathematical physics). The *vector analysis* that is indispensable to every serious student of physics today owes its form to the Yale mathematician. From the point of view of the physicist, the Gibbs vector calculus was a major simplification and improvement of Hamilton's quaternions. Yet it was received at first with a hostility akin to the initial responses to Beethoven's masterpieces, Puccini's melodies, and Picasso's abstractions. The British physicist P. G. Tait, in his 1890 text on quaternions, called the Gibbs technique a "hermaphrodite monster, compounded of the notations of Hamilton and Grassmann." Three years later, a letter in the journal *Nature* contained the New England professor's gentle rebuttal. The final sentence of Gibbs's epistle stated that "the world is too large, and the current of modern thought is too broad, to be confined to the *ipse dixit* even of a Hamilton."

By the turn of the century Gibbs had won the battle as far as the British world of science was concerned. The Royal Society of London awarded him the Copley Medal in 1901 for his thermodynamical discoveries. He was still a prophet without sufficient honor in his own land, however. When an American college president was seeking talent at Cambridge, England, he asked J. J. Thomson to recommend a molecular physicist. The letter's response was, "You needn't come to Europe for that, the best man in the field is your countryman, Willard Gibbs." "You mean Wolcott Gibbs (a chemist)," the president suggested. Thomson reaffirmed the name of *Willard* Gibbs and enlarged on the latter's contributions in the field of molecular physics. But the college president was not interested; he had already decided that a man unknown to him must lack personality and would not do for the job.

And so Gibbs remained at Yale, developing the vector analysis that was only a small preliminary to his most outstanding achievement, the creation of *statistical mechanics*, and anticipating the physico-chemical *phase rule* which he was to deduce as one consequence. Edwin Bidwell Wilson's reminiscences of Gibbs describe how feverishly Gibbs worked during the last period of his life in order to complete within a brief eight or nine months in 1901 and 1902 the entire manuscript of his *Elementary Principles of Statistical Mechanics*. In that work Gibbs developed a theory that not only provided a rigorous foundation for thermodynamics but was, in addition, of more general applicability and not limited to phenomena associated with heat energy. When some of Gibbs's assumptions are modified, his mechanics becomes suitable for various types of particles in the quantum theory today. One alteration leads to the socalled Bose-Einstein statistics, another to the Fermi-Dirac variety (Chapter 13). But the fundamental point of view remains that of Gibbs. As one of his admirers, the British physical chemist F. G. Donnan, has put it: "Of such work it is, and always will be true that the eager hand of Time may add something, but can take nothing away."

Gibbs could not have known that his ideas would involve him (posthumously) in a major crisis in modern physics and philosophy, namely, the conflict between the believers in deterministic (strictly causal) natural laws and the adherents of the doctrine that indeterminism, with its reliance on probabilistic prediction, is unavoidable in describing the physical world. In his later years Einstein placed himself firmly in the former camp. "I cannot believe God plays dice with the universe," he said. This was a reversal of an earlier attitude during the period when he had made notable contributions to statistical physics by solving the problem of "Brownian motion," or again by developing the quantum-mechanical properties of "bosons," the subatomic particles to which the Bose-Einstein statistical mechanics applies (Chapter 13).

As for Brownian motion, it is so named after the English botanist Robert Brown, who, a little over a century ago, observed the erratic paths followed by grains of pollen or tiny plant spores suspended in water. That type of motion is characteristic of all sufficiently small particles suspended in any kind of fluid—for example, the smoke and dust in our atmosphere. Such movements, which are readily visible through a microscope, were explained by Einstein as resulting from the innumerable kicks, shoves, and tosses inflicted by agitated water or air molecules in the course of their thermal motion. We cannot see this motion, but we can judge its nature indirectly from the measurement of the visible Brownian motion. Einstein established statistical (not causal) laws for this phenomenon, and subsequent experiments by the French physicist Perrin provided verification of the Einstein hypotheses. Nobel prize winner Max Born (1882–1970) says of Einstein's paper on Brownian motion. "By its simplicity and clarity, this paper is a classic of our science." Of Einstein's continued research in the same field, Born writes:[*]

These investigations . . . have done more than any other work to convince physicists of the reality of atoms and molecules, of the kinetic theory of heat and of the *fundamental part of probability in natural laws*. At that time the statistical aspect of physics was preponderant in Einstein's mind; yet at the same time he worked on relativity where rigorous causality reigned. His conviction seems always to have been that probability is used to cover our ignorance and that only the vastness of this ignorance pushes statistics into the forefront.

This attitude is not shared by other great physicists or philosophers today, and it seems to them that Einstein's dislike of statistical physics acquired exaggerated magnitude as he grew older. He expressed it in correspondence with Born, in papers attacking specific results of quantum mechanics where probabilistic methodology is used, and in many other ways. Since it has become the fashion to offer psychoanalytic interpretations of behavior (as seen in recent studies of Lewis Carroll, of Freud himself) and these are often couched in terms of "traumas" received in early life,

---

[*] Max Born, "Einstein's Statistical Theories," *Library of Living Philosophers*, Vol. 7, *Einstein: Philosopher-Scientist*, 1949.

we present the following fact for what it is worth in this connection and for its coincidental association with Willard Gibbs.

In 1901, when Gibbs was completing the manuscript of his *Statistical Mechanics*, Einstein, unaware, was starting a paper which was to duplicate all the essential features of Gibbs's *chef-d'oeuvre*. This occurrence provides one of the many instances of the phenomenon of simultaneous discovery, so often repeated in the history of science. When a mathematical or physical subject has evolved to the ripe stage that demands an all-embracing theory or a rigorous logical foundation, the foremost thinkers in the particular field—Newton and Leibniz, or Einstein and Gibbs, as the case may be—will arrive independently at the same theoretical results. The American Mathematical Society memorializes Gibbs each year because his theory encompassed and superseded all the thermodynamic theories formulated in the two millennia preceding his day. Hence anyone can realize what profound thought Einstein must have given to the simultaneous discovery embodied in his *Kinetic Theory of Thermal Equilibrium and the Second Law of Thermodynamics* (1902) and *Theoretical Foundations of Thermodynamics* (1903). Is it not possible that the youth (Einstein was in his twenties at the time) who was to create the greatest of all causal theories experienced some unconscious shock, some major frustration, in failing to be the *first* to discover the methodology leading to the greatest of all theories in statistical physics? Was it reasoning or intuition or such a trauma as we have imagined that brought about his complete withdrawal from the statistical school and his pointed prejudice against the use of probabilistic logic in physics? Since our subject is mathematics and not psychology, we shall not attempt to answer the question. In the domain of fact, not speculation, Einstein must be credited with original ideas in *both* relativity and quantum mechanics. He carried one theory to a profound ultimate conclusion, but we shall never know whether he might not have done the same with those early thermodynamic hypotheses whose methodology he renounced.

What was the actual content of the 1901–1903 statistical mechanical theory of Gibbs? As far as physics is concerned, one might say that Gibbs added little to the mere physical facts of the Maxwell-Boltzmann theory. His methods, however, are vastly superior, for he constructed a *pure mathe-*

matical subject of very great generality, one which gave impetus to the development of the modern theory of *stochastic* or *random processes*. On the basis of a small number of postulates or assumptions, he *deduced* theorems of wide applicability to a *variety* of physical situations.

One feature of major importance in Gibbs's statistical mechanics and also in Einstein's study of Brownian motion is that they were among the very first mathematical contributions to introduce ideas and issues related to *random* or *stochastic processes*. (The adjective "stochastic" derives from the Greek *stochos*, which means "guess.") We must therefore explain what is meant by such a process. But before doing so, we remark that random processes are of theoretical and practical importance today not only in statistical mechanics but also in astronomy, biology, epidemiology, economics, communication and control theory, industrial engineering, oceanography, and other subjects.

In the broadest sense, the theory of stochastic processes is the *dynamic* part of mathematical statistics. If the random variables of interest, that is, the frequency and distribution functions, change as *time* passes, the whole set of random variables is called a stochastic process. To start with a very elementary and hence somewhat trivial example, we can imagine a coin to be tossed in very many repeated random experiments so that as time goes on, wear and tear change p, the probability of "heads." Let us consider plausible values of p initially, after a million tosses, after two million tosses, etc. and label the corresponding "instants" of time as

$$t = 0, 1, 2, 3, 4, \ldots$$

with

$$p = 0.50, 0.49, 0.48, 0.40, 0.50, \ldots$$

Then if we consider a random variable with values 0 and 1 corresponding to the outcomes "tails" and "heads," respectively, the initial and the fifth frequency functions are both as follows:

x	0	1
$f(x)$	0.50	0.50

whereas the second and fourth frequency functions are given by the tabulation

x	0	1
$f(x)$	0.51	0.49

The reader will readily formulate the third frequency function and make conjectures about the functions corresponding to $t = 5, 6, 7, \ldots$. The whole *sequence* of random variables or frequency functions is an example of a *discrete parameter stochastic process*, a finite process if the sequence terminates, otherwise an infinite one.

Observe that even if the above sequence forms an infinite process, it may be one that acquires a certain stability after a while. For, if we imagine that the coin-tossing apparatus is repaired so as to make the fall of the coin almost frictionless, then ultimately we might (in theory) arrive at a situation where the terms of the sequence (rounded off to hundredths) become

$$0.52, 0.52, 0.52, \ldots \text{ forever}.$$

We have reached an *equilibrium* frequency function where the probabilities of "heads" and "tails" are 0.52 and 0.48, respectively. In other words, we might have a sequence which has a *limit*.

Since games of chance always provide the simplest illustrations for probabilistic issues, let us rely on coin-tossing experiments once more to give an example of an *finite* stochastic process. In Figure 12.1 there is a diagram of a "game tree" which was related to a strategic game described in that chapter. Let us now use the same diagram but have R and C play a game of chance instead of a game of strategy. Let there be three moves once again, with R and C playing alternately, choosing a number from the set $\{1, 2\}$. But now R tosses a penny in the first move and a nickel in the third, and C tosses a dime in the second move. Either player selects the number 1 only when the coin turns up "heads." Suppose that the probability of "heads" is 0.4, 0.6, 0.3 for penny, dime, and nickel, respectively. Then we have a sequence of three different frequency functions. If there were betting associated with the game and if it were played repeatedly, we might be interested in the expectations or means. The reader can verify that they form the sequence $\{1.6, 1.4, 1.7\}$. If one is to answer probabilistic questions like "What is the likelihood that 2 will be selected only once in the three moves?" or if, as in Chapter 12, there are payoffs at the *end* of the game, then it will be advisable to consider the process as a whole and to formulate a frequency function in which the values of the random variable are the eight paths from the base to the top of the tree (the eight ordered triples of number selections). Since the three coin-tossing experiments are *independent* trials, it is just a matter of multiplying three probabilities to obtain the probability for a particular path. Thus the frequency function for the whole process will assign to the respective paths the probabilities 0.072, 0.168, 0.048, 0.112, etc., with 0.252 the probability for the most likely path, the one corresponding to (2, 1, 2).

We might have made the above illustration of a stochastic process more general by requiring the second and third moves of the game to be dependent on the results of the previous move. Thus, in the second move, C might toss one of two different coins (with different probabilities for "heads") according to whether R chooses 1 or 2 in the first move, and likewise the nature of R's random experiment in the third move might depend on C's choice in the second move. But, in any case, the simplicity of our example would make it artificial rather than realistic. It was selected only to anticipate in a very elementary way the picture of Gibbs's stochastic process, where there are an infinite number of paths or "trajectories" about whose frequency function Gibbs theorized.

An *infinite* stochastic process need *not* be of the discrete parameter type, that is, the instants of time in the "index set" need *not* be a sequence. Instead the index set might contain the numbers in a *continuum;* for example, we might have as index set all values of t in the interval $(0, 1)$, or the index set might be the continuum $t \geqq 0$, the set of all nonnegative real numbers, arranged in order of size. In either case we would have a *continuous parameter stochastic process*. Gibbs's stochastic process was of the continuous parameter type.

In summary, a *stochastic process* is usually described as a *family of random variables*. Observe that a "family" is not always identical in meaning with a "set." In one "family" illustrated above, the numbers 0.50 and 0.49 appear repeatedly in correspondence with different index numbers. If we were considering the *set* of distinct numerical values, the numbers in question would appear only once. Another point is that, with our emphasis on the "dynamic," we have considered time to be the parameter whose values are given in the index set. But in various applications the parameter may have some other concrete meaning, whereas in the general pure mathematical stochastic process, the parameter is an abstraction with no specific interpretation.

Before we proceed to Gibbs's theory itself, we must remark that, in one respect, it is simpler than the general stochastic process, since only a single random experiment is involved, namely, the initial one of selecting the initial conditions for a mechanical system. The random variables and their frequency functions do vary in time, however, both as a result of the indeterminacy of the initial conditions and the strictly deterministic mechanical laws (which force the paths or trajectories to follow certain routes). The reader can obtain one type of picture of the Gibbs process by imagining it to be a tremendous generalization of the tree diagram of Figure 12.1. The root of the tree in the Gibbs process can be located at any one of a continuum of points. Then each one of the infinity of trees branches out in a continuously infinite number of directions. The position of the root and the direction of branching depend on the outcome of the initial random experiment. But there are no further random experiments; the initial branches just grow up and out forever, in directions prescribed by the laws of mechanics. (Our own picture, later on, will be somewhat different—in order to prevent the growing branches from getting in each other's way.)

What then were the basic axioms of Gibbs's statistical mechanics? In the first place, he postulated that certain "systems" obey the most general laws of dynamics as set down by Hamilton. These systems are mathematical abstractions, but the physical counterparts are finite portions of matter—solid, liquid, or gaseous. Each system is a mechanical one, whose state at a particular time can be specified by a certain number of generalized coordinates and an equal number of generalized momenta, these coordinates and momenta being governed by the canonical equations of Hamilton (Chapter 9). A most elementary physical realization of such a system is furnished by a single particle constrained to move in a straight line. Its position at any time can be described by giving its distance from a fixed point or origin of coordinates on the line, but this single numerical fact merely gives its "mechanical configuration" at the time in question. For its complete "state," its velocity or momentum at this instant must also be given. In elementary physics, momentum is just the product of mass and velocity, and since mass is constant (at low speeds), momentum is proportional to velocity and it matters little which of the two is used. However, it must be emphasized that the Hamiltonian equations make use of generalized or "conjugate" momenta that are very different from the mass-velocity products of elementary mechanics. From the Hamiltonian equations and a theorem of Joseph Liouville (1809–1882), the great French analyst, Gibbs was able to deduce two important "conservation" laws. We shall call the Gibbs deductions the *conservation of volume* and the *conservation of probability density*, the latter term suggesting the statistical aspect of his mechanics. Actually his "conservation" laws are just part of the integral calculus required for the proper formulation of the stochastic process he had in mind, that is, for giving algebraic expression to the continuous family of probability density functions and the ultimate "equilibrium" density function. In summary, by starting with the "canonical" equations of Hamilton, Gibbs arrived at principles essential for his own probabilistic physical laws.

A mechanical system slightly more advanced than a particle moving in a straight line is a monatomic molecule moving in space. Here *three* position coordinates and *three* components of momentum, that is, *six* numerical facts, will be required to fix the state of the system at a particular instant. In a system of n molecules, $6n$ numbers will suffice. Suppose that the system is a "gram-molecular mass" or "mole" of gas, the standard volume* used in chemistry. Then $n = Avogadro's\ number$, that is, the number of molecules in a mole of any gas. Experiments have shown that $n = 6.06 \times 10^{23}$ (approximately). Hence $6n = 36.36 \times 10^{23}$ or about 3.64×10^{24}. Thus $6n$, the number of generalized coordinates required to describe the state of a mole of gas at a particular instant, exceeds 10^{24}. Even though the gaseous form of matter is the simplest of the three forms, and a mole is a relatively small volume, the recording of the coordinates at a single instant would be a formidable task, requiring more than 1,000,000,000,000,000,000,000,000 entries! But as

---

* This is the volume of 2 grams of hydrogen at standard temperature and pressure.

soon as the gas molecules move, some or all of these numbers change—within a thousandth of a second, and change again within the next thousandth of a second! Even if the facts were observable directly or indirectly, recording them would be a hopeless undertaking.

But returning momentarily to the single particle moving on a straight line, the state at any time is the pair of values of

$$(q, p) = (\text{position, momentum})$$

determined by the differential equations of dynamics (Newtonian in this elementary case, Hamiltonian in the general case). As the point moves on the straight line, the values of the number pair (q, p) will change. To facilitate the study of the changes in state as time goes on, any number pair can be plotted as the rectangular coordinates of a point in a Cartesian graph. There will be different points for different states, and as the point moves on the straight line, its evolution through successive (q, p) states will be a curve in the Cartesian plane.

Gibbs would have referred to the state of a system as a *phase*, to the representative point as a *phase point*, and to the Cartesian plane as the *phase space*. In an earlier example, the case of a bullet moving in a vertical straight line (page 314), we considered just such a system. Let us take an arbitrary system of mass measure in which the bullet has unit mass. Hence $m = 1$, $p = mv = v$ in this elementary instance, and the formulas previously obtained give

$$q = -16t^2 + 1200t + 5$$
$$p = -32t + 1200$$

When $t = 0$, $q = 5$, $p = 1200$; when $t = 10$, $q = 10,405$, $p = 880$; when $t = 30$, $q = 21,605$, $p = 240$. These three states or phases are represented by points A, B, C in Figure 15.2.

If we were completely ignorant of the initial conditions, that is, the position and momentum when the bullet was fired, then *any point* in the phase space (Cartesian plane) might represent some possible phase or state, or *any* one of a whole family of curves (parabolas) might represent the history of successive states. But our illustration is *deterministic*, for we know both the proper differential equations and the initial conditions. The evolutionary curve is a portion of

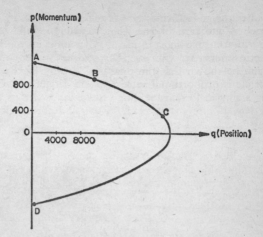

Figure 15.2   Phase-space trajectory for the firing of a bullet

a specific parabola. By algebraic elimination of t from the above formulas for q and p, the reader can obtain

$$q = 22505 - \frac{1}{64}\, p^2$$

as the equation of the parabola. When the bullet returns after 75 seconds, let us terminate the story. At that instant, $q = 5$, $p = -1200$ (phase point D). We might continue until the bullet hits the ground at $t = 75.01$ when $q = 0$, $p = -1200.32$, but this adds little to the picture.

For the sake of clarification, one usually resorts to simple instances but they often lack some of the features of the general case and may lead to some wrong impressions. In the example above, the evolution of states and the curve representing the history came to an abrupt end. This is *not* typical of the systems of statistical mechanics, where the succession of states usually goes on and on; so does the curve giving the dynamic history.

Let us consider a slightly more advanced example. A *simple harmonic vibration* will not reveal all general features but will contain aspects not indicated in the bullet example. We shall introduce the procedures of advanced mechanics and form the *Hamiltonian energy function*, which is the sum of the *kinetic* and *potential* energies of the vibrating particle. In elementary physics one learns that kinetic energy is expressed by $\frac{1}{2}mv^2 = m^2v^2/2m = p^2/2m$. It can be shown that the potential energy of the oscillating particle is proportional to $\frac{1}{2}q^2$, hence equal to $kq^2/2$, where k is a physical constant. For convenience, let us consider a particle of unit mass. Then $m = 1$ and the total energy H can be expressed as

$$H = \frac{kq^2}{2} + \frac{p^2}{2}$$

If there is no friction (only possible in a pure mathematical vibration), the total energy H will remain constant, that is, will be *conserved* as time goes on, and the particle will constitute a *conservative system*. The constancy of the total energy is expressed by the following equation:

$$\frac{kq^2}{2} + \frac{p^2}{2} = c$$

This is a relation between q and p, namely, the equation of the curve representing the succession of states (phases) of the vibrating system. The equation represents an ellipse (Figure 15.3) with semiaxes equal to $\sqrt{2c/k}$ and $\sqrt{2c}$. If c, the total energy, is fixed, one of the axes—and hence the shape of the ellipse—depends on the physical constant k. Any point on the ellipse represents the phase (q, p) at some time,

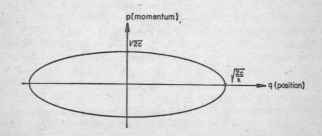

Figure 15.3   Phase-space trajectory for a harmonic oscillator

and the ellipse is described over and over again forever, corresponding to the fact that the particle is vibrating periodically in a straight line, repeating the same positions and momenta forever.

It should be emphasized that in both of the above illustrations the *actual motion* of the system takes place in a straight line. The parabola in one case, and the ellipse in the other, is the progress chart, the *dynamical history* of the system, *not* the path of the moving particle. Second, both examples are atypical because of the simplicity of the systems—the evolution of the bullet because it terminates, the phase curve of the oscillator because it is periodic.

A *general* phase curve usually goes on and on into different parts of the phase space, visiting all regions consistent with the energy of the particular system. Finally, in the actual systems with which statistical mechanics is concerned there would almost never be anything as elementary as the motion of a single particle in a straight line, and the phase space in which the evolutionary curve is described would not be a plane but an abstract higher-dimensional space. In general, then, one deals with abstract paths in an abstract space, but as in other parts of mathematics, quasigeometric terminology makes for concise, lucid expression. From what we have already explained, more than 10^{24} coordinates are needed for the specification of the state of a gram-molecular mass of gas, which is a most elementary sort of system in statistical mechanics, and hence the phase space would, even in a simple case, have a very large number of dimensions.

Thus far we have mentioned only the *mechanical* foundations of Gibbs's theory, but the huge number 10^{24} is a good motivation and point of departure for the *statistical* side of the subject. Gibbs imagined not one system with 10^{24} phase variables, but a huge set of such systems, an *ensemble*, as he called it, a "population" of systems, if we use the statistical terminology of Chapter 14. He conceived of the systems of the ensemble as macroscopically identical, but microscopically different, just as, from a crude statistical point of view, men in a population are all alike in general physical makeup but differ individually in height, weight, age, life expectancy, etc. To return to Gibbs's ensembles for an example, suppose that the system of interest, the one whose physical properties are of concern, is a container filled with gas; then Gibbs's mental construction forms an enormous aggregate of duplicate containers filled with the same gas in which, however, the phases (states)—the positions and momenta of the molecules at a particular instant—vary from one container to another. Then the values of $(q_1, q_2, \ldots, q_n, p_1, p_2, \ldots, p_n)$ at that instant are different for the different systems of the ensemble and are represented by different points in the phase space. As time goes on, these different representative points will move, describing curves or trajectories, as they are usually called, each one giving the dynamic history of one system of the ensemble. One can imagine the phase points as a cloud of dust (in a hyperspace) whose individual dust particles are in motion in accordance with dynamic laws. Then the *density* of this cloud may appear, at a particular time, to be different from place to place, or might possibly vary at each particular place as time goes on. As a result of certain *dynamical characteristics*, the dust particles (phase points) for the numerous systems never collide, and if they do not go round and round in tornado fashion, that is, if they are not periodic, each one ultimately visits every part of the phase space.

Gibbs's task, as we see it today, was to formulate the family of probability density functions for the states (phases) of the systems of his ensemble at different times. His methodology contrasts with the formulation of the single Maxwell-Boltzmann frequency function for a particular system at a particular time. If one is really ignorant of certain physical characteristics of the particular system, then Gibbs's approach permits finding statistical averages over a large number of similar systems (at a given time). If, on the other hand, one has some knowledge of a particular system (or a particular type of system) but feels that conditions are changing or evolving with time, then Gibbs's point of view permits averages for a particular system over a period of time.

From the above statements, the reader may gain the impression that the Maxwell-Boltzmann distribution is erroneous because it would change to a different one within a billionth of a second and to still another one in the next billionth of a second, etc. But Maxwell and Boltzmann *assumed* that, after a long time, a certain distribution of the speeds would be reached and *maintained* (as in the hypothetical coin-tossing sequence on page 489). At that stage an ideal gas is said to have a constant absolute temperature and to be in *thermal equilibrium*. If there is any preliminary variation in frequency functions, the ultimate distribution is that of Maxwell and Boltzmann and this *defines* thermal equilibrium of a gas as a state where the speeds of the molecules obey the Maxwell-Boltzmann law.

In certain parts of statistical physics, the whole family of random variables and their distributions as they vary in time must be considered, but the construction of theories based on a unique equilibrium distribution is a great simplification. In this respect Gibbs followed the example of Maxwell and Boltzmann, but he generalized their single system to an ensemble of systems. Moreover, he soon abandoned one of their physical postulates, namely, that of an isolated system not subject to energy exchanges with the surrounding medium. That assumption was a simplifying one because it made the total energy constant, that is, made the system *conservative*. But Gibbs did not overlook the advantage of conservative systems and, in fact, he imagined an ensemble of such systems. Now, however isolated a thermodynamic system may be, there is always some energy exchange with surroundings, and it is unrealistic to make contrary assumptions. Therefore Gibbs postulated an ensemble where statistical equilibrium is attained *not* by isolation but by free interaction. This is analogous to the thermal equilibrium described above, and if we wish, we can imagine the one real mechanical system of interest as immersed in a sort of "ice-water bath" made up of the enormous number of other systems of the ensemble. Since such an ensemble in equilibrium involves simpler statistical theory, Gibbs considered it first. For the case where the systems of the ensemble are conservative and one knows their energy, but nothing else about them, Gibbs made the simplest of all possible assumptions, namely, that for a given fixed value of the energy, the phase points are uniformly distributed throughout a "cloud" (in a hyperspace) so that the density is the *same everywhere*. This corresponds to the uniform or rectangular frequency function of Chapter 14 and, as indicated in that chapter, is the analogue for continuous distributions of Laplace's assumption of equal likelihood in the case of a finite sample space. Here it would signify that any state of a system is as likely as any other and would represent complete ignorance, as it were, of any determinate factors. The uniformity of density (for a fixed value of the energy) is what Gibbs labeled a *microcanonical distribution*.

In statistical mechanics, the frequency and distribution functions are not usually expressed directly in terms of phase variables $q_1, q_2, \ldots, q_n, p_1, p_2, \ldots, p_n$, but are given as expressions involving H, the *Hamiltonian*, which is a function of the q's and p's. The Hamiltonian represents the total energy of a system, and in the so-called conservative systems its numerical value remains constant with time. (This does not mean that the q's and p's are always the same. They vary, but whenever a particular set is substituted in the H-function, the resulting value of that function is the same.)

To make analytic handling easier, it is customary to think of such a conservative system as having a slight range of variation in energy between H and $H + \Delta H$ where ΔH is very small. Then Gibbs's microcanonical distribution can be pictured as a uniform very thin cloud in phase space. The microcanonical distribution is sometimes called an *energy shell* or surface distribution. To see why, we refer to Figure 15.3, in which the ellipse represents the evolution of one

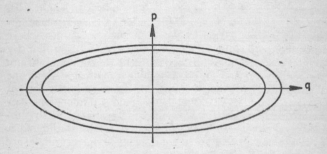

Figure 15.4.   Energy shell

conservative system with total energy $H = c$. If that system is just one member of an ensemble whose other systems may have the energy $H = c$ or an energy value slightly greater—that is, where the energy range lies between H and $H + \Delta H$ (ΔH a small positive number)—then in Figure 15.4 any points on or between the two ellipses may be phase points, and the thin elliptic cloud is the energy shell. If we conceive of ΔH as getting smaller and smaller, the energy shell will become just an elliptic curve in the limit. In general phase space, the energy shell between two surfaces (actually "hypersurfaces") would become just a surface as $\Delta H \to 0$.

But as we have indicated, both the empirical physicist

and the theoretician found the conservatism of the micro-canonical ensemble lacking in generality. Therefore the major theme of Gibbs's *chef-d'oeuvre* was the postulation of a *canonical distribution,* whose frequency function is

$$f(H) = ce^{-H/\theta}$$

where $f(H)$ is the probability or density in the neighbor-hood of a cloud in phase space, e is the natural logarithmic base, H (the Hamiltonian) is the random variable, c and θ are positive numerical parameters. (Observe that if H, the total energy, is fixed, $f(H)$ takes a constant value, and the canonical distribution reduces to the microcanonical one.)

The canonical distribution gives the probability that a system selected at random from the Gibbs ensemble will have energy that approximates an H which we may specify by particular numerical values of the q's and p's. (These values determine H). As for the parameters in Gibbs's for-mula, θ, which he called the *modulus* of the ensemble, is proportional to the variance, being small if the distribution is concentrated, that is, if most systems of the ensemble have values of H very close to its mean. Now the range of energy values in a canonical ensemble is small if one excludes the few extreme cases. It would not be mathematically cor-rect to drop these extreme states, but from their very tiny relative frequencies one can pronounce the phases in ques-tion very unlikely to occur. The parameter c varies inversely as $\sqrt{\theta}$ and also contains a "normalizing" factor which can be adjusted so that the canonical formula gives either the actual frequency (number of systems) or the relative fre-quency approximating a selected state $(q_1, q_2, \ldots, p_n)$, that is, a specified value of H.

In the special case where the ensemble systems are por-tions of an ideal gas,

$$\theta = kT$$

where T is the absolute temperature of the gas and k is Boltzmann's constant (1.38×10^{-16}). This exceedingly small number makes θ tiny, and thus the distribution is concen-trated. When this special meaning is assigned to θ in Gibbs's formula, it reduces to the Maxwell-Boltzmann distribution. But, as emphasized originally, the Gibbs ensembles need not be composed of portions of a gas, and therefore his canoni-cal distribution is of more general applicability. Thus, in relation to that distribution, Gibbs found various averages and then gave them physical interpretations. He called one of these averages the *mean index of phase probability*. He was able to show that except for a change in algebraic sign, the average in question corresponds to what physicists call *entropy*, one of the most fundamental of all thermodynamic concepts.

The use of averages in statistical mechanics raised certain challenging issues that were to provide a stimulus to pure mathematics. Gibbs himself had avoided some logical difficulties by basing his mechanics on classic probability theory, Liouville's theorem, and various bold assumptions of his own. But Maxwell and Boltzmann had felt less secure than Gibbs. They were much concerned in their kinetic theory of gases with the paradoxical situation where the deterministic behavior of individual gas molecules had to be reconciled with the indeterminate statistical laws governing aggregates of those molecules. Thus the Maxwell-Boltzmann distribution leads to certain averages connected with the enormous aggregate of molecular velocities, those overall magnitudes being considered to correspond to physical entities like pressure and temperature.

For a *direct* experimental check on the theoretical averages of Maxwell and Boltzmann one would want to measure simultaneously, at some particular instant of time, the velocities of more than 10^{24} gas molecules. To carry out such an experiment would be a sheer impossibility, and hence one might next consider whether it is humanly possible to concentrate on a single one of the vast assemblage of molecules and measure its velocity repeatedly as time goes on. It would seem that averages obtained from such figures should check with those for many similar molecules at one instant, just as tossing a single coin a million times should lead to approximately the same proportion of heads as one throw with a million coins (identical with the original one).

Following the progress of just one molecule sounds simple enough, but it is evident that this would be no more possible empirically than the instantaneous measurement of the velocity of each of 10^{24} molecules. However, we can follow the single molecule in *theory* by means of the dynamical differential equations, which give a unique position and a unique velocity of the molecule at each instant of time, providing we know its position and velocity at just a single particular instant. Then, after we have obtained a quadrillion velocities at different instants, it is possible to find their mean, median, mode, variance, or any desired average. The figures can then be compared with the corresponding averages for the equilibrium aggregate of the Maxwell-Boltzmann distribution.

But now another problem arises: Which one of the 10^{24} molecules should one select for the tabulation of velocities at a quadrillion instants of time? In terms of solving the dynamical differential equations, what initial conditions, that is, what initial molecular position and velocity, should we assign? It would be fortunate if it did not matter, that is, if the long-time behavior of one molecule were the same as that of every other molecule. Then the averages would be the same no matter what initial position and velocity were selected, as long as the numbers did not contradict given physical facts. First Maxwell and then Boltzmann postulated that this would be the case and that, moreover, the *time average*, that is, the deterministic figure obtained by averaging positions, velocities, or other variables for a single molecule over a very long period of time, would be equal to the corresponding statistical average for the aggregate of molecules at one instant of time. Maxwell called this axiom the principle of "continuity of path" and Boltzmann named it the *ergodic hypothesis*, the term we use today. The problem of the equivalence of the two types of average is not limited to kinetic theory but extends to general stochastic processes. In the case of statistical mechanics, we must ask: Is the time average of some variable associated with the single system of interest in agreement with the ensemble average computed *at any time* for the Gibbsian ensemble of "duplicates" of this system?

With all these thoughts in mind, Maxwell and Boltzmann conceived their *ergodic hypothesis* thus: The trajectory (in phase space) representing the evolution of any particular system of a microcanonical ensemble will, in the course of time, pass through *every* point of the corresponding energy surface (hypersurface). If the hypothesis is assumed, then one can deduce as a theorem: The *length of time* during which a particular system exhibits a given set of phases is proportional to the relative frequency of the latter; that is, *every* trajectory in phase space spends in a given region of that space a length of time proportional to the extent (area, volume, *hypervolume*) of the region.

No sooner had Mexwell and Boltzmann advanced this hypothesis than the physicist Lord Kelvin (1824–1907) indicated that it seemed unreasonable to him because special periodic motions must contradict it. For example, if rigid particles of some gas are bouncing up and down or to right or left between parallel faces of a rectangular container, the orderliness of the motion will prevent the frequent collisions that produce randomness in position and velocity as time goes on. As a result, the phases for such a system will not vary greatly, and the corresponding trajectory will not visit every part of phase space. Therefore, important physical quantities—time averages like pressure on the walls of the container, for example, would be very different from the corresponding statistical averages over the microcanonical ensemble. Kelvin arrived at this conclusion intuitively, but Poincaré later gave rigorous mathematical proof in a thorough study of periodic motions. Thus the ergodic hypothesis was shown to be *false*.

Although the ergodic hypothesis in its original form is untenable, various modifications, so-called *quasi-ergodic* hypotheses, have been shown to be *true*. In the applications of stochastic processes it is most desirable to be able to use time and ensemble averages interchangeably and hence to know under what conditions such equivalence is valid. The most important proof of an ergodic theorem was provided in 1931 by George David Birkhoff (1884–1944). According to Marston Morse, professor at the Institute for Advanced Study, Birkhoff was "during the major part of his life . . . the acknowledged leader of American mathematics," and of all his mathematical achievements, "popular opinion focuses attention on his proof of Poincaré's Last Theorem and the *Ergodic Theorem*" so that "much of his other work is obscured."[*]

According to Paul R. Halmos, "*Modern* ergodic theory started early in 1931 with a most significant observation made by B. O. Koopman." This thought occurred in a short paper delivered before the National Academy of Sciences. Halmos tells how Koopman inspired John von Neumann to prove a *mean ergodic theorem*. "Shortly after he proved it he discussed it with G. D. Birkhoff and shortly

* Marston Morse, "George David Birkhoff and His Mathematical Work," *Bulletin of the American Mathematical Society*, Vol. 52, No. 5, Part 1 (May 1956), pp. 359 and 389.

after that Birkhoff proved the individual ergodic theorem—the priority explained in a subsequent note of Birkhoff and Koopman."[*]

To compare the two ergodic theorems, let us state that Birkhoff's is a much more general proposition. The conditions prescribed in von Neumann's theorem do *not* lead to complete agreement in time and ensemble averages, but there is equality in the case of the mean and the variance, the most important averages in physical applications. Von Neumann's theorem shows that the ergodic hypothesis is *approximately* true and gives a way of measuring the precision of the approximation; Birkhoff's theorem establishes that the hypothesis is practically a universal truth.

A whole ergodic theory of related subject matter has grown up since 1931, always to the accompaniment of great names, and is still expanding. By 1931, however, quantum mechanics had deprived the ergodic hypothesis of most of its physical significance, but that did not diminish the importance of ergodic *theorems* in pure mathematics or their value in applied fields other than statistical mechanics.

The deductive demonstration of ergodic theorems is too advanced for presentation in a work for the general reader. But we emphasize that those propositions provide a proper theoretical basis for the computation of statistical mechanical averages. One such mean, mentioned earlier, is named *entropy*. In popularizations of science, entropy is variously described as a measure of randomness, an index of disorder, an amount of uncertainty, "Time's Arrow," etc. The famous second thermodynamic law, often called the Law of Entropy, has as one corollary the ultimate "heat death" of our universe. This is a lugubrious picture, and it is interesting that some of the apparent "refutations" of the pessimistic Second Law have come from the field of biology, where biophysicists and biochemists every now and then cite living processes involving energy transformations that provide counterexamples to the Law of Entropy.

One of Gibbs's foremost students and colleagues, Edwin Bidwell Wilson, was to devote many years to a different aspect of biological processes in his career as professor of vital statistics at Harvard's School of Public Health. His

---

[*] Paul R. Halmos, "Von Neumann on Measure and Ergodic Theory," *Bulletin of the American Mathematical Society,* Vol. 64, No. 3. Part 2 (May 1958), p. 91.

work in biological statistics was not, however, the first evidence of Gibbs's influence, for Wilson, who prepared the *Vector Analysis* textbook based on the Yale professor's superior substitute for the Hamiltonian quaternions, taught mathematics at Yale after his teacher's death, then mathematical physics at the Massachusetts Institute of Technology, where he became head of the physics department. Twenty-seven years after Gibbs's death, his illustrious pupil was asked to deliver the eighth Josiah Willard Gibbs Lecture before the American Mathematical Society and the American Association for the Advancement of Science.

The biography of a mathematician or artist or writer is essentially nothing more than the list of his creative works; legendary or fictional incidents and anecdotes arise from attempts to force "human interest" details. Therefore the *factual* reminiscences of Gibbs in Wilson's 1930 lecture are exceptional biographical material, and we shall quote some parts of that lecture.

Wilson, who was graduated from Harvard in 1899 at the head of his class, with highest honors in mathematics, had been advised by William Fogg Osgood (1864–1943), the renowned Harvard mathematician, to get a change in point of view by taking graduate work at Yale. He followed this advice and thus became Gibbs's student and disciple. We continue the story in Wilson's own words.*

Gibbs was born on February 11, 1839. He prepared for college at the Hopkins Grammar School. He was graduated from Yale in the class of 1858 at the age of nineteen. In college his interests appear to have been Latin and mathematics as he took prizes in each in more than one year of his course. He took the Bristed Scholarship of $95 for the best examination in Greek, Latin and Mathematics. He won the Latin Oration in both Junior and Senior years. He was awarded the Clark Scholarship of $120 for the best examination in the studies of the college course which was conferred subject to the condition that the recipient continue as a graduate for one or two years pursuing nonprofessional studies. He did so continue and in 1863 got his Ph.D. degree with a thesis: "On the form of the teeth of wheels in spur gearing." In the Yale catalogs of 1863–64 and 1864–65 he is listed as Tutor in Latin; in that of 1865–66 he appears as Tutor in Natural Philosophy. Afterwards he went abroad to study. In the catalog of 1871–72 he reappears as Professor of Mathematical Physics and

* E. B. Wilson, "Reminiscences of Gibbs by a Student and Colleague," *Bulletin of the American Mathematical Society*, Vol. 37, No. 6 (June 1931), pp. 401 ff.

so continues until his death. Except for his periods as Tutor he taught only graduate work, although particularly competent undergraduates might be admitted to his courses, especially the Vector Analysis.

Gibbs lectured without notes and what specific preparation he generally made I do not know. It was almost always some very simple affair on which he would go astray rather than something recondite. The year I took thermodynamics he could not make his Carnot engine run right. There was a tradition, perhaps unwarranted, that the Carnot engine was apt to trouble him. Sometimes he would unravel his difficulty before the end of the hour and it was then an especial treat to see his mind work; sometimes the end of the hour would come sooner and he would have to leave the matter over until the next time when he would appear with a sheet of paper containing the demonstration.

By far the longest conversation I ever had with him, and of course the last, took place in June 1902 when I was leaving for Paris for a year's study. He said that he did not wish to determine my line of future interest but that he hoped I would consider taking some work in applied mathematics in Paris in addition to any I might take in pure mathematics. He ventured the opinion that one good use to which anybody might put a superior training in pure mathematics was to the study of the problems set us by nature. He remarked that in the thirty years of his professorship of mathematical physics he had had but a half-dozen students adequately prepared to follow his lectures. He did me the honor to include me in the list, though I myself never felt that my preparation in physics had been adequate. I asked why he had given exclusively such advanced courses, why he had not offered some more elementary work to prepare his students. He replied that he had not felt called upon to do so but that if I were willing he would be glad to have me look forward to giving upon my return a general introductory course on mathematical physics, and at any rate he would be happy if I would bear the possibility in mind while abroad. He then went on to say that if I should choose to occupy myself somewhat seriously with mathematical physics he had a considerable number of problems on which he thought I could make progress and that he would be glad to talk about them on my return. How much I have regretted that he did not talk of them at the time, but he gave no inkling of them.

Finally he proceeded to say something of his own plans for the future. He remarked that if he could depend on living to be as old as Methuselah he would continue to study for several hundred years yet, but that as he could not expect any such span of years he had decided to set about preparing some matters for publication. There were three lines of activity he desired to pursue: (1) The revision and extension of his work on thermodynamics, to which he said he had some additions to make covering more recently discovered experimental facts not yet adequately incorporated into the theory and other additions of theory apparently not yet exemplified in experiment. (2) A contribution to multiple algebra* on which he said he had some ideas he thought worth while even though the subject appeared at the time not to be of much interest to mathematicians, most of whom were devoting their attention to analysis. (3) A revision of his method of computing orbits which should certainly be revised now that it had recently been printed verbatim by Buchholz in the third edition of Klinkerfues' Astronomy when certain important improvements were only too obvious. He asked what I should think he had best first undertake, but without waiting for reply answered that the astronomers were conservative and unlikely to be appreciative of improvements in his methods for orbits, that the mathematicians were not impatient to learn of his ideas in multiple algebra and that on the whole he felt is was more important to set about the work on thermodynamics to which he had made no published contribution of significance for about twenty-five years.

He wrote the *Statistical Mechanics* in something like nine months while he carried on his regular teaching. All through the winter and spring of 1900–1901 he worked not only by day, the light in his study in Sloane could be seen burning at night. The manuscript was finished in the summer at Intervale, N.H. After Gibbs died in April, 1903, A. W. Phillips of Yale told me that it was this severe work that killed him. He said that they had gone together to the express office to dispatch the copy to Scribners, that up to that time Gibbs had been quite himself but that from the time they turned away from the office he slumped, the elasticity was gone from his gait, he was a worn out old man, and never fully came back.

This is a thrilling story but sad. However, it may not be true. I communicated it to my old friend Ralph Van Name, nephew of Willard Gibbs, who writes: "This may be true, but it was not apparent to his family," and later, "my comment on the incident of the delivery of the manuscript of the *Statistical Mechanics* was not made in a spirit of criticism, but merely as a statement of my recollection, and of that of my sister, whom I had consulted about it. Though both of us were in Europe at the time of Willard Gibbs's death, I did not leave New Haven until June 1902, and she not until March 1903. It is unquestionably true that my uncle worked to the limit of his strength in trying to get the volume finished on time, and that he did not get over the effects for a good while. But both of us have the impression that he seemed to be in practically normal health and spirits by the autumn of 1901 . . . My uncle's final illness was a sudden and

---

* See Chapters 4 and 28, where the concept of a "multiple algebra" or algebra of hypercomplex numbers is developed.

acute attack of a nature which has no obvious connection with his overwork two years before—it was an intestinal obstruction which the doctors were unable to relieve." I may say that all through the academic year 1901–1902 Gibbs seemed to me to be in normal condition, and in his conversation of June 1902 of which I have given so long an account seemed to be looking cheerfully and healthily ahead with real pleasure in the prospect which he was outlining and with no discernible feeling that it might not be finished—indeed he spoke as one surely counting on being active on my return fifteen months later.

If I have gone at such length into this story I have done so chiefly because it so well illustrates stories which come with the best intention of truth from persons near to Gibbs, with just as high desires to tell the truth and nothing but the truth as I have on this occasion, but which none the less cannot be wholly credited, quite as I do not wholly credit as fact my own statements. There is the story that at home, where he lived all his life with his sister who had married his friend and classmate Addison Van Name, he always insisted on mixing the salad on the ground that he was a better authority than the others on the equilibrium of heterogeneous substances. A very pretty conceit, and one vouched for by a colleague much closer to Gibbs than I, but I daresay both the fact and the statement of reason for the fact would not be substantiated by the family. Another story refers to his letter to *Nature* in comment on and disproof of Lord Kelvin's proposed experiment to determine the velocity of longitudinal waves in the ether. It is said that when a colleague told him that he had just seen the letter in print Gibbs blushed and said that he could not believe the Editor of *Nature* would print it. That illustrates his modest and retiring disposition, which was a conspicuous trait, but seems hardly credible.

One often hears lament at Yale and elsewhere that Gibbs's colleagues did not capitalize his great discoveries in physical chemistry by developing the subject experimentally and intensively in New Haven from 1876 on. The comment often takes the turn of wondering how much greater role American science would have played in the growth of physical chemistry if Gibbs had accepted the offer to go to the Johns Hopkins University instead of remaining at Yale. How much difference would it have made? Perhaps very little. What efforts Gibbs made to develop physical chemistry at Yale I do not know; perhaps none. That he knew his thermodynamic work was important and knew so when he printed it I have no doubt; but I have noted above that he appeared not to have lectured upon it in his cycle of courses for about 15 years after its completion, preferring for some reason to teach other subjects, and the subject matter of the memoir is not such as would be likely to diffuse around any university without exposition by the master unless by chance there were at hand some almost equally competent person who very much needed the work as a basis for his own, and knew that he needed it. Gibbs was not an advertiser for personal renown nor a propagandist for science; he was a scholar, scion of an old scholarly family, living before the days when research had become *re*search. Probably he had faith that when the time was ripe for his thermodynamics, the doctrine would spread.

Another beautiful legend is that Gibbs was not appreciated in this country or at Yale during his life. It is probably true that his name was not well known to the ordinary Yale alumnus before the recent time when his photograph and some eulogy of him were widely circulated to the alumni during a drive for funds. But the efforts which were made to arrange for printing his long and costly paper in the Transactions of the Connecticut Academy in 1876-78 were a high testimonial to the faith of his local contemporaries in his work. He was elected to the National Academy at 40, the average age of election being 50, and only the year after the appearance of the second half of the thermodynamic memoir. In 1881 he received the Rumford Medal from the American Academy of Arts and Sciences which means that a group of his contemporaries in Boston appreciated promptly and highly his contributions in the field of heat. Of course he did not have the notice which Einstein receives today; he had no press agents and surely wanted none. There seems to be every evidence that he received the type of recognition to be expected.

There is no problem requiring more brains, sounder judgment, better total adjustment internal and external, than that of uniting the logical and operational techniques of pure mathematics with the infinite variety of observable fact which Nature offers to our contemplation with a ringing challenge to our best abilities. It was in this field that Gibbs was supreme. He had studied with Weierstrass and was not unmindful of mathematical rigor; in the paper in which he pointed out that phenomenon of the convergence of Fourier series which has come to be known as the Gibbs phenomenon he showed his appreciation of mathematical precision as he did on other occasions. But fundamentally he was not interested in rigor for itself, he was inspired by the greater problem of the union between reflective analytical thought and the world of fact.

Index